Hỏa Lò/Hanoi Hilton Stories

Hỏa Lò/Hanoi Hilton Stories

Nguyễn Chí Thiện

Monograph 57/Yale Southeast Asia Studies

Library of Congress Catalog Card Number: *2007-928756*
International Standard Book Number: *paper* *978-0-938692-89-8*
cloth *978-0-938692-88-1*

Published by Yale University Southeast Asia Studies

Distributor:
Yale University Southeast Asia Studies
P.O. Box 208206
New Haven, Connecticut 06520-8206
U.S.A.

Printed in U.S.A.

Contents

Illustrations

Foreword

IT IS, FOR US, A GREAT HONOR to publish these remarkable stories by Nguyễn Chí Thiện and, for me, a special pleasure to be able to add this brief foreword.

The austerity, menace, and extremity of long imprisonment under conditions that are calculated to defeat the spirit and body have, when, unaccountably, the victim survives, the capacity to produce great literature. At its best, it seems to me that such literature is a magical blend of extremely close observation of one's constrained surroundings and of one's interior life together with the lyricism that hopeless situations can, paradoxically, produce. It also, again paradoxically, can be productive of gallows humor and the sense of the absurd. Some of these qualities, I suspect, are the effects of a desperate attempt to rise above one's situation and above one's jailers and to seize the moral high ground—the only superiority on offer. When it succeeds, as it does here, it is evidence that for a writer of Nguyễn Chí Thiện's quality, the work of the imagination is as important to survival as a bowl of rice.

When, a long time back, I first read the translation, by Huỳnh Sanh Thông, of Nguyễn Chí Thiện's prison poems (*Flowers from Hell*), I realized that I was in the presence of a great talent, of a work whose literary importance would transcend its time and place. I suspect that those who read the original in Vietnamese rather than, as I must, in translation, would discover further vernacular poetic riches I can only assume are at work. The stories here told in matchless prose are as brilliant and timeless as his poetry. Western readers are most familiar with Alexandr Solzhenitsyn's *One Day in the Life of Ivan Denisovich* and *Cancer Ward*. Less known are the extraordinary works of Varlam Shalamov, *Kolyma Tales* and *Graphite*. These last are at least the literary equal of Solzhenitsyn's and, arguably superior in their narrative economy and black humor. The stories you now hold in your hands belong, in every respect, in the same select company. They will be read for a long time to come as testaments to the human spirit and its capacity to turn the dross of desperate suffering into literary gold.

Such stories have their time and place and serve as a monument to the suffering and injustice particular to that time and that place. Their preservation and reading by subsequent generations is, and must be part of national 'memory-work'. The danger of national amnesias—of the Holocaust in Germany, of racism and violence against Native-Americans and Afro-Americans in the U.S., of the "gulag" in Russia—is that they set the stage for further brutality. As Camus once wrote in his "Letters to a German Friend," if the French often sound critical of their nation, it is because the highest form of patriotism is to hold your nation to its highest standards and settle for nothing less. In this respect, one could say that Nguyễn Chí Thiện writes as a true Vietnamese patriot as well as a great literary talent.

JAMES C. SCOTT
Sterling Professor of Political Science and Anthropology
Yale University

Preface

NGUYỄN CHÍ THIỆN IS A DISSIDENT POET who spent twenty-seven years as a political prisoner in North Vietnam. He was first imprisoned in 1961 at age twenty-two under the "Re-education Act No.49." The charge at his only trial under the Communist regime that took power following the Geneva Accord of 1954 was "anti-propaganda." The seven stories here are about prison life and conditions during his incarceration at the Hà Nội Central Prison from 1979 to 1985. The characters are all true persons as he knew and heard them.

The character of the Old Man (defined in the glossary of prison language as a "counterrevolutionary or reactionary") is a philosopher and teacher. In keeping with Nguyễn Chí Thiện's essence of Zen—he was called "Zen Master" by his friends—sometimes the Old Man in the stories is not Thiễn but others whom he knew.

The prisoner poet survived starvation, torture, and eight years of solitary darkness. He was placed with common criminals at the Hà Nội Central Prison in hopes they would kill him. Instead, they became his friends. The real "Old Man" protected their rights by speaking up for them to the jailers.

Just as his poetry is recognized as outstanding literature, the *Hỏa Lò/Hanoi Hilton Stories* are very readable: classic themes of love (there were women prisoners at Hỏa Lò) and art flow within the grim realities of starvation, filth, and disease in Communist jails. The stories are documented with historical notes and sources in English to assist students and researchers. Each contains a poem from Thiễn's more than 700 poems composed and committed to memory in prison, for he was denied pen and paper. Folk songs and cultural descriptions make the volume ideal for Vietnamese literature or ethnic studies.

Six of the narratives take place at the Hỏa Lò/Hanoi Hilton prison. They are translated from the East Coast Vietnamese Publishers Consortium edition with Nguyễn Ngọc Bích (*Hỏa Lò Tap Truyen*, 2001), which was written in Paris with the support of a fellowship from the International Parliament of Writers. The first story, "A Short Ride," is an autobiographical narrative about carrying his manuscript of poems (known in English as *Flowers From Hell*, a bilingual work by Huỳnh Sanh Thông, published by Yale's Council on Southeast Asia Studies) to the British Embassy in Hà Nội on July 16, 1979. Thiễn asked for asylum but, with no forewarning and with the Hà Nội security police demanding his return, the diplomats accepted his manuscript but did not permit him to remain. He was arrested outside the gates and began his third prison sentence, which he did not expect to survive.

"A Short Ride" includes a portion of "Phùng Cung" (the name of another prisoner poet who was a former believer in idealistic communism) from the original *Hỏa Lò Tap Truyen*. Nguyễn Chí Thiện and Phùng Cung were fellow inmates at the Phong Quang prison camp from 1970 to 1977. Their literary methodologies for committing their poetry to memory and recitation are described in a delightful dialogue that is intermingled with the prison manner of brewing tea and smoking rustic tobacco in secrecy.

The infamous Hanoi Hilton is now a museum in Hà Nội, designed to attract American visitors (especially Vietnamese Americans) who are looking for war history. The propaganda is very crude, leaving even the most sympathetic visitors in disbelief. The exhibit shows the unhealthy conditions, leg stocks, and other means of torture used by the French during the colonial period and particularly for the political imprisonment of Communists revolutionaries until the French defeat in 1954. But there is no mention of the continued use of these devices at the prison by the Communist regime toward its own people, including the dissident poet, Nguyễn Chí Thiện, between 1979 and 1985.

It also shows the imprisonment of Americans during the war period from 1964 to 1973. Only the most gullible know it is a false presentation of the treatment of the American pilots who renamed the Vietnamese Hỏa Lò (the furnace) the Hanoi Hilton. People who visit the prison museum often post their photographs online. This is how we located Chris McCooey, an educator and portrait photographer in Japan. His "Hanoi Prison Images," were donated for the publication of the *Hỏa Lò/Hanoi Hilton Stories* after he heard the story of Nguyễn Chí Thiện's ordeal. The photograph of the mist in the mountains of northern Vietnam was donated by Jenny Dỗ, a Vietnamese American attorney who owns the Green Rice Gallery in San Jose, CA. Nguyễn Chí Thiện spent much of his life in these mountainous regions because the prison camps were deliberately constructed in very remote mountains or jungles.

Nguyễn Chí Thiện was adopted as one of six "prisoners of conscience" by Amnesty International in 1986. In 1988, his sister, the late Hảo-Thị Nguyễn, began a campaign for her brother by sending copies of the photograph that is the cover of this book to overseas Vietnamese, especially those in Europe. The image was published by Amnesty International in 1990 and resulted in an international outcry to release the poet, followed by his subsequent release in October 1991. This was at the time of the collapse of the Soviet Union in Europe. In Vietnam, many of the thousands of imprisoned officers from the South Vietnamese army were beginning to be released after the 1975 North Vietnamese invasion and victory. Many immigrated to the United States through the Humanitarian Operation (H.O.) agreement between the United States and Vietnam. Among them was Nguyễn-Công Giân, the brother of Nguyễn Chí Thiện, who had been a lieutenant colonel in the South Vietnamese army and was an advisor to his government in the Paris Peace Accords in 1971 and 1972.

In 1995, a Vietnamese American television reporter asked a retired U.S. Air Force colonel, Noboru Masuoka, who had helped imprisoned South Vietnamese officers to immigrate to the United States, if he could help get a poet out of Vietnam. Colonel Masuoka, who had been a political prisoner during World War II in America, his own country, traveled to Hanoi with his own funds to assist Human Rights Watch and the U.S. Foreign Service in securing the immigration of Nguyễn Chí Thiện. Nguyễn Chí Thiện became the only North Vietnamese citizen who was never associated with the United States or the South Vietnamese military or government to immigrate under the H.O. program. Today he is a United States citizen and lives in Orange County, California. His life purpose is to see freedom and democracy in Việt Nam.

Jean Libby
Palo Alto, California

Acknowledgments

THAT I WAS ABLE TO COMPLETE the stories of Vietnamese prisoners at Hỏa Lò is essentially due to the generosity of the International Parliament of Writers (IPW) and, most particularly, Mr. Christian Salmon, Secretary General of IPW, who invited me to spend three years in France (1998–2001). This not only helped to restore my fragile physical health, but also gave me the peace and quiet that I needed to recollect, conceive, and finally write this book. For all of that, I would like to say, "*Un grand merci!*" And to the translators of *Hỏa Lò Prison*, I would like to say "*Un grand merci*" too!

STORY 1

A Short Ride

A sudden train whistle is heard in the distance
Accompanied by cursing and dogs barking and chickens
clucking
Female voices also
Mixed with the fragrance of ripening rice and amidst birds
chirping
And children playing somewhere nearby
Plus laughter from a passing crowd
And a traditional song that is sung in a strong voice
At dusk when dew starts settling ...
Months and years have gone by, endlessly
Here I lie, like a corpse
In a cell that is like a tomb
The world is vast, and I miss everything![1]

I HAVE BEEN STANDING on one leg on the outside of the platform of the crowded train for twelve hours, but I am not tired. The train has taken me from Phong Quang prison camp in Lào Cai Province, near the Chinese border, into my home city, Hà Nội, North Vietnam.

It is July 11, 1977. About twenty of my prisoner friends, those who are called 'malcontent' and 'bad elements' because we compose poetry that is often against the regime, have been released today because there is not enough room for us in the crowded prisons. Since the fall of Sài Gòn, the machinery of the dictatorship was operating in full force over the whole country and there was a temporary

---

Sections of "A Short Ride" were translated by Nguyễn Kiếm Phong from the original Vietnamese "Phùng Cung" in Hỏa Lò (2001).

shortage of prison wardens. But ever since 1961 the North had already been turned into a huge prison—soldiers, people's militia, traffic policemen, even village registrars, village chiefs were all imprisoned by the Party. Many officers of the Army of the Republic of Việt Nam have been sent to concentration camps in the North.

I am released with writers Vũ Thư Hiên, Lê Quang Dũng, Captain Kiều Duy Vĩnh—we were all released one after the other. When about twenty of us, political prisoners, were set free, the chief warden of camp told us:

"The Party only liberates the walking skeletons, the lifeless bodies we set free to wander. We still have to make the Southerners understand what the proletariat's dictatorship really is."

The flow of prisoners from the South to the North was creating these overcrowded conditions. They were first sent to the concentration camps for 'reeducation' according to Resolution No. 49 of June 21, 1961.[2] The most severe overcrowding began on April 30, 1975 after the invasion of South Vietnam by North Vietnam in violation of the Paris Peace Accords of January 1973.

I was first put in the Communist concentration camps because I said the history textbook was wrong. In December 1960, a high school teacher of history who was one of my friends asked me to teach his class for two hours, because he was ill. The required book was *The History of the August Revolution*.[3] The textbook falsely stated that the Japanese surrender in World War II was the result to the Soviet Army's victory over the Japanese Armed Forces in Manchuria. I explained to my students that Japan had surrendered to the Allies because of the atom bombs dropped on Hiroshima and Nagasaki by the United States. Students were required to talk about their teachers and their parents to the Party and publicly denounce them. My country was becoming a land of snitches.

Two months later, I was arrested, accused of anti-propaganda, and condemned to two years in prison. In reality, I had to live three years and six months in labor camps in Phú Thọ Province and in Yên Bái Province. Although labor was hard in these camps, I was still young; in my first imprisonment my age was twenty-two to twenty-five. Prisoners could talk to one another on our way to and from work, which was primarily agricultural, growing vegetables. About ten of us enjoyed gathering in the yard at dusk to secretly read poetry and discuss literature. This was necessarily secret because the guards would break up groups, especially those who met regularly.

During those first years in detention, I created about 100 poems on the subjects of the prison scene and anticommunism. When I was released in 1964, I continued to write poetry and recite it to my closest friends who went on reciting it to others, in Hải Phòng and Hà Nội. A number of my friends offered to participate in various community activities, managing to evade capture by the police. One of them even was granted 16 certificates of merit. Eventually he too had to go to a concentration camp.

In February of 1966 I was arrested again. The security forces suspected that I was the author of the poems that were transmitted from mouth to mouth in the cities. When interrogated, I denied it, saying that I knew nothing about these 'reactionary poems.' Without receiving a trial, I was sent to the concentration camps in Phú Thọ, Yên Bái, and Lào Cai Provinces.

I could not, at that time, find an answer to all the questions haunting my mind. Why were the ordinary people who had stayed in their homes in North Vietnam rather than joining the one million who migrated South in 1954 with the protection of the Geneva Accords condemned as quislings or traitors? They stayed because the Revolution promised to continue employing them, and grant them the status quo. Especially when the promise had been made by Hồ Chí Minh himself. When in peacetime, 'There is no place like home,' they said. Yet they always lived in fear, not daring to make any move or say a word against the regime. Eventually, even they were persecuted. Eventually, we all met in prison.

It was at the Phong Quang camp in Lào Cai Province that I gained my closest friendship in life, the poet Phùng Cung. I liked and admired Phùng Cung from the moment I had the opportunity of reading his story "Lord Trịnh's Old War Horse" published in *Nhân Văn* (Humanities Magazine) magazine in 1956. Of all the articles and poems published in the spring, fall and winter special editions of the magazine (which were all banned by the Party after publication), I found this story most outstanding both in its artistic expression as well as its content, deep and very insightful, exactly like the author.[4]

A. My prison family (photo taken in Hà Nội in 1994). Left to right, Nguyễn Hữu Hiệu, (publisher of the *Hoa Địa Ngục* manuscript in 1980), Nguyễn Chí Thiện and Phùng Cung, dissident Vietnamese poets.

Portions of "Phùng Cung" from *Hỏa Lò* (2001) appear in "A Short Ride," the autobiographical first story in this volume. Phùng Cung, Nguyễn Chí Thiện's best friend, passed away at home in Hà Nội in 1997. His writings, entitled *Trăng Ngục* (Prison Poems) were published in Canada and California by Dr. Lâm Thu Vân and Văn Nghe Publishers in Westminster in 2004. (Photo by Phùng Quán)

Phùng Cung's story struck at a weak point of the Party. Because of that, the Party was enraged and put him into prison without any trial for more than 12 years. Some people believed that the story was aimed at many of the talented artists who, once they had swallowed some handouts from the Party, had lost not only their talent but also their souls. That was true. But if it attacked only the few hack writers and poets—the very people who were looked down upon by the 'father comrades' and despised by the people—then the Party wouldn't have responded with such rage. The reason the Party felt it was compelled to mete out a heavy penalty was that he dared to expose a shameful reality: the writers, the intelligentsia, in fact the whole population—like the old horse of Lord Trịnh—had been forced by the Party to wear two fig-leaf blinders that kept them looking in only one direction, not allowing them to see other things such as the sky, the clouds, the mountains, and the flowers!

There is a paragraph describing the war-horse Kim Bông bravely galloping forth, leaving behind the whole region of Sơn Nam Thượng, valiantly fighting in hundreds of battles. Yet when peace was restored, that same horse, stepping leisurely into the Lord's palace, setting its feet on the cool, blue stone floor, had cringed and trembled. It started and cowered even at the sudden beautiful singing of the birds in the green foliage. Those details were considered by the Party as disparaging innuendoes aimed at Party members. In reality, it was nothing but the sordid alienation of those who, devoid of feelings and virtue, were only concerned with protecting their own wealth and position.

In the winter of 1970, I was taken from the concentration camp at Yên Bái at 4:00 A.M. After eighteen hours of traveling by canoe, trucks, and trains—all of us prisoners handcuffed in pairs and crammed into pitch-black carriages, slimy with pig shit—we arrived at Phong Quang at about 10:00 P.M. We were all exhausted and nauseous. We squatted on the earthen yard under the drizzle and in the cold wind, listened to roll call, then the abuses and the directives of the cadres. Then we dutifully cooperated with the trusties who searched through our personal belongings consisting of only a few stinking rags. Only around midnight were we sent to our respective wards.

Among the happy chance encounters in this world, only very few could match the happiness of the encounters of former prison friends. The moment I walked into the ward, I was mobbed by four or five persons. Laughing, they showered me with questions, held my hands, shook my shoulders, and helped me put down my bag of clothing. Then they offered me tea and tobacco. I was no less joyful. We talked about everything. All of a sudden all the weariness seemed to evaporate. Friendship is really a wonderful tonic; no other fortifying drug can be so potent.

They said that Phùng Cung was also in this camp; he was now in the medical ward with tuberculosis. My eyes lit up. How fortunate! I would have the chance to talk with him, a person whom I had admired for a long time but did not have the chance to meet. A few days later I wandered down into the medical ward to look for him. It was food distribution time for the evening meal. It happened to be a special fresh-food meal of buffalo meat. The task of distributing the food is very laborious and time-consuming. The meat must be distributed separately, then the bones and then the skin; the broth had to be measured spoon by spoon. Everything was done with a makeshift scale; the scale was primitive but no less accurate than a jeweler's scale. After the distribution, the name of each person was written on a scrap of paper, which was then folded and placed against each bowl containing no more than 100 grams of food. When the name of a person was called against whatever bowl it happened to be placed, the bowl belonged to that person. The inmates crowded around in circles shouting 'suggestions' to the person who had been appointed to make the distribution. Usually he must be a person of prestige, trustworthy and with a spotless record.

Scores of patients in the medical ward, except for a few who were dying, also took part in the sacred task of food distribution. I looked at all of them, one by one. None of them looked as if he could be Phùng Cung as I saw him in my mind. I turned around and went behind the medical ward. A middle-aged man wearing a cotton jacket was standing in front of a hot-pepper plant, gazing up into the leaden grey sky; his expressionless face was equally pale and grey. This must be Phùng Cung.

"Excuse me. Are you Mr. Cung?"

Cung glanced at me and answered:

"Yes. How do you know?"

I laughed:

"I just came from Yên Bái yesterday evening. I learned from Lê Quang Dũng that you are sick so I have come to visit you. Altogether, I've been in prison for more than eight years."

"Then you are two years less than me. But you are in prison for what crime?"

"There is no need to commit a crime to be in prison! Look at many people here; what crimes did they commit? In any case, they said I wrote some reactionary poems."

With a condescending tone, Cung said nonchalantly said:

"Writing poems? Can you read me some?"

One must be very careful when living under socialism. Many people had ruined their life because of their 'loose tongue' over a few cups of tea with friends! In prison, one must be even more cautious. But looking at Cung, I felt that he was not the kind of person who would do you any harm. However I still hesitated. I chose a poem that was 'moderate,' and not too critical.

"You are in the medical ward so I'll read you a poem about living in the medical ward in prison:

Winter rushed in, a cold jungle night.
Northern wind, drenching rain drifted;
The drizzle whirled in the icy north wind
The purple potato became priceless,
My old illness made itself known.
We have predicted how many will fall;
In this winter they could hardly stand the test.
Their body is like a dummy
Hoping the winter would forgive and let them go![5]

I finished reciting the poem and waited for his comments. But he remained silent. After a moment he asked me:

"What squad are you with?"

"The bamboo-weaving squad, nicknamed 'The Graveyard Candidates.' I also have tuberculosis like you; every now and then I cough blood, but only a little bit. Whenever you feel better, come and visit me in my ward. During working days most people are out in the field. It is more convenient to talk then."

The food distribution had reached the stage of matching name to meat. I shook his hand:

"Please come in and get your meal. We'll see each other some other time. Oh! My name is Thiện, also known as Chí Thiện the Zen Master. *Au revoir!*"

Because writing on paper was never allowed, everyone had ways to meter the verses. Phùng Cung would use his fingers to count. He would do this with such concentration that other prisoners and jailers thought he was crazy. But he was not, he was simply counting words. I did not use body methods, even reciting aloud, just my memory. Most of my poems (about 300) were created during my second period of imprisonment, the eleven years between 1966 and 1977. These are the years of my twenties and thirties.

Now I am thirty-eight years old, weighing less than one hundred pounds due to the policy of starvation of prisoners that is practiced by the Communists, standing on one leg on the outside platform of the slow-moving green train.[6] The train traveled very slowly because it was so full of people. After riding all night, we pulled into the station at Hà Nội at about 7:00 A.M. I am in a good position to jump off first and I run to the houses of my friends. At 3:30 P.M. I arrive at the home of my sister (the younger of my two sisters, who were both nearly twenty years older than me), but she is still at at work. At 5:00 P.M. she comes home and is very surprised and glad to see me.

I asked her about my brother, Nguyễn Công Giân, who left home and went South with the National Army in 1954, at age twenty-two. My sister learned that he had been an officer in the Army of the Republic of Việt Nam (South Vietnam) and that he was, like many other officers, imprisoned by the Communist victors after April 30, 1975 and sent to a concentration camp—probably several because the officers were kept constantly moving in the South to North. Will my brother be brought to Phong Quang in my place? I have not seen him since I was fifteen years old.[7]

I lived again in Hải Phòng, returning to the home of my elder sister and her family. This had been my home with my parents before I was first imprisoned in 1961 and again for the two years of my release, from 1964 to in 1966. Both my parents died while I was in detention during my second period of imprisonment. My mother died in 1970 and my father in 1976. Both of them loved me and did not blame me for being a political prisoner of the Communists. They blamed themselves for not moving South with their older son, my brother, in 1954.

There are many cadres and families living in the ten-room house when I arrive, but very little food. I must sell the clothes that my mother had bought for me on the occasion of my release for eighteen pounds of rice, and wear the used clothes of my deceased father. The ward police, the district police, the city police often come to 'inquire about my health.' Denied any form of employment, I make ends meet with difficulty. I often go to bed with an empty stomach.

Millions of people lost their lives in the so-called war to liberate the South. In actuality, this 'war of liberation' was nothing more than a struggle to impose Communism, or its Marxist-Leninist brand, on the whole of Việt Nam as a stepping stone to the domination of the rest of Southeast Asia. After the fall of South Vietnam in 1975, hundreds of thousands of people went to fill up the Vietnamese gulags. There was no need for a blood bath since that would be too obvious. Instead, under the new regime, hundreds of thousands of people died of hunger and cold or simply died without notice in godforsaken corners of the jungle. Your life or death was entirely in the hands of the Vietnamese Communist Party.[8]

When Red China invaded the six border provinces in February 1979, security agents torment me ceaselessly. Afraid of being unable to survive if jailed a third time, I have decided to send my poems abroad. Those poems are the fruit of twenty years' work. It is impossible to let them be buried with me! I will take them into the French or British Embassy.

Traveling to Hà Nội, it takes three days to write four hundred poems from my memory down on paper. It would have been too risky, too dangerous to write and keep them in my room. On Bastille Day, July 14, 1979, I am outside the French Embassy with my manuscript under my shirt. But the celebrating crowd is closely guarded by police and I am unable to enter. On July 16, I put my manuscript once again under my shirt and go to the British Embassy on Lý Thường Kiệt Street

I manage to run into the Embassy, passing the guard. One Vietnamese woman and three Vietnamese men are sitting around a table in a large room. They are local people hired by the British to be a reception office for the Embassy. I had not expected to meet Vietnamese people. The situation is very dangerous. Calmly, I tell them that I came to see the ambassador. 'Where are you from?' one of them asks. 'From the Foreign Office,' I answer. They demand to see the required paper. I tell them I have forgotten to carry it. With that, I rush the door at the other side of the room. The woman stands up and grabs me; I push her down. The two men bar my way. The third Vietnamese man has gone to warn the police.

There is a young English girl combing her hair in a boudoir without a door on my right side. I say quickly in English: 'I need to talk to the ambassador. Don't fear, I am an honest man.' But she is so frightened that she drops her comb. The two Vietnamese men chase me. I run to the table and lift it up, making everything on the table fall to the floor. Upon hearing the noise, three English diplomats come out. One Vietnamese man says I am a madman. I tell the Englishmen that I am not crazy, and I have important documents to give them. I immediately run into the back door of their office. The Englishmen follow me, closing the door behind them.

Handing them my manuscript, I tell them about my prison life and the suffering of my oppressed people under the Communist yoke. I beg them to have my poems published in their free country. Finally, I ask them whether I can stay in the Embassy. They reply that I cannot, because the police are waiting for me outside. They solemnly promise that they will arrange for my poems to be published. Satisfied, I give them three photos of myself, at ages twelve, nineteen, and at thirty-nine. We shake hands. When I leave the Embassy, the security agents arrest me on Lý Thường Kiệt Street, in front of the Embassy, and drive me to Hỏa Lò Prison. It is a short ride in the unregulated city traffic of many pedestrians, bicycles, and cyclos. I find the normal pandemonium somehow comforting.

As I ride in the security car through the familiar streets, I see everything with sharp edges. Hà Nội Central Prison, which was soon called Hỏa Lò (the Furnace) by the Vietnamese, was built in 1898 to be the central facility for the French colonial government. At that time it was expected to hold 400 inmates. It was immediately too crowded and extensively remodeled in 1913, when it was expected to hold 600 inmates. It is the same prison in which the French held the Communist revolutionaries during the 1930s and 1940s, crowding twice the number of 600 into the cells. However, they were

B. The iron gate of Hỏa Lò/Hanoi Central Prison, now a museum

Nguyễn Chí Thiện was taken here after his arrest on July 16, 1979, outside the British Embassy in Hanoi where he attempted to deliver his manuscript. The inscription on his manuscript read: "I would like to have these poems published in your free country. It is the result of twenty years of work." The embassy sent the manuscript to the School of Oriental and African Studies in London, which sent it to Vietnamese exiles in Europe and the United States. Thiện spent six years (1979–1985) behind this gate—half of them in solitary confinement after the poems were published in 1980 in a Vietnamese newspaper in the United States. (Photo from "Hanoi Prison Images" by Chris McCooey, 2004) allowed books and even to hold classes (often learning French).[9] Their memoirs (those who were not executed) are now the basis for literature classes for every Vietnamese student.[10] It is the same prison that held the captured American flyers whose planes were shot down by Russian guided missiles while they were bombing North Vietnam during the 1960s and early 1970s, and which they renamed the 'Hanoi Hilton.'

I think back to my high school years in Hà Nội, from 1954 to 1956. My friends and I would ride our bicycles past Hỏa Lò, which is right in the center of town. At that time (as always) most teenagers were very naive. Whenever passing by, some guessed when the war against the French came to an end the prison would be destroyed and replaced by a university campus. Others wished a youth club would be built for young people to hang out and spend their time playing music and dancing. As for me, I dreamed the dreary prison would turn into a public park, shaded by leafy trees and adorned with fragrant flowers where the people come to relax on the green lawn.

I bemoan my lack of education, having only my miserable life to plead the case of prisoners in Communist Vietnam. In fact, during the years 1957 to 1961, I did read books on the miseries and atrocities in Russian prisons such as *I Chose Freedom*, *The Devil in Paradise*, and *Back from Russia*.[11] But I usually read them while smoking, drinking coffee, or slurping a big bowl of *phở*. As a result, my reading came to nothing.

Now, at age forty, I have deliberately taken the chance and lost my brief period of freedom. I am not sure that there is enough energy in my body to sustain my mind. I do not think that I will survive another imprisonment.

The security car turns onto Hàng Bông Thợ Nhuộm Street and drives up to the fortress known as Hỏa Lò/Hanoi Hilton to the Americans. *Clang!* The great iron doors open. *Clang!* And close again.

The original handwritten manuscripts are in the protective custody of the British government. They will be returned to Việt Nam when it is free. Written on the outside of the poems, which had been written on papers in secret from my memory of the first fifteen years while imprisoned, my request for publication does make its way to the Free World as promised:

> *In the name of the millions of innocent victims of dictatorship, of those who have already fallen and of those who are still dying a slow and painful death in Communist prisons, I beg you to publish these poems in your free country. They are the fruit of 20 years of work, and most of them were written during my years in detention. I think it's for us the victims, rather than anyone else, to show to the world the unbelievable suffering of our oppressed and tortured people.*
>
> *From my broken life there remains but one dream: to see the largest possible number of men awakened to the fact that Communism is a great calamity for mankind.*
>
> *Please accept, sir, my deep gratitude as well as that of my unfortunate compatriots.*[12]
>
> Nguyễn Chí Thiện
> July 14, 1979

STORY 2

Revolutionary Songs

Tết, the holy New Year of our land, is here
In this cell where I am all purplish, shivering with cold
Living in dank & darkness–inexorable pee smell.

Submitted at every moment to obnoxious inspections
And given two meals of dry salt-sprinkled rice a day
Or simply water for one's beriberi.

No wonder night or day he feels shaky with vision blurred
Feeling oneself entombed in a dirty, sloppy grave
Half-blind, mouth distorted, with moldy dreams
While it drizzles on outside.

That is when one's soul is awakened
To springs glorious that date back a long, long time ago
Causing me to love and miss them
Causing my palpitating heart to wish to explode.[1]

"ANOTHER TẾT![2] This is the second Tết that I must spend in Hỏa Lò prison!"

The Teacher sighs a long sigh. Right now his wife must be in the dumps. Once he was away on a mission for nearly four months. When he came back, at night, with her head pillowed on his arm, she had cried and confided to him that "Oh the house is so empty without a male presence." She then made him promise that from then on he would not let that happen again. She did not need him to be a big shot, honored and rich and all that. She said: "All I care is

---

"Revolutionary Songs" was translated by Nguyễn Ngọc Bích from the original Vietnamese "Những Bài Cách Mạng" in *Hỏa Lò* (2001).

that we stay together." His poor wife, who is prompt with tears, must be suffering a lot, crying in her loneliness until her eyes are dry. They do not have any children, so all the love and care she is capable of is devoted to him. And he knows himself to be just a nothing with no talent, not even good looks, or money. A zero, rolling into the midst of life. With his love a beauty, who is also so sweet, agreeing to marry him, he is indeed very lucky. At times when they make love, to show his gratitude he is in the habit of quoting a verse: "*Thanks to you, a beautiful vision of woman's dress has flown into my life.*" He has not quoted this verse for more than twenty-one months.

The Teacher and his wife have been together for nineteen years without ever a word of friction being uttered between them. Relatives and neighbors are full of praise for their harmonious relationship. He was a teacher while his wife knitted sweaters. With both working and spending sparingly, they still could not make ends meet.

During the twenty-one months he has been in jail, his wife still manages to bring him some provisions. Now it's a few kilograms of dry noodles, then it's a few hundred grams of sugar, or a couple of lemons. At other times it's two or three kilograms of cereals, a small bundle of roasted and crushed sesame seeds, or a bunch of bananas. As he consumed these precious commodities—their love and binding much heavier than their actual weight—he felt guilty as if he were eating or drinking his wife's life blood. On a couple of occasions he had asked those released before him to go to his wife and tell her that she should not bring him or send in to him any more provisions.

He is lucky that they made him a trusty with privileges in exchange for duties. He wants her to know that he is not too bad off. He has no way of knowing whether they managed to give the message to his wife. She still keeps sending things to him, which still fills him with great joy and grief.

It's already the 29th of the twelfth lunar month. At the latest, tomorrow, on the eve of Tết, he will receive provisions from her. He is not allowed to write letters or see his relatives because the investigation on his case is not yet quite over. Oh, how he wishes to see his wife! On some nights he tosses and turns throughout the night, loving her and missing her dearly. She must have grown pale and very thin by now. And her eyes must have black pouches because of crying and loss of sleep.

From the grey and waterlogged sky comes a spring drizzle, which blows pollution powder onto his faded cotton-padded winter coat:

"Up to interrogation!"

The warden's call takes him aback, he hurriedly stops his sweeping and looks up:

"Did you call me, Cadre?"

"Who else?"

The Teacher lays the broom against the Terminalia (tropical almond) tree and hurriedly steps into the nearby warehouse. He takes off his clothes and puts on the garb that the prisoners are expected to wear when they present themselves for interrogation. A feeling of apprehension passes through him when he must put on that paratrooper uniform, a war booty brought North from the South. These so-called interrogation suits, they are washed only once a year. There is no saying how many with pus-filled eczema, venereal diseases, and chancres have put them on previously!

He walks silently behind the warden. He hasn't been to interrogation for seven months. Now this sudden call, practically on the eve of Tết. There must be a hidden reason behind this summons. Could it be that they are going to release him? Normally at this time of year there is a small amnesty. It could very well be the case, he thinks with some palpitation, knowing that there are many arrests at holiday time—perhaps because of his exemplary behavior and the need for more room. He can even hear his heart beating in his chest.

The Teacher and the warden walk past the grapevines to the row of interrogation chambers. A huge cherry branch flushing with pink flowers can be seen near the door of the prison supervisor. Outside his window there is a kumquat tree with dark green, shiny leaves and abundant yellow fruits. A group of security officers, male and female, are standing about casually discussing their plans for Tết celebration. The Teacher tries not to look at them with envy, to be at home with their families as every Vietnamese must be to properly celebrate the Lunar New Year.

The interrogator takes over the small procession by importantly carrying a leather attaché case. He makes a sign for the Teacher to follow that dismisses the warden. Inside the familiar room, the interrogator points to a stool, then sits down, leaning backward against the chair. He opens his attaché case, pulls out a thick file of papers and a pack of Sông Cầu cigarettes, pulling one cigarette from the pack, which he lights. A younger security officer brings out a set of tea and a hot water thermos, which he puts on the table, then silently withdraws.

The interrogator pours two cups of tea and cheerfully invites the Teacher:

"Please have some tea. You smoke, don't you? I am glad that you are still in good health. Your wife must be sending you regular provisions?"

The Teacher thanks him and puts out his hand to grab the pack of cigarettes but the interrogator quickly picks it up and pulls out one more cigarette and gives to him. He ceremoniously flips the lighter and brings the light to the cigarette on the prisoner's lips. The Teacher takes a few drags, then brings the teacup to his mouth. He feels inwardly comforted. Such good treatment all of a sudden. There must be some hope.

Waiting for him to finish his cup of tea, the interrogator flashes a most friendly smile:

"With Tết here, you must miss home quite a bit."

The Teacher becomes expansive:

"Yes sir. For the last couple of nights it was impossible for me to sleep. I miss my wife terribly. As you know, Tết means reunion, family gathering. It's really a bad situation in my case. I hope you will give my case your kind consideration. My wife and I, we will never forget your kind favor."

The interrogator is noncommittal:

"That depends entirely on the level of your sincerity. The Party never hits those who run towards it. All you need to do is to repent and confess it all and the Party will be lenient towards you. Let's start."

He opens the file and takes out his fountain pen:

"You should remember that the Party punishes infringements but at the same time rewards those with merit. You may be guilty, but if you know how to repent, give us a clear report of the reactionaries' plot, then your merit will be considerable. You might even be cited in reward."

He picks up a ruler with a frown, shows it to the Teacher and takes a measure with his hand:

"Suppose this is the extent of your crime or guilt. But if your merit is this high, then one can take off the guilty part; you would still end up with this much. So let me ask you for the last time this question: who, or which organization, has crossed out the word 'our' on the slogan: 'The great President Hồ Chí Minh lives forever in our revolutionary undertaking!' and changed it into 'their' to transform the formula into a most reactionary and extremely flippant line?"

"Sir, I have repeatedly declared that I do not know who did it. Truly I do not know."

The interrogator has a smirk on his face. The smirk succeeds in killing the ray of hope that the Teacher saw only a few minutes before.

"So you are obstinate to the last, are you? Let me ask you this. On May 19, 1979, the school security guards reported that there were only the two of you at school at that early hour, you and your buddy the literature teacher. Subsequently it was discovered that the word 'our' was crossed out with charcoal. Let me ask you then, who could that be other than the two of you? The evidence is there for all to see. How can you deny it?"

"Please consider. The slogan was painted way up high on the main gate leading into the school. It was right next to the security guard's room. When I arrived, the guard was sitting there having his morning tea. How could I have been able to climb up there and cross out the word without his seeing me?"

The interrogator says in an even-tempered tone:

"Keep your cool. You are forty-five but apparently you have not had a great deal of experience in life. You must know that once in here at Hanoi Hilton it's a matter of survival. Everyone wants to keep his own skin. You are one of those innocent lambs! Let me tell you, your friend, the one you say who is closest to you, has come out with it under interrogation. He said that both of you plotted together. You deliberately went in and talked to the security guard, blocking his view so that he could climb up and crossed out the word 'our.' All it took was about a minute!"

He knows at once that the interrogator was lying. For his friend was a truthful man, one with self-respect and intelligence. Only a crazy person, one who has parted with common sense, would admit to something that he does not know or that he did not do.

The Teacher becomes more emphatic:

"Please let the two of us confront each other. Unless he has lost his reason, he would never accuse himself of something that we would not even think of doing, let alone doing it."

The interrogator stiffens his features:

"No need! Your counterpropaganda actions are in themselves a whole story. We have investigated and know everything by now. The eyes and ears of the people are a hundred times more effective than even the reactionary U.S. C.I.A. itself! On July 25, 1979, you taught your students that the law of conservation of energy was first discovered by Lavoisier and not by Lomonosov—whereas all the textbooks published by the Ministry of Education say it was discovered by Lomonosov. You even called him 'he' in a most contemptuous way, didn't you? On June 17, 1979, you told your students that the Chinese have discovered the principle of the rocket thousands of years ago, thus implying that the Chinese are smart. You also listen to Radio Beijing, read Chinese books, and have dealings with Chinese. Are you going to deny that too?"

The Teacher does his best to control his shaking voice:

"Please allow me to explain my situation clearly. What I taught about the law of conservation of energy was taught to me by Professor Vũ Văn Canh. I trusted him so I repeated what I learned to my students. As for calling Lomonosov 'he,' I had no intention whatsoever to put him down. In fact, I am full of admiration for Lomonosov, the scholar scientist. As a matter of fact, I have been called to order about this in school. As for saying that the Chinese discovered the principle of the rocket, a good number of Party publications—when there was still amity between our two countries—said so. Before the border war with China, I taught Chinese. It's only after Chinese was scrapped as a subject that I was made into a physics and chemistry teacher. As a teacher of Chinese, isn't it obvious that I should listen to radio and read Chinese journals and newspapers so as to keep myself abreast of developments? President Hồ, when he was alive, also taught us to do so. Chinese publications are available at the Foreign Languages Bookstore. My wife and I, we have lived in Hàng Buồm Street for well over ten years. All our neighbors are Chinese, so it only stands to reason that I have normal relations with my neighbors. Who has ever called that a crime?"

The interrogator points his pen at the prisoner and shouts:

"I forbid you to reason in a circle. When you looked at the picture of Guan Yunzhang, you were full of admiration for his loyalty and even said that though Guan's body was in Cao Cao's territory, his heart and mind were still with the Han. So your intent was to urge your Chinese friends to follow the example of Guan, living in Vietnam but giving their loyalty to China. Your viper tongue is thus extremely dangerous, vicious. It doesn't matter if you acknowledge your guilt or not. Based on resolution number 49 of the Standing Committee of the National Assembly that was signed into law on June 21, 1961, and written by the Great Liberator Hồ Chí Minh himself, we are sending you to a labor reform concentration camp."

The tragedy to his family looms in front of the Teacher's eyes. He feels the terrible pain, the surging anger. Such unbearable injustice makes him explode:

"I propose that you take me to court where I can be tried in proper fashion, with testimonies and evidence."

The smirk returns to the interrogator's face:

"The People's Court does not have time to try cases involving counterrevolutionary elements like you. We are the sword and the shield of the Party. No law will ever stop our hands!"

He puts a concentration order that already has his name on it in front of the Teacher:

"Sign it!"

The Teacher stands up, no less adamant:

"I won't sign. I am not guilty of anything!"

The interrogator covers his mouth and a weary yawn:

"It's all the same whether you sign or not. Those trying to reverse the wheel of history are bound to be crushed by it, that's all. I will order to stop all provisions to you from outside. Go back to your room!"

The Teacher follows the interrogator out of the room in a forlorn mood, his temples stressed and beating rapidly. After handing him over to the security officer on duty, the interrogator leaves with grumbling curses. The Teacher goes into the communal room.

Five trusties are taking out provisions bags from a large commode in the warden's room and throwing them out into the courtyard. Each bag lands at about one meter from another, thus making a series of dotted lines. Since it's Tết, most of the prisoners got provisions from outside. Rare are the families who would have the heart to leave the prisoners to their own devices, even though they may be very poor. There are wives and mothers who forego their own portions so the delicacies can be sent to their husbands or sons to begin the New Year.

Since four in the morning, the gate in front of Hỏa Lò Prison is already crowded with people waiting for their turn to come in. The majority are women of various ages, from a girl child to a white-haired grandmother. Everyone has sadness and suffering written on her face. Some women have babies in one arm and provision bags in the other. They stand bunched in groups, wearing conical hats with a flimsy nylon covering their bodies to protect them from the pollution dust sprinkle. Their faces pale and drained of blood, they stand shivering and tell one another about their husbands' or children's fates, with eyes ready to overflow with tears at a moment's notice.

One person in jail can cause so much bad repercussion on those remaining outside! Some prisoners are subject to disciplinary action, which means that they cannot receive provisions that are sent in to them. The women plead and lament in tears. The response is stone faces and brutal brushoffs by the security guards in charge of taking notes about what provision bags go to whom. So their waiting around and jostling for several hours come to naught! They end up crying, beaten, and—dragging the heavy provisions bags—return home with heavy hearts!

Inside the prison, in front of Room 10, hundreds of provisions bags have been thrown down on the floor in the courtyard. Hundreds of hungry ghosts have taken turns as they are called to sit on their haunches in front of their bags. One trusty orders them to open the bags. Everyone hastens to untie the knots, pull out the food provisions, grab at them with their hands and hastily put the food in their mouths in an attempt to swallow them as fast as they can. Some get suffocated. Ten minutes is all that is allowed, so one must do one's best to fill as much as possible the stomach that by now is crushingly hungry, so much so that one would think it can even crush iron and steel.

In a prisoner's life, the provisions bag means so much—it is news, is blood and bones, is love, is a warm breeze from home. It is testimony to the love between husband and wife, to blood ties that remain between the prisoner and his family. It makes him feel that he has not been abandoned and is thus comforted. It is also a necessary supplement to the hungry hell that prison life is, thus contributing to one's very survival. The worst off are those who receive nothing but dry noodles, rice, or bran. For this kind of food doesn't get consumed easily, it has to be chewed into a paste, which then sticks to your palate. There is no way that one can quickly swallow the dry material. In the allowed ten minutes there is no possibility that enough will find its way into your expectant, hungry stomach that by now has been aroused to claim more; in other words, there is no way to satisfy one's tortured stomach. A hunger of long date, a permanent, chronic hunger, a ruminating hunger, directs every cell in your body, every one of the senses, especially those of smell and taste, and every meridian and every gland to clamor and seek gratification!

Some prisoners with extra provisions who are sitting together in a group, give one another eyes and whisper under their breath:

"How about throwing me some sticky rice cakes and I'll throw you some candies?"

"They will beat the hell out of us if we get caught."

"They're looking the other way. Throw me some roast pork."

"No fear. They'll not know. I'll get you some pressed pork. I want a couple of oranges, OK?"

"You managed to smuggle in some tobacco? Come on, give it to me, I'll hide it for you. Those chickenshit trusties are afraid of me."

Thus, the clandestine missiles fly this way and that, in an arc as accurate as the SAM 3 missiles that shot down the planes of the American pilots who once were held in the same prison they named the Hanoi Hilton. They dart from one prisoner to another, from the one in front to the one in the back, from behind up the line to the front.

Headman—the communal room's head prisoner—rushes in yelling:

"I see you guys are exchanging gifts. Confiscate them all!"

"No, we are not doing any trading. It's really unfair suspecting us. Please reconsider."

"How dare you deny it? I saw it with my own eyes. Tie up your bags, and get back into the room, now!"

The two who had their provisions confiscated stand up, confused. But they obediently go into the room. Headman takes the two provisions bags into the warden's room and throws them into a corner.

The Teacher is cleaning up the tea set and wiping the warden's desk. He leans forward to speak confidentially:

"The warden is not here. Come, it's Tết, take pity of them and be a bit more flexible."

Headman grumbles:

"They are such dumb oxes. Provisions from their families, they don't know how to keep them, instead they violate the rules by trading. OK, this time I'll let them go. How about you? Why are you so blue since the interrogation session?"

"They've decided to send me to a concentration camp. The interrogator even said they would not allow me to receive my provisions. I just think about my wife having to bring them up here and then being forced to take them back, crying and pleading. I can't help feeling so terribly sorry for her. I feel worse for her than for me!"

"It's because you tried to act tough with them. In the end it's you who get hurt. The old have a saying, 'When one is an eel, why worry about the mud?' Our prison career will last a long time. It's best to swallow one's pride and endure. Look at me, I am at least the age of the warden's father, yet I still have to make myself small by qualifying myself as 'your grandson.' He is a mere kid, freshly made second lieutenant, yet he gives himself such air, one would think he's more important than a brigadier general."

The Teacher sighs a long sigh:

"But I didn't act tough in any way. In fact, I was as pliable as a worm. But he wanted me to accept that I was guilty when I did not do anything wrong. Should I go ahead and admit it?"

Headman replies wearily:

"You will never learn the reality of prison life."

In the big room, the tough young bullies called bear-heads are pacing around like hungry tigers. Or rather like hungry dogs. They look like ferocious beasts held in a cage who are growling to be fed. They drag themselves around the floor, faces stretched in envy, looking with bloodshot eyes out the barred door at the first ranks of those eating outside, and viciously grind their teeth:

"Hey, throw some rice cakes and peanut crunch in here!"

"Fuck you, jerks! If you don't throw us your pressed pork, I'll break your ribs!"

"Be reasonable and leave us your meat. Or else your damn father here will make sure that you will not have a single tooth left to chew!"

"Throw it in here, I tell you! Or I will give you such a beating that you will be vomiting all that shrimp-flavored noodle!"

Though they are terrified of the bear-heads, none dares answer or throw his provisions into the room for them. As they eat, they only dare to dart a glance here and there. They are so afraid that their provisions will be taken away!

"Tie up your bags!" A trusty loudly gives the order.

Everyone ties up his bag. They take their turns going into the room with mouths still full and munching away. The guard frisks every prisoner as he leaves the courtyard. Three trusties take the provisions bags away and put them in the closet in the warden's room.

From the direction of the clinic, the medic and a young nurse, wearing white, bring up a tray of medicine. Headman takes some paper and a pen with him, steps into the room and says clearly:

"Anyone sick, sign up."

Over ten inmates take turns giving their names. Then they drag themselves out into the courtyard and sit down. Suddenly the sun breaks through the drizzle. The bright light seems to emphasize their ravaged faces, which exhibit all shades of sickness—black, white, bloated, as they sit on their heels and shiver in the yard.

The medic calls out the names:

"You, what have you?"

"Doc, I have rash and eruptions all over."

"Show me your hands!"

The prisoner shows the back of his swollen hands that are covered with pus-filled dots.

"Doc, I am in such sad shape that I cannot even hold a spoon to eat."

The medic takes a Soviet truncheon and slightly hits the hands of the prisoner. Yelling in pain, the latter pulls back his hands.

The young nurse laughs out loud:

"I've told you that we will not get the eczema medicine until after Tết. So those with rash and eruptions, go back inside."

Five or six fellows stand up in disorderly fashion and step inside.

"How about you?"

"Doc, I have been having this fever all night through."

The medic hands him the thermometer:

"Put this in your mouth."

After about one minute, he looks at the thermometer and shouts:

"37.2 degrees Centigrade, what kind of fever is that? Go in!"

Others also loudly declare that they have fever. They are each given the thermometer in turn to put in their mouths, without the slightest attempt to clean or wipe the thing clean. They all show a high level of fever. The nurse gives each one a sachet of oriental medicine, the whole content of which they are told to put into their mouths. A trusty is asked to run to the water container, get a bowl of water to help them swallow the concoction.

"How about you there, what's the problem?"

"Doctor, I have diarrhea."

"Others with diarrhea?"

"Me, me, me too!"

"As for me, my stools show blood and mucus. And there's a terrible pain in my stomach!"

The medic gives each one of them a piece of paper the size of a hand.

"You go over there and try to shit in here!"

They go into a corner somewhat hidden from view. The nurse follows them to observe that each is making his own sample. A moment later they pull up their pants without wiping or cleaning their asses. The nurse briefly examines the excrements found on the papers and takes them all back.

She says to the medic:

"Only this one has dysentery. As for the others, their shit is only gooey."

The medic gives two tablets of Ganidan to the man with dysentery. Then he points his finger at the others:

"Next time, if you declare yourselves sick again, I will get you the clinic treatment."

The trusties burst out laughing.

It is well known at Hỏa Lò that the clinic is used as a threat to discourage those who declare themselves sick and ask for medicine. It's called the clinic treatment because the clinic itself is a dark and putrifying room. It has a small door that is open only during working hours. There are six individual beds therein, each about 80 centimeters wide. The bed slats are all loose or broken. And the beds are covered with dirty, tattered mats. Normally two patients share one bed. Sometimes, when the clinic is crowded, they put three patients to a bed. Only those with advanced TB or a serious case of dysentery are sent here. Rare indeed are those sent to the clinic and able to survive it. It is dubbed by the prisoners 'the hospice.' Night and day, the place reeks of an indescribable foul odor. Even the medic himself hardly ever sets foot inside it. He uses a small room about ten meters away to keep watch on the patients and give them medicine. A trusty is in charge of cleaning up the clinic and taking the patients in and out. Sometimes the trusties become ill too, if they cannot wash thoroughly between duties. They are immediately replaced with another trusty.

The medic and the nurse take the tray of medicine to the next communal prison room.

Now it is time for Headman and the other trusties to take out their provisions and have a feast. The Teacher plugs in a hotplate to boil one large tin cup of water, which he pours over his dry noodles. He also sprinkles some sesame seeds on the concoction. He slowly chews the noodles and feels intense pity for his wife, trying so hard to take care of him. The trusties are, for the most part, cadres who have committed economic crimes, hence they tend to receive large provisions bags. Fish, meat, sugar, milk, candies, cookies, fruit, all sorts of provisions.

The Teacher considers it his special luck to be able to do clean-up work, to be allowed to divide the prisoners' meal portions, to clean up the cooking utensils or to wash the dishes. All the other trusties have to give big bribes to be allowed such nice work. As well, the portion of rice that goes to the trusties is several times bigger than the one going to the regular prisoners. So he does not often go hungry. It seems that he has enough starch in his meals. As for his resting place, he is given a mat all to himself, lying near the end of the room so it's not too unbearable, like having to lie near the toilet. The others have no such luck because they have to share three or four guys to a mat that is about 70 centimeters wide, so they all crowd against one another. When he moved from cell 2 into the communal room, the warden recognized him as his old teacher. This was the reason he was picked over the others and made a trusty. As for the Teacher himself, he also recognized the warden but he did not dare to say it first.

This warden of the Hanoi Hilton prison happens to be one who is curious. Whenever he finds something in a book or a magazine that he does not understand, he often goes to the Teacher. And the latter wholeheartedly explains it to him. Thus a certain amount of deference is shown to the Teacher.

However, the job has changed the character of the original prank-loving student into a supercilious prison warden, given to fits and sometimes even to viciousness. The Teacher also empathizes with his former student's situation and environment. Hỏa Lò changes many previously nice people. The young nurse at the clinic was a truly harmless soul; when she met the Teacher she called him Uncle and titled herself 'your niece.' It took only two weeks for her to become impertinent, saying he was 'a dumb ox' to his face. She has now been christened 'the Pest' by the prisoners.

"Prepare them for taking a bath."

The warden, stepping into the room with a magazine in his hand, gives the order to the Headman, who responds in a most ingratiating manner:

"The Cadre is kind and allows us to have a last bath before the year is out."

The warden does not respond, inured to this kind of flattery. He only says curtly:

"Tomorrow I will be going home to spend Tết with my family. I won't be back until the fourth of the first lunar month. While I am away you must make sure that order reigns. Don't blame me if anything happens out of the ordinary."

Headman rubs his hands and smiles obsequiously :

"Please be reassured that we will do our best. We won't do anything unworthy of your trust."

"OK, let the room out for a bath. They can clean and wash the room as well. Not more than one hour. As for you, get me a pot of tea."

"Yes, sir," says the Teacher. Then he busies himself getting the teapot and cups ready by the time the water gets to a boiling point.

Headman goes into the room and gives the order:

"Prepare to take a bath. You go out fifty at a time. Take all your personal belongings out with you so that we can scrub the floor in the meantime."

He then picks ten men to bring in water, scrub the floor where they all sleep, and even the toilets. All the trusties are busy organizing the collective bath and the washing of more than two hundred prisoners.

The Teacher places the tea set on the warden's desk:

"Report to you, Cadre. These are the so-called tea buds from Lạng Sởn. Please try it."

"It comes from the soldier who does contraband in opium, right?"

"Yes, his wife just sent it in for him yesterday."

The warden takes a sip and nods his head with the air of a connoisseur:

"Pretty good. But it is not better than the Tân Cương tea from Thái Nguyên. By the way, what does *'sen đầm quốc tế'* mean?"

"'Sen dam' is a French term, *'gendarme,'* which has been Vietnamized. It's similar to the case of *xà phòng*, which comes from the French 'savon' for 'soap.' 'Sen dam' means 'a policeman,' someone in charge of order and security. It is a common term used to ridicule the United States for taking on the role of international policeman."

The warden seems satisfied with the answer. He points to the Thăng Long pack of cigarettes on the table:

"Have one."

Thanking him, the Teacher carefully takes out one cigarette and lights it. After a long drag he feels a real sense of comfort spreading—Thăng Long is a rare brand, in fact the best of Vietnamese brands. He knows the warden to be the son of a public security brigadier general. But he isn't sure why he chose this line of work, to become a prison warden. His father surely could find him a better employment than that. His family income must be pretty good for he does not seek to steal from prisoners. The fact that he drinks regularly, every day, tea, lemon or orange juice, is simply due to the fact that the trusties like him and want to please him. It's not something that he demands from them.

"I hear the guys talk all the time about Marie Sến. So who is Marie Sến? I ask them, no one can explain it to me."

"Dear Cadre, that's slang. When we were still young, we used it all the time. Sến is another term for 'female domestic help,' but it is a term of contempt, making fun of this kind of person. 'Sến' means *'con sen,'* denoting a young female domestic who is kept by well-off families so that she could do errands and shopping, do the cooking and washing for the family, clean house. As for Marie, that's a common personal name in France, somewhat like Oanh or Yến in our language. In other words it's a French girl's name. In the French colonial time, anything associated with Frenchmen was considered high class, swanky. So the combination of 'swanky' Marie with low-class Sến becomes a term to make fun of or discriminate against some girl.

In the old days, besides the combination Marie- Sến, we also had the term Sến-Nương, which means almost the same. 'Nương' means 'co nương,' a term for a pampered, high-class lady."

The warden's eyes brighten , and he smiles:

"You certainly know a lot of things. It's unfortunate that you are in jail."

"Oh, I only know a couple of things. The ocean of knowledge is boundless. One can study a whole life and still get nowhere. To truly understand Vietnamese, for instance, one must know the Chinese characters. You yourself in the past have learned Chinese, you should continue to build on what you already know."

"You mean I need to complicate my life by learning the language of the Chinese social-expansionists? Times change; what was good before no longer holds true. I wish instead to learn Russian. Are you good at Russian?"

"Dear Cadre, I only know some rudiments of Russian."

Suddenly there is a big commotion outside near the water tank. The lesson is over.

The warden growls at the Teacher:

"You go tell them to shut up at once. If they don't I will cut short the bathing time and send all those motherfuckers inside!"

The Teacher quickly goes out toward the commotion and says loudly:

"The Cadre orders all of you to keep quiet! If you make noise, he will send all of you back in!"

The quarreling voices are immediately silent.

More than fifty naked prisoners with rashes and eruptions all over their bodies are jostling with one another around the round basin full of water. The communal basin has a circumference of 15 meters. The weather is quite chilly. Heat evaporates from the prisoners' bodies into steam. Like a bunch of madmen, the prisoners scrub themselves continuously while jumping up and down to work on their laundry, the little clothing they have under their feet. They only have ten minutes each—that's all the time they have for both a bath and laundry.

The inside-duty trusty stands on a pedestal in the middle of the basin and shouts cadence while holding a rubber sandal:

"Second dipping of water! One, two, three, four ..."

The prisoners, each one holding an enameled bowl, dip it in the basin to pour water on themselves in exact rhythm with the counting of the guard. And, at the same time, they jump up and down on their laundry beneath their feet and use one hand to scrub themselves.

"Five, six, seven, eight, nine, ten. Put down your bowls!"

One prisoner attempts to get an extra bowl. Right away a rubber sandal flies from the guard's hand:

"Fuck your ancestors, you cheater. Put on your clothes and stand aside! Give me back the sandal!"

The prisoner throws back the sandal to the trusty. He retreats to a far corner and quickly puts on his clothes.

"Third dipping and that's it! One, two, three, four, five, six, seven, eight, nine, ten. Put down your bowls! Get ready to go back inside!"

Everyone puts his bowl down on the wall of the water basin, roughly twists to squeeze out the water from his blood-and-mucus-filled meager belongings, and puts on his clothes. Then, following one another—shivering and quaking—they make a column, sitting down in the courtyard. All is in cadence with the orders shouted by a trusty.

Inside the room, the opium smuggler is commanding nine other prisoners to get water from a small basin near the room, take it inside to do the scrubbing and cleaning of the floor. While scrubbing and cleaning, they also take advantage to wash and do their laundry at the same time in the hurried and best manner they know how. These are the prisoners with some means, so they get preferential treatment. It is very dangerous to bathe from the big basin. The trusty in charge of the clinic takes the patients' clothing and their mats full of excrement and dips them right into the basin.

Then the bear-heads in the various rooms also do their laundry by washing them inside the basin. Nearly three thousand prisoners take turns bathing and washing from the same basin. And fresh water is not put in but once a week after the basin is scrubbed. It took four batches of prisoners in the Teacher's room to get through with their washing and bathing. The bear-heads, by intimidating the trusties, use up to three times the time allotted to a regular prisoner to do their washing and bathing. This means that they are allowed to stay at the basin throughout the time given to three consecutive batches of prisoners. They pick a choice spot near the water spout, which is about the size of an ankle, so that they can get clean water right from the spout. Not having enough strength or backing to seize power in Hỏa Lò, they transform the trusties into their henchmen. As for the latter, they know they have to treat the bear-heads carefully, so they turn aside and let them threaten or rob the other prisoners. On the other hand, the bear-heads themselves also have to keep the warden in mind—for this one does not steal from the prisoners, can mete out heavy punishment, and looks after the trusties. The time is not right for them to become the masters.

By eleven, everything is finished. Having to attend to some business, the warden takes off after allowing the prisoners to take their bread rations inside to eat. *Clang!* He locks the door after giving warning to the bear-heads that if they cause trouble during the few days of Tết, they will be thrown into the dungeon and have their legs locked up!

Being allowed to bring their bread portions inside to eat is a rare treat for prisoners who always want to 'keep their happy moment as long as they can.' This happens only occasionally when it is pouring rain and it is not possible to eat out in the courtyard. The majority of prisoners, when they have a small loaf of bread in hand, are unable to resist the extremely magnetic temptation to eat it right away, biting into it and gulping it down as fast as they can, as if they were madmen. The small loaf is in constant danger of being consumed in big bites, so that in a wink it will be gone, totally disappearing into one's esophagus. Only a very small minority knows how to devote much loving care to their bread portions. They don't rush to eat them. First they only bring them to their noses to sniff them. The first such kiss is followed by a loving bite that takes no more than one tiny bit of the bread—no larger than a mung bean—which would allow one to really appreciate the bread. They keep this 'mung-bean-size bite' in their mouths until the bite blends with their saliva and subsequently melts into their esophagus, giving one a sense of something truly flavorful! Then comes the next, more passionate kiss. Such 'loving acts' can last four or five hours before the bread is totally consummated!

After the room has been scrubbed and cleaned, it smells so much better. The threadbare mats filled with body dirt are now spread out. Only the trusties, the bear-heads, and a number of rich prisoners who receive large provisions have mats worthy of the name. They huddle together, shaking because of the cold.

Headman draws in his breath:

"Boy, isn't it cold after bathing! Let's have a smoke so as to warm our bodies up!"

The Teacher stops him:

"Let's wait, the warden may still be around."

The opium smuggler agrees:

"This guy likes to stick around and snoop. One must be careful!"

Top Bear-head curses:

"Fuck him! For a mere nothing he is ready to threaten us with the dungeon!"

The Teacher asks:

"What is it like? Why is everyone so afraid even at the mention of it?"

Top Bear-head, the roughest and dominant male, pulls up his pants:

"You look at this scar on my ankle and you'll know. The tendon is already gone, so I can only hobble now; there is no way to restore it. The dungeon is way over there, in a hidden corner of the Hanoi Hilton. It is surrounded by double walls. Even during the daytime, you must have flashlights in order to make heads or tails of things. And you are allowed only shorts when you are put in the dungeon. You are not supposed to bring anything with you, not even a towel to wipe your face. And we had to lie on a cement floor. Actually, that's a shit tank. A gutter runs near your feet. So all day and all night you are wrapped in urine and shit. And you are allowed only one meal a day. We call that 'eating two shifts in one.' You eat with your fingers since you are given neither spoon nor bowl. Your rice portion is put into a nylon bag. You're given no urine basin either. So you shit right where you lie. And you have to use your fingers to pick the shit and throw it into the gutter.

About two years ago, the guy in charge of the dungeon was a second lieutenant we called "Mole Eyes." There were eight roughly cut, reinforced concrete holes used to lock one's ankles. The hole number eight was the smallest and the most miserable one. My foot was locked in there. Once the three of us had our ankles put in there, they let down a three-meter long, reinforced concrete bar, which is just dropped down on us. One motherfucker trusty stays inside to make sure while 'Mole Eyes' goes outside to lock the whole setup. He jumped on the other end of the concrete bar to make sure that it is really down before he would lock it up. And whenever he jumps he laughs hysterically. As for us, it hurts so much that we yell in pain and then faint. By then your anklebones have been crushed. I had one of my ankles in hole number eight, so after a mere twelve hours they took my ankle out and put it in another hole. The longest that they put you in the dungeon is one week. Some guys cannot endure it, and, by the third day, they're already gone."

Headman asks with apprehension:

"What was your crime to be sent to the dungeon?"

"I hit the warden, for he really went after me and gave me a beating. He wouldn't let up even after I pleaded with him. Finally, I got so outraged I gave him a real punch. He went KO right away! As for the other two guys, one was there because his provisions had been confiscated, so he cursed out the warden. The other one put a sharpened nail right into the eye of a trusty. Well, now we can have our smoke. It's really torturing me!"

A trusty takes out one piece of newspaper from a hiding place and rolls some tobacco inside it to make it the size of a fountain pen. He brusquely pulls out some cotton from his padded coat and tears it into lighter cotton. Then he brings out a 'gadget' from his pocket. It's a big plastic button with a fiber thread going through it. He rolls the thread around his index finger to keep the button steady, then uses a tiny piece of glass to strike it against a lighter lead. This causes a flash of light that catches the cotton and sets it afire. He crawls on the mat, lights the tobacco stick, and takes a deep first drag. The tobacco stick burns red at one end. He gives it to Headman. Then, one after another, fifteen privileged prisoners get their smoke. A tiny end is left which the last guy throws to some six or seven onlookers. A fight ensues. The whole group is still intoxicated, feeling bobbly and 'in heaven' as the blood vessels in the body are warmed.

Jangle. Clang! The room door is wide open. The warden walks in with his truncheon, his eyes glaring:

"Aha, so you dared! I have watched the whole proceedings. You dare to smoke thinking that I would not know. Come here you, head jailbird!"

Headman trembles in fear:

"Please forgive us, grandfather. It's because of the bath, which made us all so cold that we did have a sneak smoke. I hope you understand!"

"The hell with you! Kneel down!"

A shower of blows from the truncheon falls on his shoulders and back. The warden goes to the next:

"Now your turn!"

One after the other, fourteen of the group kneel on the floor to receive their punishment quota—a couple dozen blows from the truncheon. After he is tired of hitting, the warden wipes sweat from his forehead:

"If you had asked for permission I would have let you do it. I'm a generous fellow. But if you think you can do it behind my back, that won't do!"

He takes a look at the Teacher who is sitting petrified in his place:

"Fuck your mother! It's only because of my consideration for you."

He throws the truncheon in the direction of his old teacher, then walks quickly toward the door. Headman picks up the truncheon and respectfully gives it back to him.

The trusties are afraid they will all be put back into the prisoners' rooms like the rest of them. It would be terrible if they were reduced to being ordinary prisoners. They whisper their speculations and project a sinister future. They all have cotton-padded coats so the truncheon blows did not hurt that much. But it would be miserable indeed if they lost their privileges and status as trusties!

The Teacher consoles them:

"Don't worry too much. This warden, I know him. He used to be my student. He likes to show his authority. He likes to show that everybody is under his thumb, thus proving that he has power. He has forced every one of you to kneel down so that he can hit you—that was enough for him. You'll see. He will let things go!"

The opium smuggler tries to analyze:

"He must have been outside and tried to look in through the little window at the end of the room over there. So he saw everything. It was our mistake too since we forgot to close that 'fucking hole.' It's because all of us in the room watched only the tobacco stick that no one was aware of him; that was how he could catch us red-handed. Let us now have a depression-reduction smoke. Right now, he must be having his lunch, so he cannot be around."

Headman rejects the suggestion:

"Please, I beg you, daddy! If he catches us one more time, that would be the end of us!"

The bear-heads and the majority of the trusties, however, support the opium smuggler's suggestion. In the end the decision is made to 'start the fire!'

The trusties go back to tearing cotton from their clothes and rolling the tobacco. One laughs heartily:

"Our weapons are still intact; there was no loss. Attack the enemy when he least expects it. A sure way to victory!"

They gather once again and take turns to smoke. It was decided that no one, absolutely no one, outside the group is to get a share of the smoke!

Clang! At two o'clock in the afternoon, the warden comes back and unlocks the room, his face absolutely blank as if nothing happened. Headman opens the door and greets him with effusive respect.

The warden tells him in a low voice:

"There might be a room inspection today, you'd better be prepared."

"Yes, sir!" Headman is very happy. It's obvious that the warden is willing to drop the whole incident this morning. He even volunteers the information about a possible room inspection, so that the prisoners can hide away what may be against the regulations. The trusties are allowed out to do various chores. They do not have to worry. Besides the tobacco pouch, the makeshift lighter, and a few sheets of newspaper, there is nothing else to hide.

In the warden's office, the Teacher slowly cleans the tea caddy and cups and boils some water to prepare his tea.

Seeing that he is unhappy, the warden asks:

"You must be thinking about what happened at lunch time today, right? Do you think that I overdid it?"

"Dear Cadre, that's not it. It's just that it's Tết and I miss home, so I feel a bit depressed."

The warden points to a water pipe in a corner of the room and says:

"I brought that. From now on I will allow you all to have a smoke four times a day. It's absolutely out of the question that you smoke inside your room!"

"Dear Cadre, it's forbidden. You are most kind to us, but if the prison supervising team knew, wouldn't that get you in a bind?"

The warden stiffens his features:

"Me in a bind? I allow you to smoke, so you can go ahead! Even the supervisor of the prison owes me some consideration. I have let them alone, so they should know how to respect me too. How dare they harass me?"

The warden takes a long drag from his cigarette, blowing out smoke in small round puffs. Then he suddenly asks:

"At lunchtime, if I had hit you, how would you have reacted? Be frank."

The Teacher answers in all sincerity:

"I am a prisoner. If you hit me or put me in irons, I just have to accept. But if you asked me to kneel, I would not have done so. Even if you beat me to death. For that is just too shameful. I would not be considered human. I would have despised myself for the rest of my life. There is simply no force in this world which could get me to kneel. Ever since I was very small, I only kneel in front of the altar to my ancestors."

The warden explodes in loud laughter:

"Very good, very good. In my case I would have reacted the same way. The other prisoners, they always demean themselves by calling themselves 'your grandsons' in front of a cadre. They make themselves as small as they can. That's why I despise them. And I hit them precisely because I despise them. Come on, have some tea, have a smoke!"

The Teacher thanks him, takes out one cigarette, and drinks a cup of tea.

The warden is a bit flustered:

"When I am angry and do things that are not quite right, please disregard it. Now tell me about your case. Why do you have to be in here so long? What did you do wrong? How did the interrogation session go this morning?"

The Teacher gives a full account of his situation with his wife, then the details of his case.

The warden shakes his head:

"What a nonsensical case! I trust you. When I was studying with you I found you to be a most conscientious teacher, never a counterrevolutionary. Let me mention your case to my father. He might be able to do something about it. So don't give up hope. Don't let yourself down too much. As for the cutting of provisions, you don't have to worry. This afternoon I will go to your home and get your provisions, bring them in for you."

The Teacher is overjoyed:

"If you can help clear my case, we would be together again, my wife and I. Such a favor I will never forget. As for the provisions, please tell my wife that they are not necessary. She knits sweaters twelve hours a day and makes only 40 *đong* a month. That is not enough to even take care of herself!"

"Don't mention it. I see something that needs to be done and so I do it. It will be fine. I will tell my father in detail. At any rate, you used to be my teacher. And I will tell your wife exactly what you ask me to!"

When he sees six, armed, security guards approaching, the warden comes to military attention and calls to the trusties:

"Room inspection!"

Headman steps inside the room and shouts loudly:

"Take all your personal belongings out into the yard."

Over two hundred prisoners take their bags and bundles and follow one another out to put them into a pile near the tropical almond tree. Then they sit in rows, filling the whole courtyard. Two armed guards wearing mouth masks go into the room, ferreting out every nook and cranny, feeling holes in the walls, not forgetting the shit hole. Outside the trusties empty the bags and bundles in the open. Nothing but dirty and moldy clothing.

After the examination, each prisoner must squeeze the clothing back into his bag or bundle. Then comes the body search. Each one is ordered to take off his shorts or pants, shirt or T-shirt, to be frisked. Skinny bodies, with rash and eruptions now exposed, stand and shiver in the wet courtyard. The spring drizzle keeps on sprinkling water vapor on them. Those who have been examined take their personal belongings to a corner and sit by themselves under rows of hundreds of clothes washed in the morning, which have been left to dry—one on top of another—on a wire about four meters long. And they drip down on one's head, one's shoulders. An acrid smell of disease and decay pervades the whole place. A couple of armed guards wearing mouth masks are stationed to observe the whole inspection.

A trusty displays the rough cotton shirt of a prisoner who is half crazy and half dumb. He yells in his dread:

"Nothing but lice and their eggs! There must be thousands here!"

The warden looks up briefly from drinking tea and orders:

"Burn it!"

The mental case wrests back his shirt, lamenting:

"It's very cold! Let them eat me! For I very much pity them! I just have this one piece. You cannot burn mine!"

"Burn it! And give him one interrogation shirt!"

The trusty runs into the warehouse, takes out one paratrooper shirt, throws it to the crazy man, then flips a lighter to burn the lice-ridden shirt right there in the yard. The prisoner sitting in his corner bursts out crying.

The inspection goes on for more than one hour. Two guys from the kitchen bring the prisoners' lunch up on a pole. The Teacher wipes the cement block clean, pours the whole load of steamed rice on it and divides it into portions of one small bowl each. Then comes the turn of the bindweed, cooked with salt. Since the bindweed season is long past, what is served now is nothing but the dry roots that are left bristling with tendrils. The water in which the weed was boiled is salty and astringent and blackish. The warden looks at the rice and vegetable broth and shakes his head.

He turns to Headman:

"Let them eat early so they can go inside. Later today there must be lots of provisions from outside."

A trusty curses:

"What kind of fucking vegetable is this? They must consider us no better than animals. Throw it away!"

The Teacher knows that the trusties would not be able to swallow this kind of weed, so he doesn't bother to leave them any.

On days close to Tết, the atmosphere at Hỏa Lò is oppressive. Everyone is weighed down with memories and feels his heart sink at dim prospects for the future. They miss their wives and children and are torn with foreboding: how many more Tết s are they going to spend in jail? When will their separation with loved ones end? When will they have reunion with their families?

A few tentative explosions of firecrackers echo from the streets outside; the *bang* tree shows little buds in anticipation of the spring. The prisoners' faces, however, are dark with premonition as Tết approaches.

The hungry ghosts sit in the spring drizzle. They concentrate on chewing the tough bindweed roots, gulp down the awful salt water, which is even darker than muddy water. Their whole bodies shake violently. In prison, after each meal, one always feels terribly cold. And ravenously hungry. For the portion one gets is just about enough to stimulate one's tastebuds and stomach, so that his internal organs persecute the prisoner even worse than before the meal.

An old hunchbacked prisoner, nothing but bones and a wrinkled face, sighs and comments in his anguish:

"I am sixty-five now. Only now do I really understand the expression, 'The fire of hunger burns my stomach and a cold knife cuts through my skin.' When I was young, I heard this expression many times, but in reality I had no idea what it meant."

"Did you receive Tết provisions from outside?"

"Yesterday. My daughter gave me one steamed rice cake, a little pork, and a couple of pickled onions. That was all she had."

"So at least you have some taste of home, that should comfort you. It's not like me, naked among a pack of wolves!"

"Fuck my wife. For six months now she has left me without provisions. If she ignores me this Tết, I am going to leave her when I get out!"

"I'm afraid she's already left you. Wait until you are out and leave her? What illusion!"

"Oh, there're hundreds of those who go to prison and lose their wives. Nothing new!"

"Hey old man, what brought you in here? Did you rape children?"

The hungry ghosts laugh and laugh at the question.

Headman's voice suddenly booms:

"Inside now, let's go!"

Once again everyone must be back in rows on the floor.

A prisoner pushes up to the group a wheelbarrow filled with a few dozen provisions bags. Headman reads the names written on the bags and calls the fortunate to the courtyard. On hearing their names called, each one jumps up in joy:

"My old dad still loves his thief of a son!"

"It's obvious that my wife has not yet been carried off in another guy's arms."

"I was ready to deny my ties to her this Tết, mother or not."

"How true is the saying, 'Number one is to be released, Number two is to receive provisions'!"

Many have not received provisions for a long time now. When their names are called, they move awkwardly, as if they are dreaming. They are moved to the point of being speechless.

After having gone through the dozens of provisions bags, the Teacher goes inside the room to pee. A tough-looking bear-head of about twenty years, alert and with a bronzed body and his hair cut short, laughingly asks him:

"You didn't receive your provisions yet?"

"No, I am not allowed them any more. How about you?

The youth laughs, showing a row of very attractive white teeth.

"I'll be released tomorrow. What need do I have for provisions?"

"Congratulations! But how do you know beforehand? Have you been informed?"

"I'm going to tell you the truth. Do you know the poet Nguyễn Xuân Sanh?"

"Before 1945, he was a member of the 'Xuân Thu' group, together with Đoàn Phú Tứ.[3] I have read his poetry, have heard of him but have never met him. Let me see. I still remember one of his verses, *'At the bottom of the disk, the season goes following the rhythm of ocean and rivers.'* That's his poetry!"

"I am his son."

"Oh, is that so? So you are his son? You're entitled to go for studies in Russia or Czechoslovakia. Why are you here in prison?"

"What studies! I am born only to fool around. About two months ago, I tried to rob a foreign embassy and got caught."

The Teacher is aghast:

"For that, you can get ten years! Are you sure you're going home?"

"Of course! My father has saved me several times. He says this will be the last time he'll do anything for me."

The youth lowers his voice:

"You know, he works for public security!"

"I understand. But let me advise you to stop now. For he'll one day not be able to intercede for you. After all, your family is pretty well off, why should you?"

"Oh you just don't know. For we indulge in orgies. What family can provide for us? Even Huỳnh Tấn Phát's son has to play with guns and rob people. His dad also went around asking for leniency in his case, but it didn't do anything to his bad habit. He was in Room 12. He was released yesterday morning. A real handsome guy!"

The Teacher taps on the shoulder of Nguyễn Xuân Sanh 's son:

"You are handsome too. Handsome in a manly way. Good luck to you. Let me pee, then I have to go out and work."

The day has turned to evening, and the spring drizzle is still on, seeping cold. Those receiving provisions have eaten their fill and gone back into the room. Every one of them is filled up to their neck. They ate as if in revenge, making up for the months and days when they went hungry to the point of sickness. A couple of guys even had to throw up in the WC. It's quite a while since they have had their fill.

This time they eat fat together with sweet stuff, so they end up with diarrhea, their faces drained of blood. It's even worse than when one is hungry. But at any rate, they had a few moments of eating enjoyment.

Near 6:00 P.M., the warden walks up to them and says hurriedly:

"Go inside, all of you. I have to go back home tonight. Have a merry Tết. I'll be back on the fourth or fifth."

Headman rubs his hands together and says obsequiously:

"On behalf of all of the trusties, we wish you many an achievement so you get elevated in rank and ..."

"Thank you, thank you."

The warden turns to the Teacher and hands him a small bag:

"Now here's your provisions. She insists on sending it on to you. There's a letter also. We won't tell the interrogator."

The Teacher quickly puts the bag into the provisions commode.

"Thank you very much. Did you find my wife in good health?"

The warden hesitates before he answers:

"Generally speaking, yes. She's a little thin, though."

Another trusty says politely:

"Dear Cadre. I am afraid there are no cars left at this time."

"I'll take my bike. Come on, go on inside, it's getting late."

At the Hanoi Hilton only a couple of wardens have bikes, so this one is really proud of his Japanese-made Dream motorbike. The warden in charge of the kitchen also has one, as does the one in charge of the rooms of those already sentenced, for the last two jobs are the ones that pay the most income.

After he has had his tea and smoke, claiming he has a headache, the Teacher hangs up his mosquito net and lies down. He wants to be by himself so he can think of his wife. This is the first time after twenty-one months that he has received a letter from her. Though the letter is only a few lines long, so much love and binding have gone into this one letter! He lies in the net, reads and rereads the letter, over and over, to the point that he memorizes it! His tears start falling. She tells him to be pliable, to swallow his pride and strive to bear any unpleasant situation that might come his way, and not to try to be too upright. But hasn't he lived like that all these years? A long time ago, she was his student. She came to love him and marry him.

It was all because she believed in his good faith, his dedication to work, and his straightforward character that tells things as they are. Then from experience, she realized that a lot of people went to jail simply because they were frank with their words. She then pleaded with him to live somewhat differently, to know how to wear a mask and laugh false laughs, say the things that one doesn't believe in, and especially how to give false compliments. So partly because he loves her and partly because he too realized that he could not live truthfully as he would wish, he would have to go along if he doesn't want calamity to befall him. So year after year he became like someone who lives in the midst of life but without hearing or saying anything, as if he was deaf and dumb. He would be modest and deferential, even in front of untutored bullies known for their bad acts and shamelessness.

There is one area, however, that he could not—for the life of him—train himself to do, and that was to sing the praise of lies, of baseness, of perfidy, or to eulogize crime, repression of human dignity or common decency. The most he can do is to keep an attitude of cold contempt when he sees some of that. Such an attitude does not make the school leadership or the ward authorities satisfied, but it is usually sufficient to keep him out of trouble. When he had to go to jail, it was clearly a case of tough luck, of calamity falling from nowhere. In short, unavoidable.

Only when he was imprisoned did he realize how much he did not understand about the regime, the socialist system in which he had lived all these years. He can not imagine how, as a teacher of Chinese, the fact that he read Chinese newspapers, listened to Chinese radio, and fraternized with Chinese neighbors all these years would suddenly become a crime in the eyes of the authorities. Once the cozy friendship between China and Vietnam was gone with the wind, he should have steered a different course right away. So that is his error. And the fact that he is now separated from his wife must be ascribed to that error.

In her letter, his wife wrote: *"No matter what, I always belong to you, and only to you."* Thinking of an indefinite future of separation, he feels so truly sorry! Only now does he truly understand the Vietnamese meaning of 'heart wrenching,' for it is not just a term to describe some spiritual or emotional pain, it is actually a physical pain that he can feel wrecking him. He feels his intestines tighten and crushed inside. He wishes his heart would explode to relieve the pressure.

Jail life has taught him a great deal. When the warden promised that he would ask his own father, a public security official, to intervene, he felt that he could start hoping again. But, upon reflection, he sees that such hope is rather unrealistic. For, in political cases, no one would be dumb enough to try to intervene, not even a blood kin. People like Huỳnh Tấn Phát or Nguyễn Xuân Sanh could ask for reprieves for their children, because the latter are only involved in petty larceny or robbery. Had their children been politicals, how would these 'chairmen for show' or 'snoopy poets' dare to open their mouths? He remembers the day when he first came into the Hanoi Hilton, while he was still in the infamous cell number 1, he saw Huỳnh Tấn Phát being given a guided tour of the two memorial cells where the Communist agitators Hoàng Văn Thụ and Trần Đăng Ninh, had been kept by the French. Huỳnh Tấn Phát put his head in only one cell and straight away he fled, not daring to look right or left. He just could not bear to even take a look at other cells![4]

The Teacher lies immobile in the mosquito net and lets his thoughts wander, oblivious to all the noise and conversation that are going on outside. The whole night through he can not get a wink. He just imagines himself living with his wife. Only near dawn is he able to float into sleep, into a deep slumber.

It is the eve of Tết; the weather is beautiful. When the prisoners are allowed into the courtyard to have their meals or eat the provisions brought by their families, the golden spring sun gleams on top of disheveled or hairless heads, rough grotesque faces that are portraits of hunger. Discolored rags full of grease and dirt, limbs ravaged by eruptions and eczema: the prisoners look like so many domestic animals in their skeletal appearance, barely walking about, half alive, and only greedy for food.

Sad news comes from the kitchen area to throw even more despair and bitterness into the group. For on this Tết, there is no meat, just some pork bones to make a broth of cabbage. Thus all the expectations built up over several months for a piece of meat just crumble to dust. In the best of years, each prisoner is entitled to about one hundred grams of pork with some innards, a little bone, and some kohlrabi. And the whole thing would be divided into two meals: one on the eve of Tết and one on the first of the year. But the prisoners who go hungry all year round still entertain some expectation, looking to such a diet. For in a life of endless dry and paltry meals, to be able to lick some fat is for them already a great improvement, a joy, a festive occasion. Furthermore, on these holy days, they also have the chance to inherit portions from others who, because of the ample provisions they get from home, would not touch this prison fare. In other words, one would get filled a little better than usual. For when one is hungry, there is only one possible desire, that is to have something to eat. Anything else is soon forgotten.

Around noon, the trusties, the bear-heads, and some of the rich prisoners get together to discuss a plan. They all thought that this year they could organize to greet the passing of the year in a somewhat more celebratory fashion, *comme il faut*. The warden has gone back to his home village. With the cat away, it's time for the rats to come out and romp!

Headman is the first to speak:

"We're lucky this year that they had room inspection yesterday. So there is nothing to fear. They're not coming back for another. We can all bring the provisions inside so that we can really greet the zero hour in a grand manner, thus missing our homes and families a little bit less. Let us combine our goods in whatever way we can so that we can have fun, what do you think?"

The opium smuggler is enthusiastic:

"I'll chip in my roast chicken, two steamed rice cakes, and a box of fruit preserves."

The Teacher is somewhat more modest:

"I'll bring my share of one steamed rice cake and one Hồng Đào tea caddy."

The inside-duty trusty waxes generous:

"There are fifteen of us here, so I'll bring in fifteen shrimp-flavored, instant noodles and a kilo of nougat candies."

Headman shakes his head:

"It's not good to do ramen. It's too much trouble to boil enough water for fifteen bowls. We should bring in a small pan to boil water for tea only."

"In that case I will replace the instant noodles with fifteen soybean cakes and a pork roll."

With everyone so eager to contribute, it soon became too much to consume in one session.

The Teacher proposes:

"Let's cut down on the pork roll and fried pressed pork, or the meat and steamed rice cakes. Let's throw in more candies and crackers so that we can give some to those without family provisions. But the fifteen of us will not have enough for everybody. So I propose that we allow some with provisions to join us, with the condition that they have to bring in some extra, so that we can have enough of something for everybody. It would be heartless for us to enjoy eating and drinking while they have to look on. It would be best if we can organize so that the whole room can have an enjoyable Tết. What do you think?"

Top Bear-head is all for it:

"Right, let's have the whole room enjoy this time. I will give to each one two small pellets of tobacco. Without a smoke, Tết would not be Tết!"

Everybody agrees. So that evening when they partake of their family provisions, the trusties ask everyone to bring in a little of what they received from home, just telling them that they should keep it out of others' eyesight. Once in the room, they collect all the food meant for the celebration, put it into a single big gunny sack, which they hide under the pile of personal belongings in a corner of the room.

The last meal on the eve of Tết is exactly like the morning one: a little bowl of cold rice with a bowl of blackish, astringent, salt water. As they eat, all the prisoners curse unceasingly about the fare.

"Perverts, all of them! It's inhuman to give people food like this at Tết time."

"Even dogs in French or American families eat better than this!"

"They are worst than beasts, people who can treat others like this."

"It's the beasts themselves who have eaten all the meat and fish, what is there left for us?"

"If the day ever comes, we'll have to skin them alive, put dirt in their mouths! Only then can we forget this anger."

"Rice with salt. We'll have to make them pay for this!"

"Yeah, an enmity that will never dissipate!"

"Fuck you, guys! Are you crazy to stand there and quote Tố Hữu's poetry? Better to quote our fellow prisoner in the solitary cell, the Zen Master Chí Thiện:

The rise from apes to men took millions of years:
How many years has it required,
the fall from men to apes?

Stomp stomp stomp. Six o'clock, a guard comes. He orders all the trusties into the communal room.

Headman is agitated:

"That's it. Let's distribute the candies and cookies to those without family provisions first. Give them the tobacco at the same time."

There are seventy of them, the so-called "homeless" ones. They all sit in rows and each one is given twelve candies, seven crackers, and two little pellets of tobacco.

The inside-duty trusty tells them:

"Quiet, and listen! You can eat the candies and crackers right away or wait until the zero hour, it's up to you. As for the tobacco, let's get ready to have the first smoke!"

The whole room suddenly comes alive. How true the expression, one piece to bite when hungry is worth a whole pot when one is full.

A trusty goes around giving each one a little piece of paper so he can roll his tobacco in it. Then another makes the rounds, getting homemade matchsticks for everyone to light his handmade cigarette. Everyone is soon conked out. Some are down on the floor, others fall backward. Some have their heads leaning against the wall, others find themselves on others' shoulders with mouths foaming and eyes rolled back. Over two hundred men in the room are like that. A most unusual sight. The bear-heads and the trusties laugh uncontrollably.

Top Bear-head says with authority:

"They haven't had a smoke for a while, that's why. And when that happens, a long drag will get you into the ninth heaven. At the crack of the New Year, we'll get you your second drag—to kick out the old and bring in the Year of the Monkey.

The trusties, the bear-heads, and the wealthier prisoners start coming together to sit in a circle, relishing their tea and smoke as much as they would like.

The inside-duty trusty confides:

"This is my third Tết in Hỏa Lò. I have to admit, this is the best Tết I have enjoyed so far. The other years, they waited until the very eve of Tết before they did their inspection. Then they corralled us all at once, so there was no way to sneak in anything. Not even a smoke. It was miserable!"

The Teacher concurs:

"Right. Last year, on the eve of Tết, the whole room were like zombies. No one felt like talking to anyone."

The opium smuggler sighs:

"I have spent many Tết s in the jungle. But none was ever as bad as in Hỏa Lò. Four years ago, I turned in my captain's stripes so I could be demobilized and go home and get married. I had it up to here with the military life. It was time to say farewell to arms so that I could have a chance to rebuild my life. It's too bad I got caught, and this could keep me in here for ten years. I wonder whether those generals and colonels who were in this with me would be able to rescue me."

The whole room was alive with conversations, noisy as an open air market. At least for a moment one could forget about prison and about families.

Crash! Clang! The door to the room bursts open. Five armed guards rush into the room, shouting:

"All of you, stay put!"

The guards start looking and ferreting everywhere. They don't frisk anyone but everything they can find—candies, cookies, pressed pork, fried pork roll, steamed rice cakes, roast chicken, fruit preserves—is thrown into two big nylon bags. The whole thing takes no more than five minutes. They walk out with the two booty bags. *Clang!* And lock the door.

One guard says in a supercilious way on his way out:

"It's Tết, so we only confiscate. And let you off easy as far as the violation of prison regs is concerned. How dare you bring food in the room!"

The whole room is quiet as a church, everyone stunned by the unexpected outcome. After a while, the opium smuggler hisses:

"Fuck them and their ancestors. We've been trapped. We fell right into their ambush! We've got to admit it, these rascals had us!"

The inside-duty trusty explodes:

"And we end up empty-handed while they have a great time tonight. They will even have provisions to spare, so that they can bring some home to their wives and children. Damned devils they are! Robbing prisoners! It's just as they say, 'Ghosts don't spare sick people; neither do robbers the poor!'"

Headman laments:

"Who could have foreseen that they would lower themselves to this? Well, there goes our heroic People's Army!"

Top Bear-head mumbles:

"It would have been a catastrophe had I not been smart enough to hide our tobacco supply just in time! Imagine, nothing to smoke throughout the three days of Tết! Look at their scheme. Even ruffians have to take our hats off to these bums. We were not their equals, so it's natural we lost out."

The Teacher takes a more consoling attitude:

"Good thing we had distributed some to the 'homeless' guys! *We* failed, but at least they had a little something to enjoy. A bite and a smoke; it's not much but at least it is not something to cry about."

After many laments and begrudging thoughts, the whole group finally tires. They lie down in unison and put their arms on their foreheads. The room grows chilly and depressing.

Top Bear-head sits up full of determination:

"Let's forget about it all! The more we think about it the more woeful we become. Where's the singer? Let him come out and entertain us, so we can forget. I will give you a pellet of tobacco!"

A pale-faced prisoner, with his hair in a mess, protruding eyes, and even more protruding Adam's apple, comes forward.

"Come here. Have a smoke, so you can feel like singing!"

After a long and most satisfying drag, the singer clears his throat, hits the right pitch, and starts:

> *"The cows in the city*
> *"With their bells ringing ..."*[5]

The opium smuggler barks:

"Turn it off! What the hell do you want to go on with that damn cow song for? What a dumb ox!"

"What do you want me to sing, then?"

"A rowdy, fighting song! Grieving and lamenting will get us nowhere! Let's go. First, *Forward Soldiers*, second The *Internationale*, then *Let's Kill the Fascists, The Vietnamese Infantry Song.*[6] And you'd better sing them with your full throat!"

The singer does his best, straining his esophagus:

> *Forward soldiers go, yellow star bright*
> *Marching forth, stamping the ground to go ...*
> *Let's all stand, to break up our chains*
> *For too long we've swallowed pain ...*
>
> *Tear them up, we'll drink their blood!*
> *Let's rush to battle!*
> *Forward, let's all shout!*

After that rousing beginning, he is even stronger:

> *Rise up, o slaves of the world!*
> *Rise up, o poor and miserable!*
> *Blood is boiling in your plentiful heart*
> *Determined we are to either live or die.*

The words blow a feeling of inebriation throughout the room. Hundreds of voices join in. The whole atmosphere becomes electric, as if ready to explode.

> *Let's kill the Fascists:*
> *Viêt Nam all these years in yoke and pain*
> *As we suffer under cruel wolves.*
> *The Fascists, they rob us and they rob our rice*
> *Fill the land, now with jails and tortures untold ...*

Kill Fascists and o yes, their running dogs …
It's now time to revenge all.

The singer is now impassioned, his voice a flowing stream. Because these are songs everyone knows, the whole room is engaged. They are all standing now and sing with thunderous voices:

Fill the land, now with jails and tortures untold.
Let's go, with swords unsheathed
It's now time to revenge all.

It was exactly the right mood. People no longer sing, they shout the words. The electricity can be felt, red hot and burning. The neighboring rooms clap in unison in encouragement. Even from their faraway cells, some death-row prisoners join in the songs to give heart …

The ancient call, to break our jails!
And kill them all!

This last refrain, sung full-force by two hundred prisoners and repeated over and over again, echoes from end to end of the thick mortar walls.

Bang! Bang! Bang!

The shots ring out, tearing through the night. *Clang!* Everybody freezes as the door to the room is kicked open. Dozens of armed guards, AKs in hand, march into the room, shouting:

"So you are preparing for rebellion, huh? Who were the singers? This guy and this guy and this guy!"

They start taking the prisoners out, one by one. The trusties, the bear-heads, the opium smuggler—since they are near the door—get dragged away. They are all pushed into a large room, under glaring lights. In the middle of the room an older security officer sits beside a large table. The remains of the prisoners' food is on the table next to a couple of bottles of rice wine.

"Up against the wall!"

The prisoners are beaten on their chests and shoulders with the butts of the AKs:

"Now this is for rebelling! And this one, too! We'll just have to crush you all to death."

When the prisoners slump down, they stomp them with their boots, brutally, viciously, repeatedly.

"What crime did we commit? You have no right to hit people in such beastly manner!"

The prisoners react with one voice. For the first time, they no longer belittle themselves with demeaning conduct or by pleading for mercy.

The opium smuggler stands up, his face red and his eyes bloodshot as if he has turned into a madman. He points to the half-finished roast chicken still left on the table and yells:

"I am a Party member and a captain in the army. In the war I have had my brushes with death! On whose authority dare you rob the prisoners of their provisions so you can have a good time? This roast chicken belongs to me! I will denounce this to the supervising team, to the prison office, and to the Ministry of Public Security! If you dare, why don't you go one beating me to death? I will denounce you! So go ahead, beat me up! Kill me!"

And as he shouts, he tears up his shirt to show his chest in defiance. The whole group of armed guards stops their beatings in confusion.

The prisoners grope with their bony arms forward and stand up, adding their voices pell-mell to the charge of the opium smuggler:

"We will all denounce you, with one voice! Yes, we will denounce you! All two hundred of us will denounce you!"

The Teacher, wiping away the blood on his face, is decisive:

"You have smeared the name of the people's public security forces. We can die at your hands but we will definitely denounce you. There are plenty of witnesses, and the physical evidence is all here. Neither the Party nor the government will let this pass. I mean your unacceptable robbing of the prisoners and then beating them. All we did was to sing revolutionary songs! How dare you say that we were rebelling?"

The older officer, a captain, sitting at the table next to a wine cup, stands up and explains in a calm voice:

"You were yelling, 'Break our jails! And kill them all!' Is that not a call to rebellion? The comrades here were a bit impatient and had dealt with you a bit harshly, I will have them undergoing criticism. You can rest assured that I will not report this to the Supervising Team. Nobody among us is afraid of your denunciations, since you are by definition violators of the law. But let's drop it, since it is Tết, let's be friendly, OK?"

Having said that, he walks to the closet, opens it and takes out a carton of Sông Cầu cigarettes and a packet of Ba Đình tea, which he gives to Headman. He turns to his underlings and orders:

"Take them back to their room!"

Four guards with AKs escort them away. They walk some five or six yards behind the group in somber silence. The beaten prisoners can hardly walk, dragging along in a sorry state. The guards are patient, not saying a word instead of their normal shouting, yelling, and cursing the prisoners.

The night is bone-chilling cold. The northern wind blows the drizzle dust into their faces, wet and cold. *Clang!* One armed guard says in a quiet voice:

"Tomorrow morning we will bring you some medicated oil."

The prisoners do not answer. They all go back to their places and lie down. The whole room sits up and watches them in amazement. One prisoner, lying near the shit hole, whispers:

"They must all have had their fill of the beating."

"Whoever came up with the idea of singing in the first place?"

"That's not over yet, there will still be consequences for this!"

The hunchback crawls over to the Teacher's place to share his sympathy:

"You must be in great pain. Let me rub you, give you a massage. You will feel relief right away. For this is what I am good at. If we have real medicated oil, it will be very effective."

The Teacher whines in his pain:

"My chest really hurts. They are truly beastly. My wife just sent me a bottle of medicated oil yesterday. Could you rub it on me a little!"

"Why don't you turn around and lie on your back. Open your shirt, let me see. Gosh, it's all purple! Good thing you all wore padded cotton. For without that, you would all have your ribs crushed."

The hunchback spreads the medicated oil, rubs and massages several places. The Teacher finds his pain alleviated quite a bit. He tells the whole group:

"Sit up, you guys. Let him rub oil on for you. It really makes it a lot better."

The hunchback rubs and massages the entire group of beaten trusties, one after another. They all feel relieved, and their pain alleviated. After he is finished, he stands up to go back to his mat when Top Bear-head stops him:

"Father, why don't you have a smoke with us!"

Glancing at the opium smuggler, whose face is still red with anger, Top Bear-head laughs:

"Tonight, we realize how big your guts are! Let all of us prostrate and pay you our respects. It was thanks to you that the armed guard had to stay their hands."

"Stay only? I will sue them, 'til their stripes are ripped off, for that's unpardonable."

The Old Hunchback says sadly:

"You are still young, and do not understand the situation. It will be like the proverbial ant suing the potato. Not only will it lead nowhere, you might even end up in trouble. You should just listen to me, the advice of a dumb old man. It's best for you to drop the whole thing. For it is a most inhumane line of work, to be a prison warden."

The opium smuggler bites his lips and opens wide his eyes:

"Inhumane? Should the world turn upside down and they have to go to jail, I'll have just one wish: to be 'a tiny prison warden' to give it to them!"

Top Bear-head jumps up:

"Me too."

"Me too, me too! Me, me too! How about me?"

Snap! Snap! The Teacher can hear a few firecrackers outside, forlorn and solitary against the immense night sky …

How many million years did it take from ape to man?
How many years did it take for man to rebecome ape?

O let the world come and visit
These concentration camps in the deep jungle!
Naked, these prisoners move in bands, by the herd
Co-existing with lice and mosquitoes, ill-smelling and glum
Fighting each other for a piece of yam or manioc
In chains, they get shot, mowed down, slit up!
Far from being fast, these apes are very slow
Unlike the apes of prehistory
They are thin and hungry, like toothpicks
But are expected to produce all year round …
O let the world come and visit![7]

STORY 3

The Moon and Waters of the Red River

Once the death sentence is pronounced
One is no longer allowed family visits
And even the day of execution
Goes unannounced to one's loved ones!
Those meant for execution
Spend all their time shackled in isolation cells
And their daily diet is no better
Than those of regular prisoners:
A pitiful bowl of rice with salt-water!
And on the morning going to the execution ground
They have to be dragged out by others
Since after long shackling they stumble at every step.
They are given a couple of cigarettes
A small metal cup of tea
Plus two biscuits
Called the standard final treat
Which most of them don't even touch!
Sitting in a tomb-like truck
They still have black bands tied over their eyes
And sit with arms bound tight in the back.
The car would go at top speed
To deliver them to the execution ground.
Here, a rag awaits them
Normally a real dirty one
Would be forced into their mouths

"The Moon and Waters of the Red River" was translated by Nguyễn Ngọc Bích from the original Vietnamese "Trăng Nước Sông Hồng" in *Hỏa Lò* (2001).

And pushed far inside with a gun-cleaning rod
Lest they would emit blasphemies!
Their gums sometimes get punctured in the process
And they would start bleeding.
Strong ropes would still be brought out
To tie them up to the execution posts
Crushingly, to ill and old people alike
Enough to kill them right then and there
So that the shooting is a mere procedure!
As soon as the sentence is read
The shooting team blasts away
Unloading six slugs in each chest.
As soon as the ropes get cut
The corpse slumps to the ground
The shooting team leader
Armed with his pistol
Comes and kicks the corpse in the face
To expose the man's temple
Where he would shoot a last bullet
Called the grace bullet!
A forensic doctor would step forward
And give a perfunctory exam
And the shooting team wearing masks
Afraid of reprisals at some future date
Pack themselves onto the truck to go back to camp
To 'enjoy' a couple of beer mugs as their reward![1]

"COME, GO ON INSIDE. Others have to do their toilet, too. It's getting late."

"I've been out here only a couple of minutes, and you want me inside? I'm scheduled for execution soon; I don't have that much time left to breathe in this air. When will it be? Maybe tomorrow, or the day after tomorrow, six bullets will be lodged right here in my chest. Let me watch the clouds and the sky once more. I'll go inside in another hour."

The Warden spoke patiently:

"Look, there are so many people in line. Could you please go in.? Or else, it will take all morning and they still will not be finished with their toilet."

Death-Row, bare-chested and wearing an army-issued pair of shorts, turned his protruding eyes up in anger and shouted:

"The hell with them! I won't go in. They have all their lives in front of them; they can breathe as long as they need to."

Catching a white-dressed figure going past beyond the courtyard, he stretched his neck and yelled:

"Report to you, damn executioner doc. I asked you for some meds yesterday. Why the hell are you not giving it to me, your father? Ha, so you're slinking away? Fuck you, executioner doc! Damn you, fucking horny quack!"

The doctor came by the door leading into the cell-row courtyard and said soothingly as if he were talking to a small child:

"You have one of those chest pains? I'll get someone to bring you the pills right away. Calm down! Calm down!"

Chuckles and jeers came from the cells of both men and women prisoners. *Crack!* The Warden stood up with a murderous face, brought his fist down on the table and said:

"Shut up, all of you! Or I will have your mouths padlocked!"

A few dark green dragonflies soared by, glittering in the beautiful early morning sun.

The Warden looked at his watch and said more urgently:

"Come on, go on inside. Don't you see there are tons of people just waiting for their turns going after you?"

Death-Row laughed heartily:

"Why do they have to wait for me? If they have to, why don't they just do it in their individual pots? I have my feet in stocks 24 hours a day. I have only a few minutes of relaxation after a whole day in stocks. Why should I go in, so you can put me in stocks again? All I am waiting for is 'bang-bang-bang-bang-bang-bang' and that will be the end of me, of my suffering!"

The Warden said soothingly:

"Don't be so pessimistic! You have sent an application to the president asking for an amnesty. There's a good chance he might answer you. You've been in the army and laid your life on the line ..."

Death-Row made a face and cut him off:

"Don't you go and lull me with false hopes! I have yet to see an amnesty granted by our 'beloved comrade leader' Trường Chinh! Let me tell you, if the Chinks had not missed my heart by just three centimeters, I would have had it. And I wouldn't have to drag out my miserable life and have to suffer fools like you who so cling to longevity, people who have never seen a battlefield and yet who now try to get me inside, not even allowing a condemned prisoner enjoy a few minutes of cheap air. This air, you know, belongs to Heaven and Earth; it does not cost you a cent nor is it your property to grant or not to grant! I'll stay out here another two hours. You can go ahead and do whatever you want!"

The Warden uneasily pulled out a cigarette and lighted it. One shouldn't push a death-row inmate to the wall; he knew that. For it had happened once that a deputy supervisor got a basin full of shit dumped on his head, thus becoming the laughing stock for the entire prison. As they say, playing with lepers, one can only get hurt.

The Warden turned to diplomacy:

"Come on, why don't you go into your cell? I won't put you in stocks until after everyone is done with his toilet. You know, in my capacity I have only so much leeway. OK?"

After a minute of hesitation, Death-Row bent down, picked up his basin, and laughed uncontrollably while walking to his cell:

"OK, with that kind of consideration I'll agree to go in. I don't want to inconvenience my 'lady friends' by making them wait on

---

(*opposite*)

C. Door detail of cell #2 in Hanoi Central Prison

"As he walked past the Hoàng Văn Thụ *Memorial Room, Death-Row stopped to take a long look inside, remonstrating: 'Look at the back of the room! There used to be a huge window where the wind and the sun could come in. In front there were two breathing holes large enough for a child to squeeze through! In the early day the prison was named* Hỏa Lò, *meaning "the oven" by Vietnamese. Now the Communists cement everything up. The room becomes as dark as night, and it's even more like a furnace inside!'"*

(Photo from "Hanoi Prison Images" by Chris McCooey, 2004)

account of me. They would be too uncomfortable if they have to keep it all inside."

As he walked past the Hoáng Văn Thụ Memorial Room, Death-Row stopped to take a long look inside, remonstrating:

"Look at the back of the room! There used to be a huge window where the wind and the sun could come in. In front there were two breathing holes large enough for a child to squeeze through! In the early days the prison was named Hỏa Lò, meaning "the oven" by Vietnamese. Now the Communists cement everything up. The room becomes as dark as night, and it's even more like a furnace inside!"

Jangle! The Warden impatiently shook his key ring:

"Don't you go on with your counter-propaganda!"

"Look, the reality is right there! How can you say I am doing counter-propaganda? Why don't you look at the Trần Đăng Ninh Memorial Room over there? It is kept exactly the way it was under the French, so it has plenty of air circulating. But what's the use of talking to you anyway?"

Crash! Death-Row threw his basin violently onto the cement floor of his cell, startling the Warden.

Slam! Jangle! Clang! The Warden went to the next cell and opened the door. Two sickly pale women, one very young and the other in her midyears, holding their chamber pot and carrying dirty clothes and two towels, came out in great haste.

The Warden pronounced:

"Each room will have exactly five minutes. So make it quick!"

Fourteen people came from their cells to wash and change in the space of an hour. Shouts and yells, exhortations to rush thing up, heavily thumping feet, the crash of basin covers dropping, then doors closing and opening, all in pandemonium.

Clang! The Warden locked the door to the corridor and left within the hour.

Ten minutes later, a kitchen trusty, also a prisoner but fat and tanned—almost bursting the buttons of his green prisoner pajamas—carried the food on his shoulder that was to be distributed into the cells' courtyard. He put a darkish pan of boiled wheat flour, then a pot of blackish salted water that looked like gutter water, down on the long table next to the wall. On it were also piles of enamel bowls and platters, plus rusty, notched, and dirty spoons. He silently went about his business of serving the food, not looking towards the cells, following prison regulations to the letter by not communicating with the other inmates.

In the cell nearest the courtyard, an imprisoned Fallen Cadre had the duty of peering through the cracks between the boards that were used to board up the window.

He announced to everyone:

"It's boiled wheat flour and gutter water again!"

This was followed by angry curses, cluck-clucks full of despair, and sighs of resignation.

"Hey, Feeding Brother, are we going to have water spinach soon?"

"How about this coming August 19 Anniversary of the Revolution? Will we have some meat'?"

"How about just some rice? Can you tell us?"

"Fuck you! Are you deaf and dumb?"

Despite the questions and the foul language coming from the various cells, the kitchen trusty went on with his duties, ignoring both inquiries and taunts. When he was finished he put the empty pots and pans back into the baskets and carried them away at the two ends of his flailing pole.

Death-Row spoke up:

"Me, their father, was slapped with a death sentence yet they only feed us each meal with this gutter water and a few biscuits the size of a cat's tongue. Under the French, Phạm Hùng and Hoáng Văn Thụ were treated to a royal diet after they received the death sentence; they were given whatever they wanted, a menu that is even better than the 'Folder A menu' served at Tôn Đẩn! As for us, their fathers of today, as soon as a death sentence is slapped on us, right away we are subjected to around-the-clock stocks and prevented from seeing our families. What a fucking regime!"

"How do you know?" the Fallen Cadre with a Central Vietnamese accent challenged him: "How do you know that under the French the death-row guys were treated to a royal diet like that?"

"How do I know? Simple. It was they themselves who recounted those experiences in their collective revolutionary memoir.[2] All you have to do is to ask Phạm Hùng, who is now the Minister of Public Security, and he'll tell you. He was amnestied and therefore escaped death, that's how he was able to recount that in his memoir. He even said that the ordinary death-row fellows, criminals who had robbed and killed people, also received the same treatment—a menu to their liking! Every morning a warden would come with a notebook into the death cells to ask everyone and take down what they wished to eat. Thanh, the pockmarked, who lived in the same cell with Phạm Hùng at the time, asked for a capon and Havana cigars. As for Trần Đăng Ninh who was held in cell no. 2 over there, he recounted that Hoáng Văn Thụ had so much that he could never finish his meal, so he gave the remains to the women prisoners. These books, you can check them out at every library!"

Bang, crash, bang! From cell no. 14—where the notorious Revolutionary Phan Bội Châu was held back in 1925—came the noise of a toilet basin being banged on the boarded window.

Death-Row found the protest hilarious:

"Hey you, go on banging and soon you won't have a basin left in which to 'empty your confidences.' You know, the rats here at Hỏa Lò couldn't care less. Let them, let them eat and piss and shit on your provisions. If you are afraid to eat that, then give it to me, I'll take care of it. There are fourteen rations out there; you can give them to me, and in no time I'll make a clean sweep of all fourteen! You don't believe me, then why don't you try me sometime?"

Tramp-tramp-tramp. It's the Warden! *Jangle.* Taken by surprise, four huge city rats with dark grey fur, the size of small cats, that were exploring the boiled wheat flour dishes with their snouts, jumped off the table and disappeared into the gutter.

The cells were opened one after the other, allowing the prisoners to come out, get their rations, and take them back into the cells.

When it was Death-Row's turn, the Warden became solicitous:

"Here's the oil to rub on for the chest pain. From today, I will not put you in stocks until this time of day. You understand? And if you behave and do not cause any disorder, I will tell the kitchen trusty to save you two portions each time."

"I'll not take from other people's portions! For if you make my ration bigger, it'll mean the others will have less to eat. The whole roomful of cells will curse me under their breath. Oh no! You're just being generous at other people's expense!"

"If you still let that bother you, then let's drop it."

The Warden walked out in embarrassed silence, even forgetting to make trouble for the inmates as he did every day.

In everyday life at the Hanoi Hilton, once you had had the morning meal, half a day was already shot. All they had to look forward to was the evening meal. And after that, there went your

D. Starving prisoners

The genocidal starvation policy of the Vietnamese Communists occurred in prisons in both North and South Vietnam. These civilian prisoners were rescued from a Việt Cộng 're-education camp' in the Phú Yên province. (Undated broadside in Turner Collection at Hoover Institution Archives, Stanford University)

day. Then one started looking forward to the morning meal the day after. The two meals were the high points of one's day since every prisoner was starved, his or her stomach crying out for food, giving him the shivers, making him swoon sometimes. They starved to the point that the hunger itself seemed to be eating at their flesh, losing their bodies day after day, month after month, and year after year.

On that particular day, after the evening meal, the sky darkened suddenly. Then came howling winds and spattering rain, accompanied by thunder and lightning that felt as if the earth and sky were about to split. But, despite the breaking of branches and falling trees, and the electric poles swaying and tiles flying, the cells at Hỏa Lò remained unshakable because they had walls half a meter thick!

The agitated prisoners shouted:

"Aha, what a great storm! It's even better than a dish of fried *phở*."

"Yes, all my heat boils will disappear like magic."

"Right. Had the heat continued, we would all go crazy."

"Let the storm blow away this whole universe for all I care."

But rising above all these others was the voice of Death-Row, who was yelling like a madman:

"Long live Uncle Hoàng Văn Hoan! Long live the great Chinese Army! Liberate Việt Nam!"

After all the shouting and animated conversation, everyone gradually went into a deep sleep. For nearly a month, the air in the cells felt like the inside of a boiler. Heat boils grew all over the body. And they started to itch and demanded to be scratched. Sweat came down in streams. And it was a field day for the lice and mosquitoes. Nobody was able to sleep. But today it became cool, so that everyone soon found himself or herself deep in slumber, unconscious.

When Death-Row woke up in the middle of the night, the storm had cleared. There was total silence throughout Hỏa Lò. In his cell he could hear the breathy snores or the grinding teeth coming from the surrounding rooms. It was not clear what time it was, but Death-Row sat up and used his two hands to brush his eyes and massage his face a while to get fully awake. He then grabbed his nylon water container, drank it ravenously, spilling the water onto his throat and chest. Putting the container away in a corner of the cell, he cleared his throat a couple of times, then started singing. He had a low-pitched, warm, sad voice that in the night gave a sense of the tragic fate he was facing.

I wore out my eyes
Looking South, a lone swallow in the sky ...
Ting taang ting
O my love ... Do you feel my love ...

He stopped singing and pricked up his ears. The cell in front was quiet, totally quiet. 'She' must be sleeping. He had been moved from Division 2 to Division 1 only a week ago. For the last few nights he had been singing these verses, once he had made sure that everybody else had gone to sleep, to give 'her' the signal that they could start their heart-to-heart conversation. He waited a little longer but when he heard nothing from the cell opposite his, stretching his hand with difficulty from his position in the stocks he knocked a few times on the door of his cell.

From the opposite cell a loving, caressing female voice was heard:

"Why are you up so early today? Did you sleep well?"

"Yes, I did. How about you?"

"I was just lying here, kind of dreaming. For quite a while now I have not been able to sleep well at night. But I don't need the sleep anyway. There'll be plenty of time for sleep!"

"I am sitting up right now. Are you lying down or sitting up?"

"I am lying."

"Lying straight on your back or lying on your side?"

"On the side towards outside."

"Can you lie on your side even with stocks on?"

"I've lost lots of weight. My ankles now are truly small, and I can turn a bit."

"Would you want me visiting you now?"

"What a dumb question! How can you come into my cell? Both of us are going to die any moment. How can you still joke?"

"I'm not joking. I ask you a serious question: Would you want me by you?"

"Of course! Imagine what we can do if we had met outside of jail!"

"That's all I want to hear. Thank Heaven that they moved me into this cell so that I could be near you! Now I can lie opposite your cell."

"You put your faith in Heaven?"

"That's just a way of speaking. Neither Heaven nor Earth is to be trusted! Life is full of cheats, dirty tricksters, and hypocrites. The more honest and kind you are, the more they will suffocate you to the point that your eyes will pop out. For a long time now I no longer believe in anything. Neither Heaven nor Earth nor man! You're the only one that I trust, that I believe in."

"Why do you believe in me?"

"Well, it's something not easy to explain. The first time I saw just your silhouette going about doing your toilet I already felt something stirring wildly in me. Then when I heard you dragging your clogs in the hallway, a kind of weary, despairing gait, I suddenly felt immense sympathy for you. One day I took advantage of the fact that the Warden was flirting with the nurse at the table and opened the vent looking into your room. I saw you—so pale—sitting on the floor, your legs in the stocks. You were skinny with hair flowing down to your shoulders. The light was a sickly yellow in the room, and you appeared sad; however your features were really fine and beautiful. You were frightened when you saw me. But your eyes, they are so attractive, they could draw my soul out of my body!

(*opposite*)

E. Hỏa Lò/Hanoi Central Prison Museum exhibit showing prisoner in leg stocks

"'I was just lying here, kind of dreaming. For quite a while now I could not sleep well at night. But I don't need the sleep anyway. There'll be plenty of time for sleep.'

'I am sitting up right now. Are you lying down or sitting up?'

'I am lying.'

'Lying straight on your back or lying on the side?'

'On the side towards outside.'

'Can you lie on your side even with stocks on?'

'I've lost lots of weight. My ankles now are truly small, and I can turn a bit.'"

(Photo from "Hanoi Prison Images" by Chris McCooey, 2004)

Looking into your eyes I felt a world of dream invade my thoughts, a world of happiness. That night when you threw a string across to my room, on which you could send me sugar cubes, candies, biscuits, a needle and threads, even toothpicks. Then there was also a whole box of Yellow Star plasters. Ever since my parents passed away, I have never been taken care of with such tenderness. You know, I cried a whole lot that night. And I have loved you ever since. Once we are in love, we must of course believe in each other. Moreover, I admire you too."

"What is there to admire about me?"

"That you used arson, burning down the house of that policeman with one can of gas. That really got all of Hà Nội shook up! Now that's an achievement!"

"It was simply because I couldn't stand it any longer. All I did was trade food coupons at the government store so as to make a living. I didn't do anyone any harm. But that policeman who lived near our house was out to have a free ride everywhere. He got others to pay for his food and drinks and cigarettes; he ate off the *phở* peddlers, took drinks from the old drink-selling women, and pilfered cigarettes from poor little kids who sell them. He gave himself the right to go through our belongings on several occasions. And while at it, he took advantage and started pawing my body! I told him to go to hell. So he took me to a block meeting so they could denounce me. My mother, who was a teacher, was also called up for review sessions. I did my best to contain my anger. But when I was ordered to go to a New Economic Zone[3] because of him, I could no longer restrain myself. I decided to burn his house. I didn't know he was in it, but I am not sorry. How about you? You were just guilty of burglary. How could they sentence you to death? That's incredible."

"You don't know the full story. It was because I was the leader of the group. Normally you would get ten years at the most for burglary. But, unwittingly, we had touched upon their main stores of western medicine belonging to the Central Committee on Đinh Liệt Street near the Lake of the Returning Sword. That was how we got into real trouble. The attorney, Mr. Đỗ Xuân Sảng, when he met us the day before the trial, had warned us: 'You think you are so clever! What a thing to do! Whoever could get away with playing with the penis of a horse? There's no way to save you. I must declare forfeit right now.' What a damn unlucky life I have. I enlisted into the army at age 17. I fought against both the Americans and the Chinese. In more than ten years in the army, I have been on and off many battlefields, yet I only got a slight wound on my chest, another on my thigh, which led to my demobilization. I am an electrician by profession, never knew a thing about stealing or burglary. But I was head over heels over an army singer, and she loved to dress up. She got all kinds of presents and gifts from the officers. I was much the poorer but I still wanted to impress her by outdoing the officers, by giving her something really plush. That was how I came to organize this raid on the pharmaceutical place and got my death sentence. Ever since I got caught, not a peep is heard from her, and she has distanced herself from me as much as possible. I am really mad at her behavior. Many of my friends had advised me not to have anything to do with army performers, for they are fickle by nature. They even told me beware of 'hospital beds and the loving cheeks of army performers,' meaning anyone could lie in them or kiss them. I regret now not having listened to them. So when I met you, it was like the first love of my life. You are exactly like the woman I dream of having as a lover. But with me being such a villain, would you still love me?"

"If we two, both death-row inmates, don't love each other then whom can we love? When you looked into my room, I saw your face it was really funny because you seemed ecstatic. It must be that we have been destined for each other since some ancient time. You know, this year I am nineteen, and out there I have not had anyone to love."

"Nineteen! Just four years past fifteen, the full-moon age! And never been in love, a Maiden. You just barely started out in life and already you have had to step out of it soon. What a pity, a loss! I wish I could die in your place. Wouldn't that be much better! I am exactly twelve years older than you. But how can you be so calm? You're not like me, for I sometimes feel that I could go insane."

"I am calm, did you say? It's because I believe that we have souls and that souls transmigrate. Each one of us does not just have one life but actually many. All that remains for one to do is to live a life of decency, and if we sow the right seeds, in the next life we will be reaping good harvests. My mother loves me, so she sacrifices from her teacher's salary to keep me well provisioned. But when I see that most prisoners here just have their two meals of prison fare, and become so hungry and miserable, I feel for them so I distribute most of what I have. I may have gone thin, but it does not matter that much. Whether I am fat or thin, it does not make any difference since pretty soon I'll be lying down with the earthworms. The Old Man living next to my cell has explained it all to me, what is life and what is death, so now I understand and find peace."

The Old Man was lying straight in the stocks with his two arms lying beside his body. He had his eyes closed and breathed regularly. When he heard his name mentioned, he opened his eyes and held his breath.

"Oh the anti-revolutionary Old Man.You know he is a poet who has made hundreds of verses against the regime for more than twenty years?

"Yes, he was arrested and brought to Hỏa Lò for bringing his poems to the British Embassy on Lý Thường Kiệt Street. His poems were published by overseas Vietnamese in the U.S.A. last year."[4]

"As a poet, he made up the stories of the souls' transmigration to console you. I have been through many battles and saw lots of dead people in the fields. Never did I see any of their souls."

"Neither have I, but the Old Man is an experienced and truly decent person; he does not lie. He said that a number of people have actually died, then come back from the dead. They all tell you that once their souls have left their bodies they fly to a zone of light, with beautiful perfumes and colors, that it was fun there, and that no one for that reason wants to go back down on earth. But in their situation, because they were not yet fated to die, their souls were returned to their bodies. Then there are the stories of new births from someone else's womb—all true stories that have been documented in modern science. He said that for certain it was God who created the universe and the hundreds and thousands of species on earth. Take something simple like a bowl or a spoon, even as simple as they are, they must have been created by someone. Let alone something as extraordinary as man; he cannot just suddenly appear."

"That sounds pretty rational to me. A few days ago, I dreamed I saw my father and mother. They were smiling and said that pretty soon they will have a chance to receive me to join them where they are. So let's make a pact: in the next life let us live together! And if we are going to be reborn, let's be reborn in America so that we'll have at least a comfortable life. Let's not be reborn in this S-shaped country of ours, for that will be the end of us."

"It's too long waiting for the next life. I am afraid I cannot wait that long. After we die, we have to meet right away. Let us pick a truly lovely site, say on the bank of the West Lake, near Thanh Niên Boulevard, OK? Then on moonlit nights, with the surface of the lake spreading out immensely, peacefully and glinting under a soft, caressing wind, we will be sitting next to each other on one of those stone benches. My head will be on your chest, and you will be caressing my cheeks ..."

"What a great idea! But there are too many couples on the banks of the West Lake. Then the 'red flag youths' will be roaming around checking and harassing you. That's no fun!"

The girl giggled pleasantly:

"We'll be ghosts, how can they see us? Even if they see us, they will probably faint out of fear. How could they possibly impede our love?"

"You know what? I think that to avoid all these obnoxious interferences, let us meet on the dike of the Red River. You know, the place leading straight out from the Đồn Thủy Hospital. When we were around fourteen or fifteen, my friends and I used to play on the sand, then we swam across the river to the other side. We would sneak into the Indian cornfields and break off a few cobs, which we would roast over a fire. The moon and the waters of the Red River at that time were at their peak; they were glorious, you know. It was absolute peace. There will be no 'red flag youths' to bother us. What do you think?"

"Yes, why didn't I think of it before? When I was little, my family lived right around there. My mother actually gave birth to me there, too. On moonlit nights let us meet there then. With you by my side there are no places where I would not feel happy. Even right now when we are in these damp and dirty cells with our feet shackled in the stocks, I am happy knowing our love must be predestined by Heaven."

"I feel the same way. How strange that we both have the same ideas? There must be a destiny fated in Heaven, for God must have arranged things so that before I die I met with you, fell in love with you, and now am loved back. Yes, by now I believe there is a Heaven also. Just imagine the two of us embracing each other and entwined like two bodies inseparable, with the moon in the background and the vast waters of the Red River slapping ashore! Oh I feel so good, I no longer fear death, my darling! It's apparent that faith and love are clearly stronger than death!"

"By the way, if in the other life you betray me, I will set your soul on fire, you know that? And you will not be able to be reborn."

"By the grace of Heaven, God has given you to me. If I ever betray you it would be tantamount to betraying God's trust. You won't have to set me burning on a fire. For Heaven will have sent a lightning bolt on my head, killing me instantly. Oh darling, how I wish I could go into your room now. Just thinking of embracing you and caressing you, I feel myself in a high fever, shaking all over."

"Me too, I want you. You know, my forehead is perspiring. Let's pretend we are a couple lying side by side. From now on, let's be husband and wife, and tonight will be our first night together, OK?"

Death-Row was surprised:

"So you also thought of us marrying and considering ourselves just as good as married? I've also given thought to that, you know. What a coincidence! Do you know why I gave them so much trouble this morning?"

"Normally you are so taciturn. But this morning you were so contrary. The warden finally had to yield because he was afraid of you."

"If he didn't yield, I would have given him a taste of '*mỹ-kim.*'"

"*Mỹ-kim*? You mean U.S. dollars?"

He laughed:

"What dollars? I don't have any! But we prisoners call a bayonet or a dagger '*mỹ-kim*,' meaning 'beautiful blade,' the kind of precious metal that women would wear as adornments. I have spent time polishing a really sharp nail three inches long and it shines in the dark. Had he been insolent, I would have 'adorned' his face with a few punches so he could remember me the rest of his life. Or I could have done it in his eye, so he would have just one eye! I've been a commando and I can act quick as a squirrel. He wouldn't be able to react in time."

"So you played the recalcitrant this morning just to have a few hours of freedom?

"Right. This morning you were let out of your stocks like me, right?"

"Yes, they didn't put me in stocks until lunch time."

"See? I've attained my objective."

The Maiden smacked her lips:

"To be let out of the stocks for a couple of hours may not be worth your wasting your breath with him."

"That's not my ulterior motive. I've had this plan in mind. But you have to pardon me first before I can tell you."

"We are husband and wife now, we can put our entire body and life into each other's hands. What is there left for you to beat around the bush as if we're strangers?"

Death-Row lowered his voice and said:

"Since you are so understanding, then let me say it. Last night, while I was lying there I had thought to propose to you that we become husband and wife. Obviously we cannot have a night of love together. So I thought that maybe we could just look at each other, naked. But if we are both in stocks, of course, there is no way we could stand up and look into each other's rooms. That was why I cooked up this plan so that they would not put us in stocks until after the toilet hour. Do you see what I am getting at? Tomorrow morning, after we get back from the toilet, I'll stand on the stocks and look into your room. When it's your turn, you do the same, stand on your stocks and look over into mine. If that's still not high enough you can use something like a blanket or your toilet basin to bring you up higher. It's a good thing that at toilet time they still leave the lights on. Remember, you have to really take everything off."

"Agreed, and you must do the same. I have never seen a man. And if you see the opportunity, you must open the vent opening into my room, just like the other day. And I will put out my lips so you can kiss them!"

"Bright idea! I will kiss you, for sure. No, not just kissing. I'll breathe into your soul, darling."

"Me too, I'll drink yours also. So that our two souls can become one."

Tramp-tramp-tramp. Clang! Clang! Tramp-tramp.

Death-Row panicked:

"They may come for me!"

The Maiden heard her own heart pounding:

"It could be me."

"Whatever, we must be calm. We must be courageous. I have prepared a long time for this moment."

"Me too."

Screech! The iron door leading into the courtyard opened. The warden and four armed guards stomped into the hallway. All the prisoners in their cells sat up, holding their breath, and straining to hear.

The warden opened the door to Death-Row's cell. Two armed guards rushed in, shouting:

"Stay where you are. No movement whatsoever!"

They took his two arms, twisted them behind his back, and locked them with handcuffs. Only then did the warden come in and unlock the stocks.

Death-Row spoke only to his Maiden:

"I go first, and I'll wait for you on the bank of the Red River. Remember the moon and waters of the Red River. Don't you miss our rendezvous!"

The Maiden banged frantically on her door and yelled:

"Why don't you take me away with him. Please!"

One of the guards laughed:

"They're so afraid they both went nutty. If you had the guts to rob, you should have also had the guts to get the punishment."

Another pulled out a band of cloth and covered Death-Row's eyes, then pushed him out of the cell.

Death-Row turned back towards the Maiden's cell and said:

"Good bye, love. I am very happy having you. Do not grieve. You have to maintain your composure. Don't beg them for anything. We'll surely meet again."

The Maiden was inconsolable:

"Oh darling, good bye. How I love you! I want to go with you. We must meet again, that's certain. On the bank of the Red River, I'll make sure to be there."

Death-Row said with a shout:

"Farewell, friends, farewell! Good bye, darling."

The Warden grumbled:

"Fuck you! About to die soon, and still you are unruly! Before shooting you, we'll have to beat you up first."

"Don't you touch him!" the Maiden yelled. "Or you won't even have time to repent."

The counterrevolutionary Old Man broke in with a strong and severe voice: "At this moment and you still think of beating him. Are you out of your mind? Or are you a beast? I'll report this to your superiors!"

Two of the guards took Death-Row by his arms and dragged him away:

"Let's go, let's go!"

As he went into the courtyard, he turned back and shook his manacles, shouting:

"Don't you grieve, I'll wait for you! I'll wait!"

"You go first, I'll follow you. We will surely meet, oh my darling!"

From their cells, the women prisoners cried and cried. But there was one voice that was dramatic beyond imagination: it was a high-pitched staccato cry, a voice so tragic that it rends the heart of anyone still human.

In the distance she could still hear the voice of Death-Row becoming more and more indistinct:

"The moon and waters of the Red River .... Remember the moon and waters, my darling ...."

Silence.

Death-Row's voice could no longer be heard, only that of the Maiden sobbing. The Old Man could faintly hear an echo of a song left in the walls by the imprisoned American pilots ten years before:

Come and sit by my side if you love me,
Do not hasten to bid me 'adieu'
But remember the Red River Valley
And the girl who has loved you so true.

STORY 4

The Mist

My poetry's not mere poetry, no,
but it's the sound of sobbing from a life,
the din of doors in a dark jail
the wheeze of two poor wasted lungs
the thud of earth tossed down to bury dreams
the clank of hoes that dig up memories
the clash of teeth all chattering from the cold
the cry of hunger from a stomach wrenching wild
the throb-throb of a heart that grieves, forlorn,
the helpless voice before so many wrecks.
All sounds of life half-lived,
of death half-died—no poetry, no.[1]

THE JOLTING OF THE SECURITY CAR for six long hours on the pothole-scarred road from Camp Z8 to Hà Nội continued to make the Old Man's head spin. He never thought of his birthday, which had been a cursed day to him for a long time. It is August 10, 1983, the day he was born in Yên Đổ fifty-three years ago. *"More years of age, more of unwanted strands of ruffled hair; I am fifty plus three, now."*

At thirty-three, he was sent to a concentration camp. He was in prison four years before his wife left him. When he was released it was the end of the war with the Americans, and more room was needed in the prisons for the officers of the defeated South Vietnamese army. He was then forty-seven. Weary in body and mind, he came home only to find that his only son had been killed fighting the

"The Mist" was translated by Trần Văn Điền from the original Vietnamese "Sương Buồn Ôm Kín Non Sông" in *Hỏa Lò* (2001).

Americans at age nineteen in the Trường Sơn Mountains, and his wife had married a cadre.

His sister tearfully told him not to blame his wife:

"She loves you very much. After the day you were captured, she had to work as a peddler to earn her living. Without the cadre and his protection, she would not have been able to feed your son. Marrying her, he was subject to review and unfairly dismissed from duty. Later, he had to pull a handcart for living. It is a backbreaking job that requires a lot of muscle. He took good care of your son until the day he was drafted into Uncle Hồ's army and was sent to fight in the War of Liberation."

His sister's words danced in his head to the rhythm of the rolling movement of the vehicle, reminding him how to nurture a thankful heart:

"He has fed my wife and my son, my son and wife," he tried to convince himself; "the man stealing my wife turns out to be my benefactor."

But it was a reality he had to admit. So many of his fellow prisoners had been left by their wives. Their children were unattended, uneducated, and became delinquent. Fathers and sons were sent to reeducation camps, starved and forced to do hard labor. Women sometimes had to sell their bodies to feed themselves and also their husbands still in prison.

After being released, the Old Man lived in a small room with a few bachelors for nearly two years before he was arrested again. In 1979, the Chinese guns started rumbling at the frontier. He had to report to Public Security every day for review and self-examination. His friends were in no better situation. The news of war caused quite a stir in the Security Bureau. Vice-premier Phạm Hùng issued a decree, gathering all the persons deemed dangerous. Reading the news in *Nhân Dân,* quite a few women burst into tears. Some fainted. The Old Man knew they would be coming for him again.

Then, one morning in May, no sooner had he got up—without even brushing his teeth and washing his face—than a security agent showed up, locked his hands in metal cuffs, and took him away. After a few days in Hỏa Lò without being interrogated, he was transferred to Camp Z8 in the Nghệ An Province.[2] He had moved from camp to camp several times before; but this time, the experience was unforgettable. The feet of political prisoners were locked in stocks. Criminals were manacled in pairs. The vehicle shook violently. When the driver took an abrupt turn, all those inside were suddenly thrown to one side. The editor of the Chinese newspaper in Hà Nội was by the Old Man's side. He uttered a loud cry because one of his feet was broken at the ankle. The vehicle kept rattling on. In spite of cries of pain, two armed guards sat tight, not caring to unlock the foot-stocks for him. They even cursed the prisoners who had requested them to unlock the journalist.[3]

Surrounded with dense bamboo hedges, Camp Z8 nestled in a valley near the Lào-Việt border. He arrived when there were many cases of severe dysentery throughout the camp. The Old Man followed his fellow prisoners to the right-side thatched houses where people were held who had not been infested with diseases, because the thatched houses at the left side had been reserved for diseased people.

It was dinnertime. The irregular lines of the surrounding bare hills were being reddened by the yellow rays of the setting sun. The wind from Laos sent wave after wave of heat into the dry valley void of trees. The air was thick with blowing dust. "This is a valley of death," he thought. He sat cross-legged on the ground, trying to hold a bowl of moldy rice up to his mouth and eat some boiled manioc-leaves, but he could hardly swallow his dinner although his stomach was empty. The taste was so bitter. He put some spoonfuls of rice into his mouth, trying to swallow them, but gave up and handed the left-over to a person nearby. A prisoner muttered a curse:

"Damn it! What a picky prisoner! We have only dried manioc to chew! Months and months have passed without any fresh rice. Our complaints are just like pissing in the wind!"

The Old Man stood up in silence, letting his eyes travel beyond the campground. He could not believe his eyes. About thirty meters away, an unforgettable scene came into view. Under the saffron yellow evening light were lying or sitting hundreds of naked, pale prisoners, all skin and bone, eating rice with their hands. Unable to hold the bowls steady, some of them let rice spill out onto the ground. They shakily bent down to pick up dirty grains of rice and put them into their mouths.

Everything appeared before his eyes just like a silent movie. The striking scene was two ghost-like humans with entirely bald heads and sunken eyes who were sitting face to face in an impassive expression. Four trembling hands were clinging to a bowl of rice and slowly moving back and forth. At a closer look, he realized they were struggling for a bowl of rice left by a prisoner who had collapsed. They were too weak to speak, to curse, or to fight. An ox-driven cart rattled in. Two trusty prisoners walked into the building. After a moment, they carried out five naked corpses and threw them into the ox-cart before it was drawn away. After eating, the prisoners stood up, with a trail of blood mixed with mucus dripping from their bottoms.

"We go for a drink. Stay where you are! Absolutely no talking with anybody!" The loud voice of the guard startled him back to the reality of his journey. The car pulled over. The security guard and his driver got down and stepped into a nearby restaurant. It's Văn Điển. The streets were lined with low-roofed houses. Here and there, rather empty restaurants served refreshment, noodles, even dog-meat. At noontime, the dazzling sun blazed down on the streets. The air was filled with the smell of gas, asphalt, and food.

A road roller was rumbling back and forth. A number of workers were busy digging a ditch. Heavily loaded bicycles were moving with difficulty while antiquated bicycles hurried by. A group of cyclo drivers, with their pedicabs left under a shady tree, were drinking, smoking, and chatting in a restaurant. A gang of dirty, carelessly dressed children narrowed their inquisitive eyes to look at the black security-car and then at the Old Man. They pointed their fingers to the handcuffs, sticking out their tongues, chanting:

"Hey! Hey! Prisoner!"

He looked at them, sadly thinking: "We're only happy at the time like this when we're young and innocent, free of all kinds of worries about life-problems. It is the 'age of jade,' indeed."

Suddenly, an ear-splitting shriek was heard from a house on the other side of the street. Then the door burst open as a woman with a ruffled head of hair ran out. A man with a stick in his hand chased after her, shouting angrily:

"You, wicked woman! I'm gonna kill you!"

Some cyclo drivers ran up, trying to stop him. The woman rushed into a restaurant yelling:

"Damn you! You have abandoned your family to run after that dirty whore. I can't stand it any more. I'm going to denounce you. As a principal, you will be fired and expelled from the Party."

She repeatedly clapped her hands on her crotch, shrieking:

"You damn goat! What is this? Isn't it your much-worshipped place? Why do you have to thrust your head into that dirty whore?" Everybody burst out laughing.

The innkeeper, an old woman, came forward to pull her back, advising:

"Calm down, please! Remember you are a teacher. You'll become a target of ridicule for everyone. If something wrong happens, as husband and wife, you'd better talk to each other behind closed doors."

"How society has changed," he thought. In the old days, teachers were expected to be role models. Nowadays, even evildoers have different ways of thinking. In 1961, when in prison for the first time, he found that all the inmates were ashamed of themselves. They tried to hide their identities as thieves, because at that time criminals were held in low respect in the community. Now, they openly boast their feats of robbery. The more badly they behave, the prouder they become, because society considers them normal persons. Chairman Hồ's adage 'It's the time of heroes' should be changed to 'It's the time of robbers.'

After paying the bill to the restaurant owner's daughter, who was laughing heartily, the security guard and his driver climbed back into the car and drove away, crossing Hai Bà Trưng Street. They stopped in front of Hỏa Lò Prison. *Clang!* The iron gate closed behind them, and the Old Man was handed over to a warden on duty, who brought him past Division 2 to Division 1.

After a trusty had checked his belongings and searched his body thoroughly, the old warden with first lieutenant rank pointed at him, ordering:

"I am a member of the supervising board, in charge of this division. If you violate the regulations, I have the right to put you in the stocks and cut off all supplies at once. No talking, no communication with other cells, no praying, no looking outside, no disturbance whatever. Go in now!"

Clank! The warden opened cell 14. *Bang!* It shut. A half-naked prisoner in shorts, with a clean-shaven face and well-combed hair, was sitting on the ground waving a paper fan. The Old Man dropped his bag on the floor and lay down with a sigh, his head on the bag. He then turned to his fellow prisoner and asked:

"How long have you been here, friend?"

"Just two months. And you, where do you come from?"

"Camp Z8, Nghệ An. Many people are dying of dysentery there, and I have been moved."

"You must be very tired. Let me make you a mug of lemon juice."

The Old Man sat up, replying:

"Give me just plain water!"

His fellow prisoner smiled, showing regular white teeth:

"Let's be informal and frank! We're all prisoners. I just got some food from my wife, yesterday."

The well-groomed man of middle age pulled a bag of supplies from beside the stocks. He took out some sugar and a lemon. The Old Man stopped him.

"Thanks for your kindness. I've been in prison many times. I know food is precious in here. Supplies are from sweat and blood of the family. Keep them for your own use! Once in a while, my younger sister sends me some, though it means nothing to me. I have been used to the prison norms. I really appreciate your concern. With you as a companion, I feel happy, after all."

"Don't refuse, friend! You're still tired from a long trip. This is the first and also the last time I invite you."

He could do nothing but accept his insistent invitation. His new friend took a small piece of aluminum hidden in a gap in the stocks. He cut the lemon in half with difficulty, squeezed slice after slice into a mug of water, then put four spoonfuls of sugar in it and stirred the mixture with a plastic spoon before placing it in his hand.

"Thank you, I haven't had a lemon-drink like this for over four years."

The lemon juice flowed smoothly down his throat. The deeper it went, the sweeter it tasted. He emptied the mug and put it down on the floor, feeling quite relieved and invigorated.

"Do you smoke rustic tobacco?" the Old Man asked.

His friend's eyes brightened.

"You've got tobacco? I'm craving for it."

He smiled:

"Sure, we can have a puff, right now."

His cellmate put a finger on his lips to silence him:

"Be quiet! Not now! We have to wait until dark. The warden is still somewhere, out there. He is a power monger, ready to put us in the stocks or cut off supplies at any moment. That's why we call him 'Buffalo King.' Lie down to rest! You're still tired."

He lay down, eyes closed, thinking about his fate. His father was both Chinese and French-educated. As a man of wide knowledge of things past and present, how could he accept communism? Finally, his father was denounced in public and died a tragic death by execution. He did not follow his National Army companions to the South in 1954 because his father advised him to stay. He later realized that not only his family was ignorant, but almost all other people had been deceived by the Communists, due to ignorance. If the nation had known the Communists well, how would they have been able to bring the entire country under their control?

Trailing a dog's life in various camps, the Old Man met numerous Christians, clergymen, writers, journalists, teachers, monks, soldiers, even cadres, Party-members. Nobody among them could give him a logical reason for his arrest.

He remembered the ceremonial visitation of General Lê Hữu Qua, head of the Lao Gai (Goulag) Bureau for Viet Nam. Resplendent in his uniform and gold-rimmed spectacles, he praised the Party, saying proudly to the inmates:

"Our Party is very lenient. Not everyone is arrested. Only 130,000 persons who have served the puppet government and army are kept in concentration camps for reeducation."

He had to wait until 1976 when he met a senior prisoner at Camp Phố Lu who was a genuine reactionary, wholeheartedly against the Revolution and the Regime. He was not like those the Party grabbed indiscriminately in the streets and dumped into prison. Questions that had tormented his mind during fifteen years of imprisonment were clarified by the senior prisoner:

"It's understandable, very understandable. First, economically speaking, prisoners provide the best source of income. It takes 50 cents a day to feed and clothe a prisoner, including medical expenses. For example, in a group of weavers, most of them seniors, the least efficient labor force, the money each senior makes averages two piasters a day, four times the amount of money spent on him. And a 'so-called' carpenter or locksmith or forester makes ten piasters a day on average, the amount 20 times larger than that spent on each of them. Therefore, you see, the more prisoners, the better. As the poet, my friend, phrases it:

They are thin and hungry, like toothpicks
But are expected to produce all year round ...
O let the world come and see![4]

Second, from a political point of view, in order to build socialism, each person must be reeducated into 'a new man.' No matter how clever you are at masking yourself; they know you don't like them. However, they don't think you are able to overthrow them. Why do they fear you whereas they are not scared of the French and the Americans? They know for sure you don't have the guts to publicly oppose the Regime. Under their strict control, each move you make is being watched. What's more, you toil day and night and still do not earn enough to feed yourself and your family, let alone to think of rising against the Party. Their stomach-controlling policy guarantees it. The only thing, however, they cannot control is your busy mouth. Millions of gossiping mouths create a significant obstacle to their political propaganda, which deceives young people and turns them into new persons, in other words, robots.

The young people today who have grown up under the Regime do not know a thing about the past. With them, the Party feels free to distort history and boast their clown-performances they think to be the best, the greatest, trying to mold them into whatever they wish. Therefore, they pin all their hopes on the young generation. Each time they take the census it shows the number of old people dwindles, whereas the number of young increases. They happily boast that the country is getting younger and younger as they often say: 'Youth's ready where we're needy; and youth's at hand where trouble lands.' One man I know, already 70 when arrested, begged for release on the grounds of old age, in order to live the rest of his life in peace with family. His interrogator smiled indifferently, saying: 'You're old, but your mouth is not old.' Alas! The old man finally died in prison.

Romantic literature, sentimental music such as 'Poor Fisherman,' 'Dreaming Rivulet,' 'Paradise'—songs totally unrelated to politics, are all forbidden. Those who sang such songs like 'Bushy-bearded' Toán or 'Yellow Lộ were sentenced to ten-to-fifteen years in prison. One day, when Trần Hoàn, director of Hải Phòng Bureau of Cultural Affairs, heard his employee whistle a song entitled 'Young Mountain Girl' that Trần himself had written during the war of resistance against the French, he hastily waved his hand, saying: 'Please! Another song, please! Those songs are forbidden as they are not favorable to the formation of new socialists, and tend to weaken the strong ideas of Bolshevism.'

Thirdly, in wartime, those who do not sympathize with the regime are considered reeds, and those who are enemies as tigers. Reeds, a hiding place for tigers must be cut off. Therefore, those who have been released, are captured again because the policy of the party is to remove reeds in order to kill tigers. The Party also arrests people due to their life history. This policy must be carried out naturally, as class struggle requires. Actually, bourgeois and landlords in prison are not many, if compared with other elements. As a long-time prisoner, you certainly know that political prisoners are many, but criminals are still more. They are the inevitable products of poverty and misery, products of an education devoid of national tradition and moral values.

Those criminals are young. The Party considers them garbage, not susceptible to reeducation. The best way is to put them in concentration camps and force them to labor. Remember 'reeducation' is an empty word. Do you think the Party sincerely believes in what the word means?[5] They know deep down inside those who, in society, already hate the regime, never grow to love it after ten or fifteen years in prison camp with all the torture and suffering. Therefore, you should never pretend to say to the Communists that you have achieved good results from reeducation and regretted your faults and mistakes. If you say so, they will laugh right in your face.

After hearing the senior prisoner comment on the Party, he respectfully joined both hands and bowed to him the same manner that Liu Bei did to Kong Ming:

"Master! Hearing your precious advice, I feel as if I were a blind person who has just recovered his sight. All dense fog has cleared, revealing a wide expanse of blue sky. Many thanks! Many thanks! Master!"

A voice from cell 7 interrupted:

"Peeping Tom, how many wheelbarrows of vegetables have you counted today?"

The Old Man opened his eyes and saw his cellmate looking out through a slit in the wood planks, and answer in a loud voice:

"Forty-two wheelbarrows in all, Bear-head. Tomorrow, each ration must be a bowlful."

Bear-head burst out laughing:

"Don't worry! Tomorrow, we'll be full."

Peeping Tom sat down with a smile. He then said to the Old Man:

"Here, they call me 'Peeping Tom,' because I am assigned to peep and count the number of wheelbarrows of vegetables. Honestly speaking, I deserve that nickname. As a man who has a strong interest in women, I usually stand up and look out the hall, watching the girls walking in and out of the bathroom. By the way, Buffalo King has just left."

The Old Man sat up:

"Can we have a deep inhalation to release tension, now?"

"No hurry! Dinner is almost ready. Buffalo King will come back to unlock the door for us to get our food that is placed outside the cell doors. If we smoke now, he will smell it. It's so dangerous! Wait till after dinner when kitchen people come to collect dirty dishes at the door; he will be off duty after that. Recently we have only pulverized salted fish. Those who have supplies from family don't eat that kind of food and give it to others. If you can swallow it, my ration is for you."

"I'm a kind of homeless prisoner. If you don't use it, leave it to me. I can eat anything."

Bear-head raised his voice, asking the Old Man:

"You've just come here, haven't you? Where from?"

The Old Man stood up, answering:

"From Camp Z8, Nghệ An Province."

"Even a number of jailers have fled from that deathtrap. All of my friends died there. Miraculously, you have survived. How long have you been arrested?"

"Twenty years, in all. And you, how long? And how old are you?"

"I'm twenty-five. I was a thief since my childhood. My prison life began when I was fourteen. I was recaptured after being released for over one year. This time, I may be sentenced to be shot or to life imprisonment."

"Is your crime serious?"

"I stabbed a customs officer, because I was checked while trafficking in tobacco along Hà Nội–Lạng Sơn Road. I jumped out of the train to escape. Unfortunately, I was recaptured in Hà Nội after two weeks. I succeeded in bribing my way out. I kept bribing him until the day I ran out of money. His sudden turn-about made me mad. So I stabbed him with a bayonet."

"My young friend, you're too aggressive. Don't waste your young age recklessly. You should have acted more carefully."

Peeping Tom warned:

"Buffalo King is coming back!"

The Old Man sat down and shook his head, saying:

"Nowadays, young people are easy prey for voracious beasts called 'prison.' Many are put in concentration camps for years just because they have stolen a hen, a bundle of rice, or a bicycle. Most of them die in prison. The longer they stay in prison, the worse they become. A great number are arrested again after being released. This young man is right. Life imprisonment or at least 20 years in prison is certain. He can only find a life inside—that is why he is a Bear-head, the roughest of the bullies!"

Clink, clank. Buffalo King opened every door for prisoners to go out to the corridor for their food rations, which the prisoners brought back into the cells. He stayed in the hallway, keeping a threatening eye on male and female inmates scurrying back and forth.

Peeping Tom handed the Old Man a bowl of pulverized dry fish. The Old Man tasted a spoonful, then spat, saying:

"How awful! It tastes saltier than salt. I can't finish my own ration. How can I eat this kind of food? I'm gonna die of thirst, now."

Peeping Tom opened a bag of meat, took four morsels and put them into his own bowl and then invited him:

"Share some with me. It's my wife's cooking. Let's enjoy a little bit of daily life's pleasure."

The Old Man refused again, but Peeping Tom kept insisting, forcing him to accept:

"This time only. Don't force me, please! Go ahead with your own food! It makes me feel more at ease."

Peeping Tom ate his food while fanning himself and said:

"There are altogether four divisions, here. Division 4, over there beyond the vineyard, is considered the best as it is reserved for high-ranking cadres. Division 3, near the kitchen, is suffocated with smoke. Division 2, with a cell dedicated to the memory of Trường Chinh, is very dark and stuffy, with floor covered up all over. It's entangled with pots, cans, and containers of all kinds. Division 1 here is rather airy. If the back wall upper window is not covered with planks, it is not as hot and dark as this. As for Division 3, it has a good point thanks to its proximity to the communal room of women. It's fun to hear them sing, yell at each other, and then fight every evening. During the day, we can watch them at will while they're marched to the interrogation room."

With much experience from long years of prison, the Old Man knew that surveillants, called 'antennas', are planted in prison. Lonesome people often are so naive that they believe others and confide to them what they hold close to their hearts. Most antennas are sweet, nice and helpful, which touches the hearts of newcomers in need of many things. As soon as the Old Man stepped into the cell, he saw the clear complexion of Peeping Tom. He thought: two months in prison are not enough for Peeping Tom to get such a bourgeois complexion, the complexion highborn European ladies adored in the 19th century. He had no doubt the moment he asked Peeping Tom how long he had been in prison.

Looking at Tom's belongings—well stocked with a fan, cans, plastic containers, spoons, not to mention a bag of winter clothes and blankets hanging on the wall—he knew right away Peeping Tom was an antenna. If not, why had he lied to him, he asked himself? A prisoner's belongings reveal themselves. He must have written to family or have been visited many times before he has stuff like that. It's impossible for a newcomer still in the period of interrogation to get all those things. The fact that he knows all four divisions in detail proves he has been through them. Such minor mistakes a malicious surveillant never commits: might Peeping Tom be a reluctant antenna?

Clink, clank, bang. The used dishes are rattling, put outside by prisoners. Here comes the kitchen helper collecting them, All the doors close tight again. Clink, clank, bang, down the row.

"Hurry up, I want to get out of this hellhole early tonight," Buffalo King angrily urged the employee.

After Buffalo King's departure, freedom time in the division began. Every cell resounded with male and female voices, calling and joking.

"Cell no. 8, have you got supplies, this month? Your husband must have left you alone. Sorry for you, dear!"

"Do you know how your love is, after enjoyment? The stick being lifted, the hole is left empty."

Amidst the roars of laughter and 'Amen!' Bear-head called out:

"Order! Order! Where is Driving Gangster? Let him continue the story left unfinished last night!"

"We, as truck drivers, are called 'Driving Gangsters.' During the bombing by the Americans in 1965 and 1966, only one trip to Quảng Bình, "the land on fire" won us 300 piasters in extra money, six times the monthly pay of a cadre. Though not one of us wanted to face death, we all had to go anyway. People tried to stay away from us. We were considered pests. Wherever our trucks stopped, American aircraft arrived to drop bombs. The air strikes often caused heavy casualties to innocent people.

But no matter how much they feared our arrival, at nightfall village women flocked to where we stopped along the Ninh Bình–Quảng Bình Road. A few coupons to buy 250 grams of rice were sufficient for us to get them under the trucks. They were of different sizes and shapes. They also varied in age, from young girls of fourteen to middle-aged women of nearly fifty. They all tasted good, no matter the flavor. Exactly as a song goes: *'So beautiful the road to battle, this time of the year!'*"

Driving Gangster paused, and several male voices called out:

"More, more! Tell us more about the juice!"

"No, there are ladies here. You must only imagine. The only detriment was that they were too thin (due to malnutrition) to create in us the mood for total enjoyment. I gave a box of candies or a bag of instant noodles as humanitarian gifts to any girl who knew how to please me with a better technique. She was deeply touched! We strictly cooperated with one another and coordinated our activities to achieve our goal. Those of us who survived the bombardment tried to gather as much war booty as possible and declared the truckloads had been destroyed. Back in Hà Nội, we were free to go on a binge. You know, very few people came back alive from the battlefield. In wartime, we just tried to enjoy life to the fullest whenever we could.

Ironically, during wartime we drivers received certificates of merit and letters of commendation. Now, in peacetime, they receive death sentences for stealing small amounts, only three or four truckloads of rice. They are insignificant in comparison with what was taken during the war."

The Old Man asked with concern:

"Do you have anyone outside who can help you in court?"

Driving Gangster continued:

"I have gone to the court of appeal. Still, the verdict is upheld. My only hope now is Trường Chinh's amnesty. At the age of forty-one, I don't want to die. What a destiny! When I took the rice, I thought that if I was caught I would just have to compensate for the loss or possibly be sentenced to seven years in prison, at the very most. Sadly, it was not so."

The Old Man replied:

"You're right, Driving Gangster! It's too bad, you have been chosen as a typical target for the government's fight against corruption. So, you're finished. Only heaven can help."

Peeping Tom said in a low voice:

"Let them do the talking and gossiping. We can allow ourselves to get drunk, now. We haven't smoked for weeks. I feel so miserable!"

The Old Man pulled a handful of tobacco from his foul-smelling blanket.

Peeping Tom said with admiration:

"Long years in prison have really taught you a lot. Such hiding is quite an art. It's impossible for them to find out. But, there's no more flint in the lighter. What can we do, now? I have only a small piece of paper."

"Don't worry! Everything will be OK," the Old Man said.

With an easy smile, he ripped a large plastic button off his coat and held it up, saying:

"This is the lighter. I need the hemp string in your pocket. With that string threaded through the button, I can make fire."

He bent down to pick up his rubber sandal and pulled a shard of glass out of the sole of his shoe. He tore off cotton and paper to make a roll long enough for two of them, and handed it to his friend.

"You go first! Rustic tobacco is very heavy. Be careful! You get drunk easily."

After a good long drag, Peeping Tom staggered. He leaned his back against the wall, dropping the roll on the floor. The Old Man picked it up and smoked to the finish. The air was filled with smoke.

Bear-head roared from cell 7:

"What a torture for me! What a delicious smell!"

Prisoners in adjacent cells joined in the excitement:

"It smells so good! Where does it come from? From what cell? We want to know, friends."

"It certainly comes from our 'Uncle,' the new prisoner from the camps. None of us has had it for several weeks."

"Don't forget us, dear Uncle! It's no good to keep it all for yourself."

Bear-head insisted:

"Don't act alone, please! Share your happiness with others! Don't you know that everybody here is one prison family?"

Recovering from ecstasy, Peeping Tom asked the Old Man:

"What do you think?"

"We should share with everyone. How many people smoke here, anyway?"

"Everybody, except women and girls. Is the leftover sufficient for seven persons?"

"Don't worry! I have enough."

The Old Man took another handful of tobacco from his blanket.

"How can they get it now?"

Peeping Tom smiled:

"You still keep a lot in your blanket, don't you? Well, let me tell them to 'drive over.'"

He then stood on the stocks and shouted:

"Cell no. 7! Drive over to receive the order!"

"At your command!" Bear-head answered.

Right after that, a toothbrush tied with a hemp-string flew through the door into the Old Man's cell. He nodded repeatedly with satisfaction.

"It's so wonderful! The target is hit from such a distance, right the first time."

Peeping Tom tied a box of tobacco with the string and ordered:

(opposite)

F. Hallway in cell block of Hanoi Central Prison

"Right after that, a toothbrush tied with a hemp string flew through the door into the Old Man's cell. He nodded repeatedly with satisfaction.

'It's so wonderful! The target is hit from such a distance, right the first time.'

Peeping Tom tied a box of tobacco with the string and ordered: 'Drive it back!'

The toothbrush was again pulled through the door to the other side. The Old Man shouted into the corridor, saying: 'Remember to give an equal share to everybody.'"

(Photo from "Hanoi Prison Images" by Chris McCooey, 2004)

"Drive it back!"

The toothbrush was again pulled through the door to the other side. The Old Man shouted into the corridor, saying:

"Remember to give an equal share to everybody. Have you got fire?"

"Don't worry, Uncle! We're well stocked. 'Fuel' is what we need. The amount you gave will be divided equally."

"I just had an idea to share some with you when I heard all the hustle and bustle. It's so much fun!"

Peeping Tom said:

"Goods going through cell gate no. 7 must be heavily taxed. I'm afraid there's not much left for others."

"It's normal. Loss and damage cannot be avoided in transit."

The hall was crisscrossed with toothbrushes whisking away from cell to cell. The whole division smelled of tobacco smoke.

Bear-head raised his voice with satisfaction:

"Thank you for your tobacco. What a treat! It's so delicious! So satisfying! Uncle, what have you done to be kept in prison for so long like this? What are you? A counterrevolutionary? A counterpropagandist? Or a misfit always complaining or blaming the regime?"

"As a former captain in the National Army, I am innocent. My only sin is stupidity. When I had the opportunity according to the Geneva Accords in 1954, instead of going to the South, I remained in the North and was put in a concentration camp for reeducation for 16 years, from 1961 to 1977. I did nothing against the regime for two years after release in 1977. I was arrested again in 1979 when the Chinese made a surprise attack on the border provinces. After almost four years in the Bamboo Gulags, I have been transferred to the Hanoi Hilton for a reason I don't understand."

"Dear Uncle, you must be careful. The less said the better."

"My wife left me. My son was killed in battle with the Americans. Now, family being lost, I'm finished. I have nothing to lose. Why do I have to be fearful or watchful? It makes no difference to me to be in prison or not. If I am released now, I don't know what to do for a living. As a civilian, I will be continuously harassed by local authorities. I am fed up with all the bother and trouble. I'm old enough to die. I'm fifty-three this year. Today, August 10th , is my birthday."

"Damn it! We have nothing to celebrate your birthday."

"I never bother to remember my birthday. I don't know why the date suddenly comes to my mind."

A soft female voice with a Southern accent was heard:

"I have a small gift for your birthday, Brother."

He laughed:

"Thank you very much for your concern. To me, birthday is a day of curse, rather than a day of celebration."

Peeping Tom came close and whispered:

"She is from Sài Gòn, married to a Chợ Lớn, a Chinese resident. She's a merchandise trafficker, very rich. She and her son have been imprisoned for fourteen months. It is rumored that she has bribed the security with 150 *taels* of gold to buy her way out. As a generous woman, she has a lot of gifts for the homeless. Buffalo King treats her very nicely, as he has been well fed by her. The amount of supplies she gets every week is more than enough for four persons. A big bag each time. It is unlikely that the capitalists can be exterminated. Even in prison, they're still happy. As for the proletariat, they always suffer, inside or outside of prison. The fact is that poor people are the only ones who bear the full brunt of the dictatorship of the proletariat promoted by the Communists. Do you know there have been 52 suicides a day, on average, since South Vietnam was 'liberated'? All the victims are poor people. A member of the executive committee in Hồ Chí Minh City has told me so."

A horn comb flew into the Old Man's cell. The woman raised her voice:

"Pull the string and get it!"

He stood up quickly, answering:

"Thank you, I don't need it. I have been used to prison life. Keep it for yourself!"

"Pull it in, please! Hurry up! The armed guard on duty is coming."

Peeping Tom said:

"Come on, take it! She's sincere."

No sooner said than done. He jumped down and pulled in flattened nylon bags of sugar and various kinds of cake.

He unfastened the bags, saying:

"Pull the string back, ma'm!"

The horn comb followed the string out. After that, two more combs flew into the Old Man's cell. Each comb was attached with a nylon bag of gifts.

The Old Man stood up and said in a quavering voice:

"I thank you, ma'm and all my children. My heart is really touched by your sympathy."

A male voice sounded irritated and envious:

"What a lucky guy! Even your wealthy dad can't do it better."

The Old Man asked Peeping Tom:

"Who is it?"

Tom waved his hand:

"Don't pay attention to that homeless guy. A first lieutenant. He has been here for five months. For what reason, I really don't know. Everyone hates him. He's in a permanent state of hunger, as nobody gives him anything. He often boasts that his unit was the first to liberate Sài Gòn. Even the Sài Gòn Woman does not give him food. He deserves it, as he's a snitch by nature. However, he has given up that bad inclination since the day Bear-head in cell 7 slashed him in the face with a razor blade. The ten-inch scar is still on his cheek. Bear-head had the opportunity to carry out his plan one morning when Buffalo King, in a hurry, let the two do the toilet cleaning together.

"Was Bear-head severely punished?"

"He was put in the stocks for only three days, thanks to the wealthy woman's intervention with Buffalo King. Money talks, you know. This warden should be put in prison. Human hearts can be filled with love only when their stomachs are full. Education and cultural activities are secondary. Beautiful lofty ideas cannot bloom in an empty stomach. The Sài Gòn Woman is an example. She is able to help others thanks to her wealth. You and I, no matter how generous and helpful we are, can do nothing because we ourselves are in need. If she had come here earlier, the young man in cell 6 would have not died."

"How did it happen?"

"About seven weeks ago, he committed suicide by cutting a vein in his arm with a broken piece of glass. He was only twenty; tall and handsome. In his life, he ate like a horse. Without supplies from his family, he could not stand the pangs of hunger. So, he preferred to die. If the Sài Gòn Woman had fed him, he would have not killed himself, I believe. There are a number of prisoners in the communal room who have committed suicide like that, some bumping their heads against the wall, others slashing their necks with a piece of glass."

Noticing Peeping Tom's crow's feet, the Old Man asked:

"How old are you, friend?"

"I was born in 1928. I'm fifty five now. *"Happy birthday to my 55! There are still 45 years left."* I still remember those verses by Dương Khuê. I'm from Vân Đình, same village as he."

"Are you a member of the Party?"

Peeping Tom was surprised:

"How do you know that?"

"I just guessed."

"You guessed right. I joined the Party in 1953."

Peeping Tom continued with his story.

"As a resistance fighter, I participated in the campaigns of the Frontier and Điện Biên. In 1956, I was transferred to the Foreign Trade Department. I got disillusioned relatively early, but too late to start a new life. Since the Land Reform and Literary Movement, I knew I was going in the wrong direction. The following years awakened me even more to the realization that I had been cheated. After the country had been unified, I had a chance to go to the South and saw with my own eyes Mê Kông Delta farmers feed pigs with rice. People lived in abundance. They treated one another with humanity. Setting foot in the city of Sài Gòn for the first time, I was startled to find that life was so prosperous and people were happy; children were well behaved and polite. I realized what the Party had said was sheer propaganda. What a big lie! It's a shame. They don't know how to maintain such a beautiful life. Back in Hà Nội, I happened to meet the elderly Vũ Đình Huỳnh. I had met him a few times before during the resistance war against the French. He is a stately old man with a thoughtful face hardening with determination. In a melancholy mood, he said to me: 'Dear friend, Sài Gòn has been occupied, not liberated as they said. I guarantee it will become like Hà Nội in a few years. I have devoted my whole life to the Revolution, and sacrificed everything for national independence and freedom, and for the well-being of my compatriots. Such a beautiful dream of mine is not achieved, alas! I feel really guilty towards the country and my people.' To be honest with you, if every member of the Communist Party Politburo were like Mr. Vũ, you and I, we would not be here. Unfortunately, they are only a bunch of opportunists, demagogues, hypocrites, and power-hungry, foxy guys. They do things against revolution and progress in the name of Revolution. They do things against people in the name of People. They speak highly of Humanity while they act against human beings."

The first moment the Old Man heard Peeping Tom's confidential words, he doubted if Tom had trapped him. But noticing a tone of sincerity in Tom's voice, he thought this guy might be a reluctant antenna. But it was not a problem for him. He did not have to hide his identity or put on an act. With a closer look, he found Peeping Tom's eyes, especially his smile, sincere and honest.

He then advised Peeping Tom with all sincerity:

"You're an outspoken person. You will be in trouble if your remarks are reported to the security. Many have become victims of their mouths. Why don't you fear when you raise your voice against their propaganda in front of me, a person you've just met? From now on, be more vigilant, friend!"

Peeping Tom smiled brightly:

"With a discriminating eye, I know you're not a decoy. Later, you will hear obscene curses and words of blame at every corner of this division. Being repressed, the inmates cannot keep their mouths shut. I know how to watch my mouth. Knowing you are a gentleman, an understanding person, I just vent my anger, that's all. We need a little bit of mutual confidence. How can we live in a society where suspicion and mistrust prevail?"

The Old Man laughed:

"Honestly, let me ask you. How long is your sentence? How many years are left? When will you be released?"

Peeping Tom slapped himself on the knee and laughed.

"How smart I am! I know I cannot bypass you. I was sentenced to three years. There are four months and ten days left. I have already been in prison for 32 months. They want me to play their ears and eyes and help them investigate political cases, because they know I am a former Party member. Actually, I haven't done anything wrong, only embezzled public funds. Everybody does it if he can. But to take advantage of my friends' trust to harm them is what I am not able to do. It is so vile! In addition, I really admire my fellow prisoners. Without brave people like them, the current situation cannot improve. The Party promised me to cut down my prison term to six months if I would be an antenna. If I had complied with their requests, I would be released now. "

Why didn't they put you in a concentration camp as the result of your disobedience?"

"Money talks! Most of us here have to spend money."

"Why did you lie to me at the beginning that you had been arrested for two months?"

"Everyone knows I have been in a cell for more than six months. How can I lie? Bear-head knows I am an informer. Therefore he's just reminded you to be vigilant. Interrogators are a bunch of idiots. They always recommend me to tell people that I've just been arrested and to keep it secret. How can I? Just looking at my belongings, quick-minded people know right away I have been here for a long time. I confess to anybody around me I've just been here for two months. To say so is to indirectly tell them to be on guard. If I work for the Communists in earnest, I must be wise enough to devise my own scheme."

Stomp-stomp. Clink! Clank!

The guards walked from cell to cell to open peepholes to check inside before closing them. At Sài Gòn Woman's cell, one of them looked in, whispering something. Peeping Tom stood on the stocks stealthily watching. He saw four Chinese sausages pass through iron bars. The guard secretly wrapped them up with a piece of newspaper.

"It's so hot here! Please, leave the peepholes open for us to get some fresh air."

"Okay, but no looking into another cell! And no talking!"

Peeping Tom sat down on the floor in a hurry. The two guards went to every cell to open the windows again. After that, they locked the gate and went away.

Bear-head laughed heartily and said to Sài Gòn Woman:

"Indeed, you're the benefactress of this division. We can never get them to open the peepholes, even though we beg them on our knees."

Peeping Tom's voice dropped to a whisper:

"What large sausages! Even in prison, the capitalists are still powerful. Wardens, armed guards—all are at their command."

The Old Man added in a sad voice:

"So it is in camps. Wardens treat wealthy prisoners as their superiors. Only the proletariat suffers. Standard rations all year round: torture and locks considered normal; death insignificant! Now, it's my turn to invite you to celebrate my 53rd birthday."

He handed Peeping Tom two pieces of green bean cake and two pieces of sweet short cake. Tom took them with open smiles.

"I'm not formal like you, Old Man. I'm going to eat them right away. From now on, we're friends. I'll see my wife in a few days. I can ask her to deliver a message to your sister?"

"Please, tell her to inform my sister that I've been transferred to the Hanoi Hilton prison, and to send me some vitamin C, a toothbrush, a tube of toothpaste and some clothes, and also to let her know I am reasonably well."

"Is that all?"

The Old Man sadly replied:

"Her family is poor. To request so many things might hurt her financially. I feel very guilty."

Bear-head's voice was heard resoundingly:

"Girls! I suggest you to sing a song to wish our Uncle a happy birthday. Cell 9 first, then cell 8, and cell 10 please!

A girl spoke up:

"I'm going to sing: 'Waiting for your Return,' wishing Uncle a quick release, OK?"

Wait for my return, dear!
Keep waiting, my dear!
Forget about heavy rain,
And endless sad days!
Keep on waiting until the day
I'm home, my dear!

The Old Man asked in surprise:

"What a singer! Who is she? Is she a professional?"

"She's a mulatto, from Từ Sơn in the Băc Ninh province, the result of a rape by a colonial African soldier during the resistance war against the French. She sings Băc Ninh folk songs very well. Her voice is very powerful. This division would be sad without her."

"What has she been charged with?"

"We don't know, as she never reveals her identity. We don't care to ask. She's possibly an informer. In the same cell with her is another girl guilty of U.S. dollar trafficking, who's just been arrested, a girl with lots of sex appeal. After searching her and finding 600 dollars, the police brought her here right away. She has been here for almost two months. No food supplies! No dress to change. It's terrible. The Sài Gòn Woman was kind enough to give her another dress."

The song resounded loud and clear, with words repeated again and again.

Wait for my return!
Wait for my return!
I brave death amidst laughter!

Then the refrain slowed to a mournful pace:

In spite of falling snow and heavy storm,
In spite of the scorching sun, my dear!
Being forgotten, by old friends
Keep waiting for me, dear!

The Old Man was lavish with his praise.

"It's really a God-given voice. If trained, she would fly high. It's a shame, so many talents have withered. This song is Simonov's best poem set to music. The regime's national poet Mr. Tố Hữu translated the French version badly. '*Quand la pluie au ton cuivre seme la tristesse*' has been translated in the following words: "Heavy rain and endless sad days." Such a translation cannot describe the color of copper, a dull yellow color, expressing the boundless sadness overwhelming the heart of a lonesome woman who is waiting for her husband's return from battle. Poet Lê Quang Dũng, my former fellow prisoner, translated those two lines much better:

The falling rain is tinted with the evening-sun;
Your sadness is as yellow-ripe as the color of the sunset.

Two more verses in French are as follows:

Attends-moi, quand l'été rayonne, mais tout l'hiver attends.

'L'été rayonne' meaning 'Summer shines' can revive the instinct for life. It has nothing to do with the 'scorching sun.' When writing: *'mais tout l'hiver attends,'* the poet wishes to convey the idea that 'throughout the long wintry days, she needs to be warmed by his love. Still, she silently waits in loneliness.' 'Falling snow' and 'heavy storm' are superfluous. It just doesn't work that way."

Peeping Tom said, with his eyes opened wide:

"What a multi-talented person! As a military man, you're also a poet, a professional poet. I really admire you, friend."

The Afro-Vietnamese girl said:

"I'm gonna' sing another song to you, Uncle, entitled 'The Fisherman's Song.'"

"Please, go ahead! Your voice is so beautiful!"

Silence reigned over the whole division. The song painted the picture of a vast expanse of water, which has the power to lift the human soul from a dark, stuffy prison to the open sky and sea.

Oh, my friends! I remember an evening,
When warm, friendly flames flared up,
Higher and higher, up and down with the tidal waves.

A voice echoed from Division 2, near the vineyard:

"My dear nightingale! Louder for this side to hear!"

The Sài Gòn Woman said:

"I give you, dear, some lemon candy and salted dry apricots to sweeten your voice."

"Thank you, Auntie! Let me finish the third song. This is my native village folk song I learned from my mother when I was a small child."

Driving Gangster spoke up:

"Go ahead! Just hearing your voice, I love you already, my sweetheart!"

The black-skinned girl with a Vietnamese soul raised her voice again, a voice laden with homesick tears, reminding them of a deep attachment that lingers, never ending

My dear, stay home! Don't go away!
Away from me. Don't you miss …
Let your dress not be soaked
… in the rain of tears.
You, my love, stay here!
Don't go away!

The Old Man stood up looking out the hall, his voice still filled with emotion.

"Thank you, my child! You sing so well! This is the first time I celebrate my birthday, friends! Tonight is the happiest day of my prison life. I'm so happy I don't want to go anywhere else. If I am ever released I will miss this moment forever, so much that my clothes will be soaked in the rain of tears."

"Don't get too emotional, Uncle! Now, it's cell 10's turn to sing."

Bear-head's request was followed by a coarse voice shouting from the yard:

"Shut up, everyone! I'm gonna' put anybody who sings in the stocks. You know the regulations!"

Peeping Tom whispered in the Old Man's ear:

"He's the assistant supervisor, void of human feeling and expression. Whenever he is offended, he threatens the stocks. Sometimes he means it. We call him 'God of Stocks.'"

When God of Stocks had moved on, Peeping Tom said loudly:

"Excuse me, listeners! Tonight's show must end due to technical problems. See you again tomorrow night, for 'Saturday Night Live'!"

Bear-head growled:

"We're harassed by the enemy while we are in Heaven. Let's have an inhalation. He began to sing:

Too homesick, I light a cigarette,
Watching smoke spreading upwards to the trees.
Is my soul heavy
With age-old melancholy,
This evening?

"Damn it! All kinds of torture! What a persistent pain of missing wife and children! What a craving for canine meat!"

The Old Man lay down wearily:

"I've got to sleep now. I feel so tired, tonight. Have you gotten any sleep yet?"

"No, not yet. So many mosquitoes here! You need a mosquito net. The wall is scarred with holes stuffed with rags and strings. You can hang your net on them. Take this piece of cardboard to fan yourself. It's too hot in here!"

"I'll lie down here for a moment to have some fresh air. It's very stuffy in the net."

"It's up to you. Goodnight, my friend!"

The Old Man soon fell asleep, partly due to the long journey, partly due to a full stomach. When he awakened it was almost dawn. He was surprised to see Peeping Tom, a short pencil in one hand and a piece of tea-wrapping paper in another, looking up at the ceiling in deep thought.

"Didn't you sleep? It's almost daybreak. What are you writing?"

Peeping Tom smiled:

"I'm writing a poem to 'her.'"

"Your wife?"

"No, to my new love, in cell 9, the Dollar Trafficker. She seems to accept me. Each time on the way to the bathroom she looks at me and smiles."

"How can you manage pencil and paper?"

"Thanks to Sài Gòn Woman. She can get anything she wants."

"Be careful! If Buffalo King knows it, you'll be in big trouble. I worry about you."

Peeping Tom calmed his friend:

"Don't worry! I'm always on full alert. I even hide razor-blades for a shave, you know. Hey, my new friend! I'm writing a poem, but don't know how to conclude. It's so hard!"

"Poetry is not needed for expressing love, my friend, prose is sufficient."

He shook his head:

"Don't talk about prose with me! I knew how to write poems since I was in the Army. I sometimes have my poems printed in the

Literature and Arts Magazine. I want to create a new form of poetry without a cliché-ridden style, that suits the modern world—the post modern world—I would say: 'Here, read it!'"

The Old Man took the piece of tea-wrapping paper. After reading several times, he asked in surprise:

"What do you intend to convey? I don't understand at all. Why are the lines arranged in the shape of an upside down triangle with a slit in the middle?"

Peeping Tom grew serious:

"If it is understandable, how can I call it 'new'? The upside down triangle with a deep crack in the center represents my basic instinct. It's also the symbol of the arrow of cupid, god of love. This is a kind of concrete poetry, which catches the eyes of the readers. The language I use is to express repressed emotions, throbs of desire and passion, a mental state of hesitation and confusion, something unclear, indiscernible, obscure in my subconscious. No wonder, you don't understand. A special key is needed to decipher the code. That's what I mean 'new.' Modern poetry should be something transcendental, supernatural, and abstract, rising above the dull realities of life, above a stagnant society with its conventional ways of doing things."

"Why don't you decipher the code now, so that I can understand?"

Peeping Tom looked embarrassed. He might not have the key.

Feeling sorry for him, the Old Man relented:

"Let's be honest, friend! How long ago did you get the idea of creating 'new poetry'?"

"Since the day I went to Singapore to buy machines. I happened to find some essays on literature by French and American scholars. Frankly, my English and my French are poor. I can hardly understand, even with the help of a dictionary. When I quote a number of English, American, and French authors, many people, especially the young ones, think I am an erudite person. Sometimes, I go so far as to quote from the documents written in Greek, Latin, or Chinese, although I'm totally ignorant of those languages. I just want to show off, you know." Peeping Tom let out a satisfied laugh.

The Old Man continued with a smile:

"Briefly speaking, you only repeat what others have said. Such repetition is nothing new. It's new to you, but very old to them. You have stayed awake all night, only to draw an upside down triangle and to write an incomprehensible poem, a type of poem even you cannot explain. And now, you're going to show it to the Dollar-Trafficker. What for? You'll make her think you are a rotten, ill-bred guy when she looks at the picture. Your purpose is to win her heart, not for her to taste the 'new' in your poem. A normal letter will do. Half an hour is enough for you to achieve your goal. Leave that kind of revolutionary poem behind!"

Peeping Tom responded as if awakening from a long dream:

"You're damn right! It's really a waste of paper."

"Not a waste! We can use this piece of paper for a roll of tobacco. The day is breaking. Let's have a puff to keep ourselves awake."

After a deep drag, Peeping Tom told the Old Man to keep a watchful eye on the corridor, then boiled some water for tea. After three minutes, tea was ready. They both sat in the morning stillness, sipping tea.

With a plastic cup in hand, the Old Man said confidentially:

"In prison, I have had a good chance to meet quite a few writers and poets. They all wish to create something new. To their knowledge, the word 'creation' itself requires them to do something new. They feel an obligation, an urge to do it. They don't need foreign writers to teach them. A true literary work must have something new, in other words, something typical of its author. 'New' however is not enough. 'New' must be supplemented with 'good.' In the last century, after composer Franz Liszt had listened to a piece of music written by a young man, he said to him: 'Your music is both new and good.' When the young man got exhilarated, the composer added: 'Regrettably, there is no 'new' in the 'good,' and no 'good' in the 'new.' In the century before that, Voltaire received a literary work from a young writer. As the young man considered his work extremely new, beyond his contemporaries' understanding, he entitled his book 'To Posterity.' After reading it, Voltaire said: 'I'm afraid your book won't reach its destination.'

You must admit that no matter how new, how beautiful, how superior a thing is, it must be rooted in life. Without life, it's just a vacuum. Life is the mother of all things. Without much experience of life, writers or poets who wish to produce great works of literature are just like women who wish to give birth to a baby without being pregnant. No matter how hard they contract their muscles, no baby spurts out of their womb. You see what I mean. You waste the whole night, staying awake. You have alienated yourself from the source of life when you look for the 'new.' Eventually, you have concocted something you don't understand yourself. Life never accepts something that doesn't come from it and serve it back. It keeps eliminating what is useless and harmful. It treasures all forms of beauty, because it needs beauty, except the kind of beauty that causes disaster and catastrophe. Living in the woods for years, I know all types of poisonous mushrooms. They look gorgeous and taste delicious, but they scare animals, even snakes away. Wherever we find them, we destroy them before they can harm others. So are songs and poems extolling the merits of Hitler, Stalin, Mao Tse Tung. In fairness, some of them are artistic achievements. But life does not accept that kind of art because it attacks life, insults the good, the beautiful, and praises the wicked, the bad."

Peeping Tom nodded his head repeatedly, asking:

"You have said that the beautiful and the new are found right in the realities of daily life, haven't you?"

"That's right! Being here, in this prison for less than 24 hours, I have discovered many beautiful and new things. Let me ask you, where on earth can you witness such a beautiful birthday celebration everyone prepared for me, last night? Me, a stranger. Isn't that new? Isn't that beautiful? If your heart beats to the rhythm of life, you can capture many new things that are elusive, able to slip out of hand in a second if you don't pay close attention. A piece of wood can talk. It talks to someone who knows how to listen to it. A rustic hut has its own beauty for those who know how to behold it."

"I have to admit you're right. But a European essayist considers poetry as a mere technique of disposing words."

"That's formalism. It perceives a poet as a person who juggles with words, bringing poetry down to the level of circus or magic. You try in vain to create a new form. Only substance can create form. When substance changes, form must change accordingly to suit the new substance. In other words, without new themes, new feelings, new ideas, and new facts, the writer is not expected to create a new form. Even a number of writers in the Western world try hard to create something, but they produce only deformities and then label them 'modern.' Actually, they destroy literature and stamp out the avidity for reading, even among well-educated people. Life has gradually cast aside persons of small talent, those harboring a big ambition to become founders of schools. As far as I remember, several years ago, a modernist boasted that with a stroke of the pen, he could each month complete a novel as mediocre as Balzac's. Now, life has driven those kinds of people into oblivion."

Peeping Tom emptied his cup, heaving a sigh of satisfaction:

"You're a very knowledgeable person."

The Old Man laughed:

"As a military man, my knowledge is very limited. I just repeat what I overheard from a number of imprisoned writers."

"Did they discuss the use of words and music rhythm of a poem?"

"Their primary guideline is not to adopt formalism. They usually read a poem to one another and elaborate on it for a long time. One evening, hearing singing from a far-away cell: *'Old mother's eyes are filled with tears; the Thao river is still flowing between its banks'* a poet immediately replaced the proper name 'Thao' with a verb 'Thao Thức (to throb with emotion) as follows: 'The river is still throbbing between its banks.' He said that the verb 'throbbing' adds life to the river.

Another prisoner went so far as to change Văn Cao's marching song. To him, *'The triumphant, blood-stained flag carries the soul of the nation'* is not as lively and powerful as *'The triumphant, blood-stained flag reverberates with the soul of the nation.'* They even corrected Vũ Hoàng Chương's poems. Let me remember—Yes, this verse: *'Life dies down in the back alley, as the wind blows in the attic'* was rewritten as follows: *'Life dies down in the back alley, as the wind blows through the attic.'* In their opinion it is better to avoid the repetition of 'in.' Consider the verse *'Let's hang high the sail and raise: Heave Ho! Heave Ho!'* To gain more momentum, it should be modified as follows: *'Let's raise: Heave Ho! Heave Ho! Higher and higher with the rising sail.'*

They praised Vũ Hoàng Chương for his great art of translating Chinese poems. This is the original verse:

Sorry for the bamboo bush at the mountain crack,
Still there in the rain, waiting for someone's return!

It turns so beautiful and poetic under Vũ Hoàng Chương's pen as he wrote:

The young girl's room is left open,
The bamboo bush still waiting, as green as ever.

"Did they touch upon the themes 'art for art' and 'art for living'?"

"Their viewpoint is very simple. To them, if something is bad, and not beautiful, it cannot be called art. Art is beauty itself. Whether a poem describes a beautiful girl's eyes or the ugly body of a skinny, starving person, it cannot be accepted as an art form if it is not beautiful. Every art form, in other words, every form of beauty—except the kind of beauty that causes disaster like I have mentioned before—is devoted to the service of man, the enrichment of the human heart and mind and the uplifting of the human soul. Actually, the debate about art has been going on for a long time. The main cause is that those who advocate 'art for art' take a narrow view. To them, social and political issues are not part of art. Victor Hugo answered them, saying: 'The liberation of man as well as the amelioration of human condition never degrades beauty and hurts poetry.' George Sand, Tolstoy, Dostoevski, Goethe, and Rene Char thought in the same manner. They used to read to each other beautiful poems, even those about daily life activities, like drinking wine.

Listening again and again, I can remember some of them. For example:

I pour wine by myself, and by myself I drink.
I hardly get drunk when loneliness builds up I think.
I keep drinking, drinking and keep pouring,
Like a whale emptying the ocean while swallowing.

Peeping Tom said with great satisfaction:

"Excellent! Do you know who wrote it? It must be from someone untamed, unsubmissive."

"It might be from Hoàng Công Khanh, my fellow prisoner at Yên Bái, a member of an art group."

Peeping Tom was angry:

"When released, I will dump that kind of cheating stuff in the waste basket."

"No! You must read them to keep yourself informed of various literary movements: post-, ante-, super—provided you don't re-use what have been thrown away and think they are new. It's not late yet. You still have time to write 'her' a letter."

"No more paper, friend! Tonight, I have to ask Sài Gòn Woman for some. I'm gonna' take some exercise, now. I have a half-hour workout, every morning. Living a stationary life, I will lose muscle."

"For me, there has been too much manual labor in camp, already. I don't need more exercise. I just want to practice some basic techniques of Qi Gong for relaxation."

After that, the Old Man sat upright, massaged his entire body for a moment, and then, his eyes closed, took regular, deep breaths. Not far from him, Peeping Tom jogged on the spot, breathing noisily, his feet raised high. After a moment of exercise, he jumped up several times like a grasshopper, trying in vain to reach the high ceiling. His hand was still several inches away.

Peeping Tom panted:

"I try to reach the ceiling, but I can't. I don't think you can."

The Old Man stood up and said:

"Let me have a try!"

As agile as a monkey, he launched himself, applying his hand flat on the ceiling. Then he turned his body upside down, walking on both hands very deftly.

Peeping Tom was amazed:

"All skin and bone as you are, you are still very swift and strong. You did it just like magic."

"I will perform martial arts for you to see now."

With lightning speed, he began a flurry of hard, fast blows and throws and kicks with his hands and feet. After about a ten-minute performance, he sat down, his face looking normal, his breathing regular.

He said to Peeping Tom:

"I can teach you if you want. But you've got to train your will first, your breathing second. Martial art comes last. This is a special method of maintaining energy in hard times. When I was at Heaven's Gate Camp, I learned this art from an old monk."

Peeping Tom sat up:

"I want to learn, too, to be strong enough to serve young girls. I want to learn, right today, please!"

"Okay, but remember to be patient. Take your time! In a haste to do something, you achieve nothing. Let's have a puff before I put the tobacco in a hiding place."

After smoking and drinking, Peeping Tom pulled a razor-blade from under the stocks and began to spruce himself up, shaving beard, trimming eyebrows, side burns and unwanted hairs in his nostrils. It took him half an hour to get the job done.

He asked the Old Man with a smile: "Do I look 55? I've told 'her' I'm 48."

"You look much younger than your age, thanks to your smooth and clear complexion. If you don't tell your real age, she will think you're younger than I."

"And you, a miserable life in prison for many years makes you look 70, with all bone and skin and beard growing wild. Without the beard, you would look younger. Shave it off, friend!"

The Old Man smiled, saying:

"How can I shave my beard? Without it, I would be sent back to hard labor for sure. In addition, if my beard suddenly disappears, Buffalo King will ask me where I have found the razor. As a result, you have nothing left to spruce up."

"What a clever idea! I never thought of it."

Stomp-stomp.

The Old Man urged:

"Hurry, hide the razor blade! I hear footsteps. Maybe Buffalo King is coming."

"Don't worry! Not yet. Well-supplied women enjoy special privileges. Their cells are always first.

Clink, clank. Peeping Tom was right. Buffalo King came to the cell of Sài Gòn Woman first. Then he stepped out and sat at a table, plugging in the kettle to boil water for tea. The water bubbled noisily in his bamboo pipe.

Tom whispered to the Old Man:

"Stand up to observe her. Nearly fifty. Still in good shape."

The Old Man stood on the stocks, looking out. A slender, rather good-looking woman with curly hair and clear complexion stepped out, a chamber pot in one hand and a bucket in another. She stopped at the door of the Old Man's cell, looking at him with a smile. He raised his hand in reply and sat down on the floor.

Peeping Tom whispered again:

"Do you notice a big box in her bucket. It's for Buffalo King. Two other women often bribe him too; but they are not as rich as this one."

The Old Man asked:

"Why do the women have to do so? How much can they get in return?"

"Nothing, except to stay in the bathroom longer to bathe and wash more freely and to boil water for tea and noodle. His monthly pay of 80 piasters cannot compare with what he receives from those women. They just buy an easy life with some of their wealth, you know."

After about half an hour in the bathroom, Sài Gòn Woman went to the yard to dry her laundry. She then went back to her cell, brought out a mug and a bowl to boil water for tea and noodle.

"Chief, I would like to report there's plenty of water in the tank today. My cell smells bad. It really needs washing and cleaning."

Clank! Buffalo King opened Bear-head's cell door:

"You do it."

Bear-head uttered a loud "yes" before hastening to the bathroom for a broom and a bucket of water, and began to work away, giving her cell a good scrubbing.

The Old Man stood up to observe Bear-head. He's a slender, young man with a ruffled head of hair and big, alert eyes. He carried water, waving happily to the Old Man, who nodded back with a smile. After the washing and cleaning, he returned to his cell. The Sài Gòn Woman brought in her tea and noodles. Buffalo King opened cell 10 for two middle-aged women. The Old Man waved to them, smiling.

Peeping Tom said to the Old Man:

"The woman who goes first gave you a birthday gift yesterday. You remember? Both have been charged for the embezzlement of public funds."

Clink, clank.

"It's the cell of the Dollar-Trafficker and the Afro-Vietnamese girl."

The Old Man waved to both of them. When Peeping Tom blew a kiss to the Dollar-Trafficker, she looked up, smiling.

"Thirty years old already. What do you think? Is she still good?"

"Yes, she's still fresh and pleasant looking. As for the other, she does not look Vietnamese at all, although she carries the Vietnamese blood in her veins. The African gene is dominant, you know."

"This girl is crazy about boys. She fell in love with a hardened criminal, a few months ago. She gave him a pair of jeans, even her gold ring. He has been transferred to camp."

Peeping Tom waited for the dollar-trafficker to pass by in order to blow her another kiss before sitting down.

Clink, clank!

Buffalo King came to the cell of Driving Gangster and the First Lieutenant and then to four or five more cells of male prisoners. The Old Man waved his hand to everyone.

Peeping Tom sat motionless on the floor, growling:

"My turn is always last. No water is left, I'm afraid. Buffalo King always means to harm this cell."

"Why?"

"He hates me, because I do not call him 'chief.' Some people, even former directors shamelessly call him: Chief! Chief!"

Tap-tap-tap. A prisoner knocked at Sài Gòn Woman's door.

Buffalo King shouted: "Why did you knock at her door?"

"I didn't, Chief!"

"There's no denying. I saw it with my own eyes. Flirtatious behavior does not fit a prisoner. Being well-fed, you're hungry for love, aren't you? She's been married already. Without supplies for four months, I'll see if you are sexually aroused or not."

Bang! The door shut.

"Now comes the turn of Bear-head's lover. Let's stand up for a look! She's not beautiful but good-natured. Everyone loves her. She gave you a gift last night, didn't she? In the same cell with her is an actress of the Hà Nội troupe. She is a foul-mouthed girl; even foxy guys cannot outswear her."

The Old Man stood on the stocks, waved to the ladies and sat down, saying:

"I think I have met everyone in this division. Buffalo King is a really rude guy. I feel sorry for the First Lieutenant. He looks so thin!"

"As a snitch, he deserves it. Many guys locked in communal rooms are much thinner than he. Being fed with a starvation food ration allowed by the regime, the human body could hardly survive. You're not better than he, friend! To survive twenty years in prison is a miracle. Now, let's get prepared! Our cell is the last one. If we're late, there is no water left."

"That's too bad. I planned to take a bath today!"

Peeping Tom explained:

"You cannot have a bath today even if there is water left. It is only allowed once a week, on Wednesday. If we are caught bathing on other days, we are forbidden to go to the bathroom and forced to urinate in a can, which we are not allowed to dump into the toilet."

"You can go now. Be quick!"

Peeping Tom and the Old Man ran like crazy to the bathroom, pot and bucket in hand:

"Hurry up! Have a quick wash! You can go back to the cell for teeth brushing."

Peeping Tom got the job done in five minutes. He then brought the pot and the bucket full of water into his cell. The Old Man was washing his trousers when Buffalo King shouted, pressing him. He rushed into the yard to hang the laundry and came back.

Buffalo King glowered at him:

"Next time, if you keep procrastinating, I will box your damned ears."

Hearing those words, the Old Man turned back, his face serious:

"Watch your tongue, man! Remember you're in front of a person of honor."

Buffalo King shouted at him:

"Watch your impudence! A reactionary has no honor. I have read your biography sent from camps. To curse the Party and our leaders is your profession."

He drew his revolver and pointed it at the Old Man:

"I'm ready to shoot you on the spot now. I dare you to curse the Party and our leaders again."

The Old Man burst out laughing:

"You can only threaten those who love life and fear death. Let the entire division bear witness for me. This morning, August 11, 1983, the warden in charge of Division 1 has excited me to curse the Party and leaders. Take me to the main office right now for the chief to solve this case."

Buffalo King raged:

"What a slander! Who excited you?"

"I request you to take me to the supervisor's office."

"He's not here."

"If so, give me a pen and paper, so I can write down what has happened. Your duty is to let the culprit report an incident and to send his report to the main office."

"I don't have no paper, no pen. Get into your cell!"

"I would like to let you know I don't care about the trivialities you have done. But, if you don't treat me fairly, I have the right to clarify everything with the chief supervisor, and with the director too. The Hanoi Hilton is not a wasteland where you can do whatever you wish. There still are the Party and the government above you. As you know, a number of wardens have been put in prison." With those words, the Old Man stepped back into his cell.

Clang!!! Buffalo King shut the door after him with a bang:

"I'll talk to you later!"

Clang!! His steps grew faint in the distance.

Bear-head shouted with joy:

"You're super, Uncle! You're really a hero. This is the first time he is made to blush."

The Old Man stood up, answering:

"You mean 'hero' at this corner of the Hanoi Hilton? Oh, no! Prison has turned quite a few heroes into cowards and ridiculous clowns. My weak point is not to be able to swallow humiliation. Besides, I'm too tired of life to fear death. To me, concord is the best policy. But I cannot let him go too far. Yesterday, I did not mind his threatening gesture when he pointed his fingers at me, but now he uses a pistol ..."

Sài Gòn Woman spoke up:

"Dear Brother, you have made me admire you so much."

"It's a small thing to admire. Being pushed to the wall, I don't care about anything, that's all."

"The more humble you are, the more I admire you, dear."

"No, I just tell you the truth, I never pretend to be humble. I'm not conceited either. If I were a little bit smarter, I would not be here, in prison for years."

Bear-head let out a loud guffaw and spoke with a forged Southern accent:

"'Dear Brother! You've made me admire you so much.' Uncle, you have been touched by such intimate words, haven't you?"

His lover warned him:

"Hold your loose tongue."

"You're selfish, dear! Why don't you want her and our Uncle to be as happy as we are?"

"Stop joking! She and our Uncle don't like it."

Peeping Tom said confidentially to the Old Man:

"You just hit the jackpot, friend. She's so sweet on you."

The Old Man sat down, shaking his head:

"You're truly a poet, rich in imagination."

"Frankly, I have more experience than you in this matter, my friend. Time will prove it. Now, I would like to ask you a more important question. Do you think Buffalo King can cause you trouble?"

"Don't worry! A guilty conscience needs no accuser. He seemingly wants to yield. You should know under this regime, the Party has succeeded in creating fear not only among people, but also among cadres and Party members. They fear the Party more than people do. Because they fear one another and their bosses, they have to be always on guard. Starvation and prison are permanently threatening their lives. Fear leads to submission; and submission turns them into docile servants, entirely at the Party's command. Only when people no longer fear, can the Party not exist."

Clang! Buffalo King opened all the cells for everyone to go into the corridors for food. The entire division was in high spirits when they saw a bowl full of water vegetables for each person. In the Hanoi Hilton, such a sight is rare, even when vegetables are in season. Family-fed prisoners can make a wonderful kind of salad by mixing salt and sesame with chopped hot pepper, flavored with a few drops of lemon juice.

Buffalo King told the Old Man:

"Go out for a haircut and a shave. Be quick! "

The Old Man went to the yard and sat on a stool. A trusty began to cut his hair and beard swiftly with a pair of scissors.

"I allow you to take a bath."

The Old Man hurried to his cell for a towel. Peeping Tom handed him a cake of soap. After a good rub, the Old Man returned to his cell.

Peeping Tom appeared joyful:

"How clever you are at dealing with him! You know when to press and when to release. He fears you. He has never given anyone such a privilege. Before, only one haircut in months for each prisoner during the bathroom hour."

Bear-head declared:

"Look, Auntie! Being spruced up, our Uncle looks twenty years younger."

"I have noticed that too." Sài Gòn Woman said.

Peeping Tom said to the Old Man with satisfaction:

"Don't you see she always keeps an eye on you? Hurry up! Go for it!"

"But what for?"

"For relaxation, for fun! To forget a little bit about the prison life."

"To me, love is not for fun or something you can play around with. Now let's eat!"

The Old Man was about to eat some vegetables when Peeping Tom stopped him:

"No! Too dirty. Pluck off withered, rotten leaves before you eat! Sometimes, bugs, even leeches are found. Do you know how vegetables are boiled? Vegetables fresh from the garden are thrown bundle after bundle into a wok, without being washed. They picked up boiled vegetables and spread them on the cement ground. They then put other fresh bundles over them. After that, they boil the rest, and again lay them on top of the fresh ones. They keep doing like that, alternating boiled vegetables with the fresh ones, thinking eventually the whole pile will be steam-worked. Not because they have no conscience or are lazy. There are not even ten cooks altogether. How can they get the job done in time while serving nearly three thousand prisoners? They cannot do otherwise."

After eating and smoking, Peeping Tom asked:

"Do you know how to play Chinese chess? I have a whole set of chessmen made of paper. Someone has drawn the chessboard on the floor, here. If you don't take a siesta, why don't we play a few matches to kill time?"

"Okay! But I'm very bad at chess."

"I'm no better either."

Both of them focused on the chessboard. Peeping Tom was very competitive. Whenever he beat his opponent by one move, he shook his knees as a sign of complete satisfaction. Then he would croon:

To be pitied are only a few of the pawns:
Sent across the river, how many ever come back?
Generation after generation is sacrificed by their victories
and losses:
Are they awake or dreaming as they play this chess game?[6]

After losing three matches in a row, the Old Man lamented:

"Too bad! I can't beat you. Let me lie down for a while."

"Use this mat, friend! It's cool to lie on the bare floor. However, I don't know why whenever I wake up, I feel very tired. Perhaps cement absorbs energy. The mat has been used by a ringworm-infested person. But I have washed it rather thoroughly."

The Old Man spread the mat on the floor and lay down, his face to the wall. The wall was stained black with dried blood. It must be dead bugs. He turned up, facing the ceiling. He was thinking hard, trying to find the reason why he had to leave the camp for the Hanoi Hilton. Do they plan to release me, he asked himself? They don't have to bring me here. They can release me right from the camp if they want to. Why not? It's incomprehensible.

He heard the students of Tận Trào School playing noisily in the playground. Hàng Bông Thợ Nhuộm Street is right on the other side of that wall. It's only about a 20-minute walk to his sister's house. So close, yet so far away. Suddenly, he felt much more miserable than a dragonfly or a sparrow. They are so free, free from all kinds of ties and bindings. The 6-meter-high wall topped with barbed wire and broken glass over there is insignificant, compared with the whole network system of prisons cast over his country like a huge spider's web.

The Old Man had first been arrested and put into prison in '61, when his son was only eight, a second-grade student, whom he and his wife treasured. They were frugal with their own food and clothes for the sake of their son. They saved their portions of meat and sugar for him, fearing that a malnourished child would not develop in mind and body. The child took after his father's eyes and nose and his mother's smile and ears. He often let his son sit on his lap, thinking man can never perish, that after he passes away, a part of his body and mind still lives in his son. The same thing has happened to his parents. They are not alive any longer, but they're still living in him. Life goes on and on without end, generation after generation.

He got married at the age of twenty. His marriage was pre-arranged by his parents because they wished to have a grandchild to enjoy their old age. Despite the marriage set up in a traditional way, he and his wife lived together in great happiness. She was an elementary school teacher. Her beauty was average. Yet, she was so mild, so sweet, and so good! A pleasing, caring wife, a loving mother, a delightful daughter-in-law and a wonderful housewife. He spent many nights in prison regretting not being able to love her more during the nine years they had been together. Sometimes, he had shouted angrily at her, making her cry. She was too gentle and submissive. She never argued with him.

Back home from prison in 1977, he learned she was living with a marketing manager and had three children with him. He told his sister not to inform her of his release, for fear of troubling her while she was enjoying a peaceful life.

But then, in 1980, she and her family, including her new husband, became boat people, escaping from the 'unified' Việt Nam.[7] His sister had no news of them, although three years have passed. She might have fallen prey to the sharks at the bottom of the sea like many other ill-fated refugees. Or to the pirates who waited off the coast of Thailand for the emigrants who were carrying their best possessions converted to jewelry and gold coins to fund their new lives. He heaved a deep sigh, remembering the verses:

Our country's fallen in a pit of spikes.
We can't escape in just a day or two
to reach high seas a boat must wait for winds.
To break the chains, it takes a hammer blow.
And with our bodies we must make a raft,
Must pour our blood and make a stream, a tide.[8]

Peeping Tom was walking back and forth on the floor. He stopped short, asking:

"What makes you sigh, my friend?"

The Old Man sat up and opened the bag of tobacco to smoke:

"I can't get to sleep. I feel sad, thinking about everything."

Peeping Tom said:

"That's why I'm scared of lying down. Walking the floor releases stress. I only lie down when I'm too tired. When I am walking, I dream that I am strolling along 'Sunset Boulevard.' I usually walk at least 10 kilometers a day. During my months in prison, by my calculation, I have covered one-eighth of the distance around the earth."

Exhaling smoke, the Old Man related:

"In camp, I vegetated, oblivious to everything. Here, I have become a thoughtful person. I don't mind staying here or going home. But I don't understand why they still keep me here when the war with China does not materialize. It's nonsense!

There's no rhyme or reason in this society. Without Russia's intervention, our own country would have been destroyed. The so-called 'forever tight friendship' has turned loose. My youngest brother was killed in the '79 border war. He was stationed in Lào Cai when Chinese troops arrived. Seeing the enemy's tanks cleverly camouflaged with yellow-starred red flags, we mistakenly believed they were ours. That's why our troops were heavily defeated."

The Old Man shook his head:

"It's ridiculous! After the battle, both sides claimed victory."

Peeping Tom explained:

"They both told a big lie. Chinese troops suffered heavy casualties, but ours were no better. The fact is both sides took human lives very cheap. To be honest with you, I have never seen the Party leaders in such a state of apprehension. They showed composure in the fight against the French and Americans. But in this case, no sooner had our troops been attacked than *Nhân Dân* had a headline printed on the front page urgently calling for the Soviet's immediate intervention. Brezhnev warned: 'China must withdraw from Việt Nam before it's too late.' So many people were mobilized to build the Sông Cầu defense line to protect the capital. Even chemical weapons were ready for use at Yên Bái. Well-trained soldiers were airlifted from Cambodia. Although Việt Nam's rough border terrain is ideal for defense, the Chinese succeeded in penetrating about 40 kilometers deep into our territory in a few days. Lạng Sơn front and the capital of Hà Nội were no more than 100 kilometers apart. No wonder our leaders got scared. They were prepared to move to Thanh Hoa. Ethnic minorities were on the Chinese side. On March 5, Deng Xiaopeng declared troops' withdrawal and warned Vietnam against any surprise attack during the time of withdrawal. Not a gunshot was heard from our side.

The Chinese had a trick for winning people's hearts. They distributed food supplies and clothes to the Vietnamese people. However, factories, mines, bridges, public buildings, and offices—all were swept away under their advancing footsteps. Even Pắc Bó Cave, where Hồ Chí Minh was living during the 1940s, was destroyed. Without Russia's support, while hundreds of thousands of soldiers were stuck in Cambodia in 1979, Vietnam would have been swallowed up. If China's henchman Hoàng Văn Hoan were in power, our people would be much more miserable. Russia's puppets are much better, anyway. During the Sino-Vietnamese War, besides the dead and the wounded, Vietnamese refugees were the worst hit. When they returned home, nothing was left. Poultry, cattle, everything that moved were all killed by Vietnamese troops."

"I've also met quite a few mountain people in prison. They all live along the border. They told me they were lucky to be in prison. So many of them were killed and thrown down the canyons just because they were Chinese sympathizers. You're right! Without the Soviet intervention, we would have been in danger. At war with the Chinese, we suffered serious disadvantages in many respects. They knew our terrain like the back of their hand, because they had been stationed in North Vietnam for years. Furthermore, when the two countries still kept strong ties of friendship, our department of defense went so far as to have army maps printed in China. A great number of Party members and soldiers were among Chinese sympathizers. Our people were exhausted whereas the Party got stuck in Cambodia. The Chinese forces were ten times stronger. Logistics were favorable to them as the two countries share the same border."

Tramp-tramp, tramp-Tramp.

"Stop for a moment! Buffalo King is coming."

Clang! After unlocking the doors for prisoners to get out for food, Buffalo King told the Old Man:

"Go for interrogation! Today you do not have to be in uniform."

The Old Man followed the duty warden, walking past the closet where the pus-infested South Vietnamese officer's uniform was kept for the interrogation of prisoners. He was brought into a rather large room, decently furnished, well-ventilated by a swift-running ceiling fan, and decorated with a large oil painting on the wall. This was certainly not an interrogation room. A stocky, middle-aged man, with hair cut short, a golden watch and a short-sleeved shirt introduced himself as a staff officer. Two young men in civilian clothes were sitting beside him. Their respect for him indicated he was a high-ranking cadre. One of the two poured tea into cups. The officer pointed to a packet of Thăng Long cigarettes on the table, saying with a smile:

"Have tea and a cigarette! Are you in good health? We brought you here with the idea of giving you a way out. How long have you been imprisoned?"

"The first time, sixteen years. This time, since the border incident took place in 1979, over four years."

The interrogator nodded repeatedly in agreement:

"It's really a big loss for you! We're in wartime, you know. During the Second World War, the U.S. gathered all the Japanese residents in prison camps in the mountains and deserts, even citizens. When China invaded our country, the ex-prisoners of the puppet government and Army in six cities along the border followed the Chinese.

They were sentenced to death at once, according to martial law. You were lucky to be in Hà Nội at that time. I have reviewed your files. During nearly two years in freedom—from '77 to '79—you did not work for a living, except that you did some illegal business."

"I was jobless, sir. Hair-cutting is the only trade I've learned while in camp. But quarter security agents forbade me to practice my trade under the pretext that as an itinerant barber I have more chance to contact people. I was chased away while working with a bicycle pump at the roadside. I was fired again after working for a while as a mason's helper. The reason: ex-prisoner. Consequently, I had to sell tea and honey bought from Phú Thọ, Lạng Sơn. Some kilograms of tea or some liters of honey for each trip, just to make both ends meet. Very often, goods being confiscated, I lost everything, capital and interest. Sometimes, I went without food for days."

"Why don't you get married? You want to be free to do politics, don't you?"

"It's hard, I should think, to find a girl who sincerely loves you, especially a girl who agrees with you on everything. When I was released, my wife had married another man, and my son had been killed without a trace in the woody Trường Sơn mountain range. I am too disappointed to think of marrying again. My life is not settled. I can't afford to support myself, let alone to have a wife again. Do you think I purposely stay single for politics? How can I get involved in political activities while my stomach is empty? Like you, most revolutionaries were married. Revolution does not require you to be single, does it?"

"Well, you have suffered a lot in life, I know. Now, we wish to give you a chance to start a new life. You're just fifty-three, seven years younger than I. There's still plenty of time. Now, I have a personal question to ask you. Do you want to be released?"

"Living in a kennel, even a dog wishes to get out, let alone a human being. As for me, sincerely speaking, I'm utterly tired of everything. Long years in prison have made me a callous person. It makes no difference to me whether I'm in prison or out of it. Different circumstances create different problems. Living outside, I don't really know what to do for a living. I am continuously vexed by police and security. Life is no better out there."

"Therefore, we would like to give you a better opportunity and compensate you for the loss you have suffered. We will make necessary arrangements for you to be in Hồ Chí Minh City. You don't have to worry about board and lodging. We might be able to find you a woman to live with, which makes your old age less lonesome; on condition you will help us achieve a number of things. Actually, we're not short-handed. But, it is more convenient for us to use you. Anyway, our main purpose should be perceived as a compensation for your loss. How do you think?"

"Can you let me know something more concrete?"

"You must serve the Revolution unconditionally. You have to complete whatever the Revolution entrusts to you. Of course, the job is not beyond your capacity. Now, I need to know if you accept or not."

"I cannot accept, unless I know something more concrete."

"No problem! We're not in a hurry. Take your time to think about it. When you're ready, let the supervisor know, and I will see you. Today I've already made myself very clear. You should weigh the pros and cons carefully. Don't let your chance slip away. By the way, do you wish to write to your younger sister? We can post the letter for you."

The Old Man asked for paper and a pencil, wrote a few lines and handed the letter to one of the two young men. The interrogator stood up. So did the Old Man. The other young man handed him a nylon-bag containing a box of sugar, two cans of milk, a parcel of tea, a carton of Điện Biên cigarettes and a lighter, and said:

"These are gifts for you from our chief."

"Smoking is forbidden in the Hanoi Hilton. There is no boiling water either. This stuff might be confiscated."

The interrogator smiled:

"Don't worry! I'll let them know. Think over what I've said today. I'm waiting for your answer."

The warden on duty brought him back to the division, and said to Buffalo King: "Our Comrade General has allowed him to smoke and drink tea."

Buffalo King showed noticeable respect for him. Without searching the Old Man, he opened the door for him and said:

"Use a mug for boiling water!"

He thanked Buffalo King and went in to take Peeping Tom's mug. Tea was ready in only two minutes. He carried the mug of tea into his cell and warmed it up with his cotton coat.

Peeping Tom asked:

"Any good news?"

He shook his head:

"No! Not at all. I'll tell you after the meal."

Click-lock. Click-lock. Buffalo King puffed at his tobacco pipe and left. Quite a few inmates congratulated the Old Man on the good signs indicating he would be released soon, especially on those gifts from the staff officer.

Bear-head said aloud, without reservation:

"Our Uncle and Auntie are leaving us soon. Once released, you both are free to pamper and cherish each other. Please, don't forget your unlucky nephew."

Sài Gòn Woman responded with joy:

"When I'm free, I will send you gifts."

Driving Gangster asked the Old Man:

"As a long-time prisoner, can you let me know, is there any chance Chairman Trường Chinh will grant me amnesty? Death sentence is too heavy for me. It's only 28 tons of paddy that I took, you know."

But the Old Man could not hear. Being locked in the stocks, Driving Gangster could not stand up to raise his voice loud enough. Peeping Tom had to remind him to speak louder:

"Louder! Our Uncle cannot hear you."

Driving Gangster's question had to be repeated. The Old Man tried to console him:

"You cannot control your destiny. Death or life, I can't tell. Too much worry doesn't help. Keep hoping for the best! Who knows? Your sentence may be lifted some day."

Peeping Tom said to the Old Man:

"What a tragedy, I think his death is certain. Trường Chinh has never forgiven anybody. How about you? Don't be too pessimistic about life!"

The Old Man talked confidentially with Peeping Tom:

"I know they want to use me to harm others. I am a former captain in the national army, living in prison for 20 years. They know I can easily win the trust of opponents. Therefore, they intend to use me as a trap. I can never accept such a dirty job. Now, I come to understand the reason why I have been transferred here."

Peeping Tom shook hands with him in admiration:

"You're really a noble person. I totally agree with you on what you've just said. It's a shame to betray your friends. That is not the price you pay for being released. I have contracted terrible vices but not the vice of betraying friends or cheating women. I can be a Don Juan, a ladies' man, not an unfaithful womanizer. I am a hot lover, not a cheating lover. I bitterly hate those who cheat women."

"When he offered me gifts, my first impulse was to refuse. However, I thought again and realized those gifts were what he had stolen from people, not his own possessions. With that idea in mind, I took the gifts, with a clear conscience."

"I had the same idea when I embezzled the public funds. I think if they cannot buy you off, they will send you back to camp."

"My life has been ruined. It cannot be worse."

That night, the whole division was bustling with life. Female and male prisoners joked with one another. They sometimes used obscene words, but it was all in fun. Combs and brushes were whisked from cell to cell. Gifts were exchanged. Those without supplies were given some gifts. The small amount of food they received from friends was not enough to satisfy their hunger, but enough to warm their hearts. Peeping Tom stood, looking out for the armed guards who might be around.

The Old Man said to him:

"I have been in many prisons before, but I see that nowhere can be found inmates as nice as here. Most of them are newcomers, so they still have something to give. I feel sorry for the first lieutenant. Nobody cares to give him some food."

"Everyone hates him, because he's a snitch. Besides, he is far from here, in cell 1, next to the bathroom. Gifts must go through our cell in order to reach him."

"He stopped being an informer since the day he was slashed in the face, didn't he? I think we may give him something to eat."

Peeping Tom said in a moving voice:

"You're right! We should give him some. Let me drive to his cell."

The Old Man put two sweet short cakes, some sesame-sprinkled gums into a nylon bag. Receiving gifts for the first time, the first lieutenant was deeply moved:

"Thank you, Dad, for your loving concern."

Bear-head scolded him:

"I have met many guys of your type. Being given something, you say: 'Dad! Dad!' If not, you curse: 'Damn it! You old fool!' Are you still proud of the Revolution? Stop your tell-tale mouth! If not, I'm gonna slash it, not your face this time."

The Old Man told Peeping Tom to distribute cigarettes to every cell; three cigarettes to each person. He then stood up, asking:

"Brothers and sisters! Do you smoke?"

The actress of Hà Nội troupe giggled:

"I can smoke rustic tobacco, even 'cigars,' Uncle!"

Everyone burst out laughing.

Sài Gòn Woman said joyfully:

"I'm not an addict. But I smoke to share your happiness, dear brother! You're going home soon, aren't you?"

"It's not true, dear. As for the singer, do you smoke?"

"Yes, I do, Uncle! I smoke to sweeten my voice in order to entertain everyone here."

"Only three among women who smoke?"

Other women just said "Thank you," refusing to smoke. The show did not end until ten o'clock. Everyone had to sing even though they did not know how to sing. At everyone's insistence, a number of women stood up and declaimed some lullabies. One of them was brazen enough to recite:

"Lullai, lulli, little baby!
When you're evacuated,
your mommy goes hunting for another daddy!"

Everyone applauded, convulsed with laughter.

"Hip hip hurray! Come on, let's sing again. It's better to sing often than to sing well."

The Actress sang most often. As for the others, more than ten songs each. All the songs were sentimental music.

Peeping Tom said to the Old Man:

"In wartime, we need energy to fight. This sort of music is too weak. It's so exhausting, so paralyzing! No wonder, we have been defeated. It's the music that cost us our country, home, and even wife. Do you have enough energy to fight when you sing:

> *Atop a towering warship, perching high,*
> *I watch the stars, missing your eyes?*

The Old Man heaved a deep sigh:

"We've heard *Thái Thanh sings a song of separation in a café* and now, we are really separated for hard labor while a warden hurls insults at us. We have heard: *From now on, weapons won't divide our love anymore,* but now concentration camps divide us much more effectively. Without a strong will, or knowledge of politics, how can we win the war against the Communists? Let's blame ourselves first, the Americans second. Don't talk about it anymore! Let bygones be bygones! Go to sleep!"

"You sleep first. I have paper. I must write to 'her.'"

The Old Man lowered his mosquito net and lay down to sleep. He got up at about 4:00 A.M. and began his routine of respiratory exercises. A moment later, Peeping Tom woke up. He boiled water for tea. While the others were still sleeping, the two sat sipping tea and smoking. The old man felt relieved while enjoying the fragrance of tea.

"This is a rare moment. Even in the outside world, we can hardly afford such a relaxing time. Out there, people are busy day and night, working for a living. They never have time to sit down together, drinking and talking confidentially like this. How precious the present moment! Exactly as the old adage goes: 'I take the person I drink with, face to face, as my wife.' In prison, we are deprived of almost everything; yet it is a place where we feel closer to others, a place where we treat one another more nicely. Any newcomer is considered as a special guest. I've just been here not even two days, and I have the feeling everyone is a close friend. It is not so easy to get acquainted with others in the outside world. In crowded communal rooms, prisoners struggle for life. Hunger robs them of human feelings. The situation in camps is no better. Cells are desolate cemeteries where the inmates are always in stocks, suffering too much hunger to care to talk with others."

"Prisoners love one another because they are in the same boat. To share happiness is much harder than to share suffering. Too much suffering however can turn human beings into cruel beasts. Here, all people, except Sài Gòn Woman, receive supplies only once a month. Although used sparingly, food is hardly sufficient. Still, we're not too hungry to become heartless. Look! Your shoulder is bruised with bug bites."

"Here, bugs and lice are our companions. There's no way to get rid of them. By the way, have you written to 'her'?"

"I have. To me, love here is just for fun, to chase worries away. We must go our separate ways, anyway. Everyone has got up. Let's have some exercise! In prison, exercise is a must for everyone."

Bear-head crooned:

One sad Sunday, is there anybody, anybody ...
Your lips are full, sensuous ...

Peeping Tom cursed:

"Damn it! Always your lips, your shoulder ... while the war is raging. It's an anti-war song. I don't know what type of people they are."

Stomp-stomp. Peeping Tom stood up on the stocks to look:

"Buffalo King is off today. A warden from the South takes his place. This man is as good as Buddha. I don't understand why they haven't dismissed him from the job, which requires brutality and unscrupulousness. I think he will be transferred sooner or later."

Clink! The new warden opened the door and stepped into the Old Man's cell first. Peeping Tom whispered to his friend: "We're free to go bathing and washing today. Let's take everything out to wash." They did not squander water away, trying to save for the others. They were about to get back to their cell when the warden said:

"Feel free to stay outside for awhile, to enjoy the fresh air!"

After that, he went to open Sài Gòn Woman's cell. During such a rare moment of relaxation, Peeping Tom happily ran around the yard. He looked very young. As for the Old Man, he raised both hands, inhaling the fresh morning air.

The new warden sat at a table, puffing twice on his bamboo pipe. He looked toward the yard gate and said to the Old Man:

"Go close that gate, for convenience and privacy!"

But Peeping Tom did not wait. He hastened to the gate to close it. Seeing that the warden did not drink tea, the Old Man said:

"I have tea, sir. May I make tea for you?"

"This morning, I forgot to bring tea along. Go ahead! We can have some together."

He took out a bag of Ba Đình tea and plugged the boiler in.

"You've just come here, haven't you?"

"Yes, I came the day before yesterday."

"You look so thin! You must have been in prison for some time."

"Twenty years, altogether."

"Why so long?"

He began to tell the whole story of why he had been arrested and put in prison.

The warden smacked his lips:

"In '54, you remained in the North, whereas I left the South to regroup in the North. Your wife left you; as for me, my wife died in 1969, and I did not hear the news of her death until after the country had been unified. Your son was killed by the Americans somewhere in the woods of Trường Sơn mountain range, whereas my son was killed by Pol Pot's troops in Cambodia. Now I'm living by myself as you are. I'm going to retire in one year."

"Have a drink, sir, while the tea is still hot!"

"Thank you, you drink first. Each person's destiny has been decided. Worries won't help. My younger brother, a major in the Army of the Republic of Viet Nam, is currently at Tan Lap camp. He's as skinny as you are. You don't want to be in prison. I don't want to be a warden. Still, I have to be."

"Sir, a warden like you has brought us prisoners a lot of consolation."

"I always nurture a hope that when the war comes to an end, the number of prisoners will decrease. But reality proves the contrary. You crave rustic tobacco, don't you? Take a quick puff, now! I will hand you a bag later this evening; and you can distribute it to others. Don't tell them the tobacco is mine. I don't want to ask for trouble."

The Sài Gòn Woman brought out her laundry to dry. She said 'hello' to the new warden.

The Old Man stood up, saying: "Thank you, sir, for the fresh air."

"Keep drinking tea before you get in!"

Jogging for a while, Peeping Tom felt tired. He stopped, winking at the Old Man.

The warden invited Sài Gòn Woman to drink tea with him:

"Have a drink, please!"

"Thank you, I have my own tea. I ask your permission to plug the boiler in."

"Go ahead! You don't have to ask."

She brought out a mug of water and a nylon bag of about three kg of roasted glutinous rice and said:

"These are for my Brother, here."

Hearing that, the Old Man refused:

"It's very kind of you, dear. But how can I take your gift? Please, keep it for later use."

The warden smiled:

"Come on! Take it! She notices you're skinny. I order the bag be brought into your cell!"

Peeping Tom carried the bag in. The Old Man said, "Thanks," in embarrassment before walking in and claiming it.

All the prisoners took turns washing and bathing to their hearts' content. They opened the windows to look into other cells and talked freely with one another. The warden sat smoking and drinking in silence. He seemed tired of life. His bamboo pipe was bubbling without interruption. Tobacco addicts wish to use a water pipe to freshen their throats, because a roll of rustic tobacco wrapped in paper produces so much heat. He distributed tobacco to everybody and allowed them to smoke freely.

Bear-head stood at his lover's door, whispering to her for a long time. The Actress urged him:

"Go ahead! Kiss her!"

"I'm trying to, but the iron bars are too thick, too close-set. My lips cannot touch hers. Only a finger can go through."

His lover said:

"You fool! Why do you curse everyone without discrimination? I've told you many times, and you don't listen. As for our Uncle who's just come, if you curse him, I will break off all relations with you."

He seemingly got tamed:

"I never curse our Uncle. I protect him, instead. I don't curse even the antenna who is with him. Sometimes I only warn him against any report about the events happening in prison."

"Get in! We have gone too far already. We must not take advantage of our good warden. Let's hold him in some regard!"

Peeping Tom waited for the Dollar Trafficker to walk out. He stooped to look through a two-hand wide window. The Singer walked out first, then the Dollar-Trafficker followed. He handed her through the iron bars a neatly folded letter the size of a matchbox. She took it furtively and went into the bathroom.

Peeping Tom's face brightened:

"The first step is considered a success. I have to go for it. I'm gonna take the next step."

The Old Man smiled:

"This warden is so good! Male and female inmates are free to talk with one another, and he pretends not to know it. He is a person of great compassion. I have in my life met some wardens like him, and we, even bad guys, respected them very much. They're just like those who don't get soiled while wading in mud. Indeed, he's a really good-natured person."

"Don't you see that female and male prisoners appear much happier while living together?"

"Naturally, man is not born alone. A male must be coupled with a female. That's the law of nature."

Peeping Tom kept listening. Hearing the sound of sandals approaching from bathroom, he jumped to the door. The Singer went out to dry her laundry in the yard. After carrying a pot and a bucket of water into her cell, the Dollar Trafficker walked out. At Peeping Tom's cell she stopped short.

Peeping Tom raised his voice, with a smile:

"Dear, your jade ring is so beautiful! Let me have a look, please!"

Seeing a tapering finger jutting out from iron bars he suddenly seized it and began to caress it amorously on and on. The Old Man turned his face away.

"Why do you look out, friend?"

He turned back, answering:

"I just want to leave the two of you alone. Congratulations!"

Peeping Tom said, his eyes sparkling:

"She has succumbed to the temptation after reading my letter. Everything happens just as anticipated. How about you? Why are you so indifferent! Follow in my steps, friend! Long years in prison have made your heart stone-hard, haven't they?"

Bear-head observed what had happened from the start. He laughed:

"I have to admit Peeping Tom's saw is a genuine one, made in Czechoslovakia. It's powerful enough to saw down the Dollar Goddess at a single stroke."

Clink, clank! The warden locked the door and jangled away.

Sài Gòn Woman said heartily:

"This warden is truly a Vietnamese Gandhi. He's truly an honest person. He doesn't put on an act, like a bunch of hypocrites. From now on, let's call him 'Gandhi'!"

"Agreed! Agreed!"

At about 4:00 P.M. Gandhi came back. He opened the doors for prisoners to go out to get food and to bring the laundry in. The Old Man was the first to go. Gandhi handed him one hectogram of Thống Nhát tobacco.

The Old Man sincerely thanked the new warden:

"You're so nice! Here, we call you the Vietnamese Gandhi."

The warden smiled sparingly: "I don't deserve that name. Suffering too much in life, I find it easy to feel compassion for the sufferings of others. I have a deep affection for the prisoners. My younger brother is also a prisoner. Looking at your food ration, I feel sorry for you, but I don't know what to do."

"I find that most Southerners, especially the farmers are very frank and straightforward. In 1960, when I ate folded sizzling pancakes in the street, I asked the seller, who was a Southerner: 'Is this the kind you have in the South?' He gave me an abrupt answer: 'In the South, even a dog doesn't care to eat this kind of cake.' He continued to talk, saying that sizzling pancakes made in the South must include various ingredients such as coconut milk, shrimp, etc., ..."

Gandhi smiled: "That's right! The Southerners always speak their mind. Were you upset to hear that, by the way?"

"On the contrary, I found it very interesting. Hearing such an abrupt statement about the pancakes he was selling in front of me, his customer, I thought nobody could be more sincere. I came to like him more. Since then, I often came to eat his sizzling pancakes and we became close friends. Allow me, sir, to share tobacco with friends, now!"

The Old Man went from cell to cell to distribute tobacco.

The First Lieutenant begged him: "Give me a flint, Dad, for a spark of fire. I'm very hungry, Dad! Please give me something to eat!"

The Old Man hurried to his cell. He brought out a flint attached to a button, and one kilogram of roasted glutinous rice for the young man. After that, he went to the cells of women and girls to thank them for their birthday gifts. He also went to see the Singer, the Actress, and Bear-head and gave one packet of cigarettes to each of them. Arriving at the cell of Sài Gòn Woman, he handed a packet of cigarettes to her, saying:

"I know you are not a smoker, dear. One cigarette after a meal does no harm, but gives you a pleasant taste."

"I accept your gift, dear Brother, on the condition you have to take whatever I give you. By the way, tell me your sister's address. When released, I will stop by to see her, and through her I will send gifts to you. Do you think you will be released soon? Twenty years in prison is long enough. How much longer do you have to wait? They are so cruel!"

"Not a slim hope! Security promised to set me free on one condition, I have to cooperate with them in harming others. I cannot accept their condition. They have used those dirty gifts just as bait to lure me. I'm giving you my sister's address tonight. Your kindness touches my heart immensely, dear. Thank you so much!"

"Don't mention it, brother! Please, consider me your own sister."

"I do."

After waving 'goodbye' to her, the Old Man went back to his cell at the time Peeping Tom was leaving the Dollar Goddess's cell. He asked the Old Man:

"You have 'opened fire,' haven't you? How is her reaction? It seems to me both sides are very friendly."

The Old Man shook his head:

"Just friends! That's all."

"For my part, success is beyond my expectation. She pledged to look for me, when she is released. I have given her the address of one of my friends, so that she may keep track of me. She divorced a long time ago. My wife is, alas, as fierce as a tigress."

"Let's eat something. And we'll drink tea, lest it be cool down."

In the evening, everyone in the division lavished praise on the new warden. The air was filled with the fragrance of rustic tobacco and cigarettes. Peeping Tom was in high spirits. He stood up to declare:

"Tonight, I'll sing to honor the 'Vietnamese Gandhi.' I would like to open the show with a song entitled 'Blue Danube.'"

He sang the song both in Vietnamese and in French, which impressed the Dollar-Goddess. He sang the next song entitled 'Return to Sorrento,' and concluded with 'The History of a Love Story.' Everybody gave him a big hand. The Singer and the Actress took turns to sing. They sang tirelessly. The more they sang the more they got excited. After eating his fill, the First Lieutenant also stood up to sing. What an amazing performance! His voice was so warm, so sweet! He continued to sing a series of revolutionary songs, and closed with three Laotian folk songs both in Laotian and in Vietnamese. Everyone applauded him enthusiastically.

"We have discovered a new talent in this division."

"We have a wonderful duo now."

He said proudly:

"If I have enough to eat, I'll sing much better. That's the best I can sing while I'm hungry."

Bear-head scolded him:

"You hungry fool! Always asking for food."

The Old Man intervened:

"Stop it! From now on, in this division, everybody is part of a family. Let bygones be bygones! Don't take it to heart, friend! Talent should be appreciated and misfortune understood."

Peeping Tom stood up and declared the show closed. The hustle and bustle went on and on, and did not stop until late at night when the footsteps of an armed guard were heard.

The Old Man said to Peeping Tom:

"I'm going to teach you some techniques of Qi Gong."

He smiled:

"Thank you, friend. I'm too excited to learn now. Let's wait for some more days. Her 'vitamin' is very effective."

"If so, let's have a puff. Then I will go to sleep. As for you, keep pecking at her 'vitamin.' I do not know if she dreams about 'your vitamin' or not."

"She is a very sensuous woman with sparkling lascivious eyes, thanks to my 'vitamin.' Why don't you go to bed now? Let me have time to dream for a while!"

Days passed in and out, the Old Man had been in the division for two weeks. He did not want to ask for another meeting with the staff officer, because he knew when he refused cooperation with the security, the prison door would shut tight. He had expressed his determination not to serve the revolution. He heaved a deep sigh, thinking: "I have no choice."

Peeping Tom had became a confidential friend. He found him well-educated, straightforward, good-natured and totally against the regime. Tom often remarked:

"Regrettably, instead of liberating the North, South Viet Nam has itself been 'liberated' by the North. As a longtime member of the Party, I can state that this authoritarian regime was a disaster to the country."

As an extensive traveler, he thought those who had been in foreign countries and still accepted the regime must be mental cases.

The Old Man's sister had sent him some gifts and a letter in which she advised him to welcome the overtures made by the Party. After reading the letter, he shook his head. They even asked for his sister's cooperation in an attempt to shake his spirit. Her gifts were only a few kilograms of roasted noodle, some hectograms of Cuban sugar and a little bit of salt mixed with sesame. He felt guilty though, because he had nothing to give back those who gave him gifts.

Peeping Tom tried to console him:

"Don't worry about trivialities. Everyone knows you're poor. The Sài Gòn Woman has given you so much! You do not look as thin as before, and now you look much younger as well."

"I know, but I still feel embarrassed. As a general rule, a satisfactory relationship should be a fair give-and-take."

"Everyone in this division knows you are generous. If you trade the amount of your tobacco and cigarettes for food, you will have enough for at least one month. Everyone admires you because you don't forget the First Lieutenant."

"It's too bad! He keeps asking for more, because he does not know how to save."

One evening, after a meal, Buffalo King came to his cell. *Clang!* He opened the door and said:

"Get prepared to move to cell no. 1!"

At those words, Peeping Tom's face turned pale. He felt dazed for a moment. He and the Old Man were living together in happiness. He was not used to such a sudden separation while living in prison. The Old Man packed his few belongings and went to cell 1.

The First Lieutenant appeared joyful. He said:

"I'm happy to be with you, Dad! If you need anything, I'm at your service. I can give you a good massage."

"This cell is too close to the bathroom. It's too humid and smells very bad. We must report to the warden and ask for a good rub and wash."

"Let me do it, Dad! Old as you are, you should relax. I'm still young, you know. I can give you a helping hand whenever you need me."

"How old are you?"

"I'm thirty-one.

"How long have you been arrested?"

"Just ten months. After a few months at Bất Bạt, an army-controlled camp, I was transferred here for a reason, I really don't know. My condition was better over there. I'm too hungry here."

Bear-head shouted to the old man:

"Uncle! There's no way you can be happy in that cell."

"No problem! We're still in the same division. We're only four meters apart."

Bear-head raised his voice again:

"Young man, I warn you against any misconduct toward Uncle. I won't let you do anything disrespectful."

Peeping Tom added:

"All of a sudden, you have to move while we're happy together. I'm so sad, friend!"

"We're still friends. A short distance cannot separate us."

The First Lieutenant continued his begging:

"Give me something to eat, Dad! I'm too hungry."

The Old Man said in surprise:

"I just gave you one kilogram of roasted noodles, the day before yesterday. Why don't you save?"

"I have swallowed it in one gulp, Dad."

"Don't eat that way, young man! You have to use food in small portions. Never eat to your heart's content. Eat just to maintain your health. Here, I'm lucky to receive each month a couple of kilograms of noodles from my sister. When I was in camp far away over there, she could see me only once a year, on New Year's Day. Prison term is still long. We have to train ourselves to survive torture and hunger."

He stirred sugar in a mug of water and handed it to the young man. He then gave him some roasted noodles. He took for himself a few handfuls of noodles and put them on a piece of cardboard often used as a fan.

"Don't you drink, Dad?"

"I did. I only drink once a day."

The young man emptied the whole mug in one gulp and greedily swallowed up the amount of noodles in a few minutes.

"What did they charge you with?"

"With corruption, Dad. When my troops stationed in Laos, I was assigned the task of transporting food supplies to Thailand for Thai guerrilla groups. I took bribes to let people cross the border. Unfortunately I was caught after a few times."

"Don't you have anybody to provide supplies for you now?"

"My parents are dead. I'm still single. My only brother has fled to Australia."

"When did you enlist in the Army?"

"I enlisted at the age of 18, my false age. Actually, at that time my age was 17. My native city is Thái Bình, called 'Việt Nam's granary.' But in reality, Thái Bình residents are starving. Each person receives only 9 kilograms of rice a month on average. As you know, young people, including girls, need at least one kg of rice a day to survive. As the saying goes: 'At seventeen, he or she can break a buffalo's horn.' Every year, when going digging ditches for irrigation, each person must contribute one kg of rice, a day. People have to eat as fast as possible because if they are slow, they will starve. Let me tell you this story, Dad. That year, a girl who lived next door to me took along a couple of sardines for a trip to the fields. After ten days, all the sardines were brought back, untouched. At the sight, we laughed convulsively when we knew the reason why. She did not eat her fish for fear that those who sat with her around the same tray of food would eat up her portion of rice in case she happened to be caught in fish bones. We joked: 'What homesick fish you have! Fish to go and fish to return,' making her blush with embarrassment. I had known what hunger is when I was a child. I still remember the day I was only 10 years old, my dad was swinging in a hammock, sighing deeply for lack of food. Suddenly, he shouted angrily: 'Damn it! We still have a basket of potatoes. Son, have them boiled right away! And tomorrow we can go without food.' At those words, I happily hastened to the basket and tripped over the doorstep. As a result, I broke a front tooth. Since then I was nicknamed 'toothless guy.'

He smiled, pointing to his mouth and said:

"Look! Dad! My broken tooth is still here."

The Old Man finished the remaining noodles, drank some more water, and asked:

"Did the army accept you right away?"

"Yes, when I heard the news, I felt happy as if my mother were being resurrected. From now on, I thought, no more permanent twinges of hunger. Those who were rejected because they were underweight appeared sad as if they were mourning the death of their fathers. Some of them broke into tears."

"Do you know at that time those who went to the South fell like flies?"

"Yes, I know. So many village lads lost their lives. My two cousins were killed in the Battle of Khe Sanh during the Tết Offensive of 1968."

"Didn't you fear death?"

"Yes, I did; but a state of permanent hunger was much more fearful. In the army, death was something I had not met yet; but food, plenty of food was right in front of me. Twenty-one kilograms of rice, one and one-half kilograms of meat, one kilogram of sugar a month are what made my mouth water. I lived like in a dream. In addition, I might be promoted to officer for bravery in battle. The condition was much better than that of volunteer youth forces."

"Have you ever been in Cambodia?"

"Yes, I have. In 1979, we advanced to Cambodia through Laos. Laotian and Cambodian girls are very easy going, Dad! To be honest with you, when in Cambodia, I even ate human liver so that I could prove myself a warrior. It's very nutritious, Dad."

"You did? Was it raw or dry?"

The young man expressed some regret:

"I ate it dry. Some of my friends were luckier. They ate it raw, fresh from bodies. They even drank alcohol with it. It's so brutal!"

"You're still very lucky to be alive. Poet Chế Lan Viên reported in *Nhân Dân* that, of more than 3,000 cadres sent to Lam Dong in 1975, only 30 survived. A security general declared victory each time one truck out of 40 reached its destination."

"That's right Dad! Heavy casualties were reported. People died in various ways, especially truck drivers. Some were killed in a bomb attack. Others died of diseases; some others were killed in an accident .... It's a price to pay for victory."

"Are you a Party member?"

"Of course I am. If not, how could I be promoted to first lieutenant?"

The Old Man stood up:

"I'm going to take some exercise. Go join the others!"

He walked back and forth on the floor listening to the songs. When the show ended, he sat down and gave himself a good massage. After that, he practiced some techniques of Qi Gong.

"Let's have a smoke, Dad!"

"You smoke rustic tobacco or cigarettes?"

"Give me a cigarette!"

After finishing the cigarette, he asked again:

"Do you still have glutinous rice, Dad? I remember the Sài Gòn Woman has given it to you. I think you are still very handsome and attractive. She's crazy about you."

"Don't talk nonsense! She just gave it to me out of pity."

"Let me cook glutinous rice for you, Dad!"

The Old Man was surprised:

"What do you cook with? We have no boiler, no pan, nothing…"

"I cook in a chamber pot. Don't worry! I have washed it thoroughly. I'm gonna' tear up this blanket and burn it for cooking."

The Old Man furrowed his brows, saying:

"Chamber pot? It's so disgusting! We are not allowed to cook although we have a boiler. Don't you fear you'll be put in the stocks? About two minutes are sufficient for me to boil water for two small cups of tea. I need someone to watch out for the guards who may be around. Cooking glutinous rice takes at least half an hour. How can we cook anyway, as everybody in the division will smell something burning? In case we're caught, we'll be accused of destroying public property. If you still crave it, I will have the kitchen people cook for you tomorrow. Now go to sleep!"

The next morning, Buffalo King allowed their cell to be cleaned. Both of them worked hard, trying to get rid of the bad smell.

The Old Man said:

"We have to maintain hygienic conditions as much as we possibly can, in order to survive in prison."

The First Lieutenant pulled a nylon bag full of banana skins and other dirty fruit peelings from under the floor and began to eat them voraciously.

The Old Man tried to stop him, saying in disgust:

"Stop it! Is this dirty stuff from the bathroom? It's unspeakable! That rubber basket is full of used toilet paper and sanitary napkins. You rotten fool! Are these the kinds of foods you eat everyday? Throw them right away, will you? Let me give you some roasted noodles."

Hearing that, the First Lieutenant stealthily wrapped them up and hid the whole bunch under the floor. The Old Man warned him:

"Next time, if you continue to eat those dirty things, I will report it to the warden, and you shall be cut off all supplies, including tobacco."

That night, the Old Man softened his voice, talking confidentially with the young lieutenant:

"What I've just said is from my heart. I care about you. I plan to save glutinous rice until noodles run out. But seeing you hunger for glutinous rice, I've told the kitchen people to cook it for you. You know, candy, cake, sugar, noodles. Whatever I eat, you can too. I'll share with you what I have. I know the amount of food is not enough even for me, let alone for you. We're short of supplies, you know. What can we do now? We can stuff ourselves in two days and do without food for a whole month. However, such an eating habit is harmful to our health. Besides, where can we find medicine in case we fall sick? I can bear the pangs of hunger better than you, because I have been in prison for 20 long years. You should train yourself to be used to the situation in prison. You must be kept in prison at least five more years. Later, you may be transferred to camp. You will die easily if you continue to eat rashly like this. You're still young. Try to live! Mind my words: 'Eat to live, don't eat to die!'"

"Like anybody else, I cannot eat dirty stuff. I have my own dignity as a revolutionary fighter. But I cannot control myself, because I'm too hungry."

"I understand; during the starvation year of 1945, I saw with my own eyes people eat more rashly than you do. They even ate human bodies. In China, during the starvation years, quite a few parents exchanged their children, because they did not have the guts to eat their own. They had to do so because there was nothing else to eat. As for us, we are not so hungry. We still have three hectograms of rice a day. In spite of food shortage, we can drag out our lives for years. I don't talk about dignity with you, much less about revolution. I'm not sure a few words of advice can help you when you have not awakened to the realities of life. I just want to emphasize one point: your own life. Absolutely no rash food, if you want to go home safe and sound. The unique method of fighting hunger is not to think about it. Practice some techniques of Qi Gong and you will forget it. Look at Bear-head, the Singer, the Dollar Trafficker, and those who have no supplies. They are as hungry as you, except that sometimes, they receive some cakes or candies. However, they do not look so miserable as you. Follow their example!"

"Yes, I will."

"If not, you have no other way to fill your stomach. You'll just torture yourself."

It's so boring to be with the First Lieutenant, the Old Man thought. That young guy had nothing interesting to tell him, because he was always obsessed with the idea of getting something to eat.

One day, seeing Sài Gòn Woman receiving gifts from her family, he urged the Old Man:

"Ask her for some glutinous rice, Dad! I'm dying for a mouthful of meat."

The Old Man said in a sad voice:

"I don't even care to take what she gives. How do I have the face to ask?"

"This is not a matter of saving face, Dad. She likes you. I'm sure she will give you anything you ask."

"I have told you, no!"

The former officer lay down on the floor, depressed. The following morning, after the bathroom hour, Buffalo King came and told the Old Man to go for interrogation.

Same room. Same staff officer. Same two young aides-de-camp. The officer pointed to a chair for him to sit on.

After a few meaningless introductory words, he came to the point: "I'm sure you have thought over my proposal. I come here today to know your decision."

"Yes, I have thought it over. I cannot cooperate with the Security."

He seemed a bit surprised: "May I know why?"

"When I was young, I only knew the Army, and fought like a professional soldier. I never thought of politics. Now, after 20 years in prison, I feel tired of everything. I just want to live in peace as a simple citizen. If I had wanted to fly high, in 1978 I would have risked my life on the ocean, with so many others, instead of living in prison like this."

"Don't you wish to serve the Revolution to redeem yourself?"

"To be honest with you Sir, I don't have any faults to redeem. In 1954, I did not go to the South as suggested by the Revolution. I have never said or done anything against the regime. You have an absolute right to keep me in prison or set me free. My destiny is in your hands."

"Do you think when cooperating with us, you would have a guilty conscience?"

"Every country needs a security service. I haven't liked it since my childhood. Different jobs for different persons. I do not accept your proposal just for the simple reason that I don't like that job. When I don't like the job, how can I fulfill it? Furthermore, it's not safe to be engaged in security activities, especially for a person whose history is like mine."

"Not safe? I don't understand what you mean. I need to hear more of an explanation."

"In my opinion, security service as well as politics is not safe. Those who wish to live a peaceful life don't want to participate in it. So many pro-Russian politicians have been arrested. Now Chinese sympathizers are, in turn, captured and put in prison. Those devoted revolutionaries have been imprisoned; let alone me, a captain of the Puppet Army of the French."

"Briefly speaking, you don't accept my proposal, do you?"

"No, I regret not being able to accept your proposal."

The staff officer stood up, his face indifferent.

"You can go now. If you reject our friendly overtures and want to continue your prison life, your wish will be met."

"As I've just said, my life is under your control. I have no power to determine my fate."

Back at the division, he felt sad. But his conscience was clear. A clear-cut choice had been made. Buffalo King let everyone out to take food. Checking his bag, the old man found that the amount of sesame salt, noodles, and sugar had been reduced by one-third. He asked the young man:

"You have eaten my food, haven't you?"

He denied it:

"No, I have never touched your bag."

The Old Man was angry:

"There's no denying it. The bag was not tied like this. I know because I have my own way of tying my bag. I have treated you so well. I have shared with you whatever I have. And you stole my food during my absence. From now on, I will give you nothing. You hear me?"

Throughout the day, the old man did not give the lieutenant anything to eat, nor did he give him tobacco to smoke. He did not talk to him either.

That night, the young man kept lying with a grim expression on his face while in the division, some were singing and others were talking. The Old Man sat in silence, his eyes closed, practicing some techniques of Qi Gong.

Suddenly the First Lieutenant sat up, cursing:

"Damn it! I'm gonna take it by force and eat it. I can fight for it. I don't give a damn about being reported."

The Old Man opened his eyes and turned to him:

"You've just aimed abuses on me, haven't you? You want to rob me of food, don't you? I won't report you, I promise. But if you have the guts to touch my bag or utter another insulting word, some more of your front teeth shall be broken. Go ahead! Do it! And you will see. You damn fool!"

Seeing the Old Man's eyes roll strangely, he remained quiet. After a moment, he lay down to sleep, his mouth wide open. Looking at his gaunt face and skinny body, the Old Man sighed deeply.

Next morning, Peeping Tom announced a piece of good news:

"It's Gandhi's shift today."

Another rare chance for prisoners to open the ventilator windows, to go to the bathroom, and to talk freely. Those who passed by the Old Man's cell stopped to inquire about his situation.

Hearing the story, Peeping Tom gave him much praise:

"You have acted right, friend. It's a great sacrifice on your part. Far from you, I feel very sad and lonesome. No more chance to smoke, drink, and talk together."

Bear-head threw tobacco through iron bars, and said to the Old Man:

"This is from my friends, Uncle, I have a lot. When you run out of it, just let me know."

"I still have some, thanks."

"Please take it Uncle!"

He then turned to the young man and said, his eyes rolling:

"You're really lucky to be with our Uncle. Treat him nicely, will you? Or I will give you another slash in the face."

Sài Gòn Woman looked into the Old Man's cell, inquiring:

"How about your interrogation, Brother?"

The Old Man smiled brightly:

"Still in prison, for sure. The officer told me so."

She appeared sad:

"They're so cruel! You were right. We'd rather die than cooperate with them. It smells bad, here. Let me give you some bottles of perfume."

"Thanks, dear! Later, when released, I will seek every possible means to go to Sài Gòn and have a meal with your family."

"You will be my guest of honor, dear Brother. I will buy a railway ticket for you."

Gandhi came to the Old Man's cell. As usual, he handed him a box of rustic tobacco, a package of Hồng Đào tea, and said:

"This packet of tea is for you only. As for tobacco, you can share with others."

"I know you're living on a modest income. You should not give anything to us. Your presence is sufficient to make us happy."

"Living outside prison is always better than living in it. Take it! We must be discreet."

Sài Gòn Woman asked permission to give the Old Man some gifts.

Gandhi smiled:

"It's truly a sentimental relationship, isn't it?"

The Old Man answered:

"We consider each other as brother and sister."

He then went to every cell and distributed tobacco. At the cell of Bear-head's lover, he joked:

"Later when released, can you come here with supplies to visit him? Do you wish to act as the legendary 'Tô Thị' waiting in vain for her husband to return?"

"I certainly do. I love him."

"He's very energetic."

The Actress pouted her lips:

"Inside, she swears by seas and mountains to love him to the end of her life. Once released, she may easily say 'goodbye' to him and run away with a new love. Let's wait and see!"

Whenever Gandhi took Buffalo King's place, every cell enjoyed an occasion of great festivity. A good heart can soften sufferings. At night, when prisoners in the division stopped singing, the Old Man started eating the food Sài Gòn Woman had given him. The First Lieutenant was lying flat on the floor, with a long face. The young man knelt down on the floor, repeatedly bowing his head, saying:

"I beg you to forgive me! I'm ready to accept any kind of punishment inflicted on me. I beg you! I beg you, Dad!"

The Old Man's heart sank when he looked at the young man, thinking to himself: How can a man behave in such a humiliating way, just because of hunger?

"Sit up!"

The First Lieutenant began to cry:

"If you don't forgive me, I'll continue to beg on my knees all night."

The Old Man ordered again:

"I have told you to sit up. I don't mind your offensive words in the past."

He sat up and whined:

"Everybody hates me, except you, Dad. Only you love me and consider me as your son. Please, forgive me for anything wrong I've done."

The Old Man pointed to the bag of food, saying:

"You have bowed to this bag, not to me. I intend to punish you one time only. I know you curse and want to rob me just because you're too hungry. Being with you in the same cell, how can I swallow my food while you're lying there with an empty stomach. From now on, stop asking! Just eat whatever I give you!"

He then unfastened the bag, took out some steamed sticky rice, a few slices of pork paste, a piece of short cake and handed to the young man who said again and again: "Thank you, Dad! Thank you, Dad!"

Waiting until he finished his meal, the Old Man rolled tobacco for him and sincerely advised him: "Your sentence being made, you will be sent to camp, I know. As a Party member, you may be privileged to do a job that can satisfy your hunger. However, it's so dangerous to live among criminals. To avoid being beaten to death, being seriously hurt, or becoming handicapped forever, you must necessarily live an honest life. Habits of reporting, gossiping and pilfering are taboos. Death comes as easy as winking. If you are appointed head of a group, remember never to suppress your inferiors or force them to labor to get credit for yourself. You can lose your life as easily as in a dream. No wardens can protect you. Bear in mind that you live with your fellow prisoners, not with cadres. Don't be a gang member's opponent. Murder is their profession. They can kill in cold blood. Your physical strength, your martial arts are of no avail. They can act stealthily, suddenly, any time day or night. There's no way you can find out. Being in prison for twenty years, I know even well-trained commandos are afraid of them. The simple reason is that, as daring, reckless guys, they make light of death. Keep my words in mind! If not, you have no hope of going home safe and sound."

"Yes, I will never forget your advice, Dad!"

The Old Man had been at the Hanoi Hilton for nearly three weeks. He taught the young officer some Qi Gong techniques, trained him how to breathe properly, sermonized to him on moral values and told him to join the fun organized by his fellow prisoners. His intention was to help the young man forget his own hunger. He had truly made progress.

One morning, the division received two newcomers. They were two women. One was middle-aged; the other still very young. At the sight of the two women walking in the hall, the Old Man knew right away the middle-aged woman was a snitch. She was encumbered with a heavy bundle and always kept a watchful eye on her surroundings, whereas the young girl with tearful eyes carried a small bag of clothing.

Taking advantage of Buffalo King's short absence, Bear-head asked the older woman:

"How long have you been arrested?"

"Just this morning."

"What is your prisoner number?"

"X1025."

He turned to the young girl, asking: "And you, stop crying! You have just been arrested too?"

"Yes, just this morning."

"Remember one of the regulations here is: no confidential talk, no confession of sins to others. Violation invites the stocks."

"Thank you for reminding me."

The Old Man thought to himself, this rascal is pretty smart, despite his poor education. My prisoner number is Z4257—hers is X1025. Evidently, she was arrested a long time ago, not this year. The younger girl is however very naïve and credulous. I must warn her against any mishap for prevention. She is unable to understand what Bear-head has hinted at.

The Old Man stood up and took a length of wire off a rusty wire threadbare net on the window, he then slipped the wire through a crack in the window, and pulled at the bolt to open the window. He waited for the two newcomers to go to the bathroom. He waited and waited until the Old Newcomer walked out. Seeing her carry a bucket of water, he nodded a greeting to her. A minute later, the young girl stepped out, a towel, a toothbrush, and a tube of toothpaste in hand.

He raised his hand as a signal for her to stop, and said in a soft voice:

"Remember never to tell your companion what you want to hide. It's very dangerous, my child."

The girl nodded her approval: "Thank you for your advice, sir!"

He urged her: "That's it. Get moving!"

On the way to the bathroom, Bear-head stopped at the Old Man's cell and looked in the opened window, saying:

"Uncle, you have to tell the girl to be careful because the woman is an antenna."

He smiled:

"Don't worry! I have just told her so. Would you please close the window for me!"

"How could you open it?"

"It's easy. I used a piece of wire as a hook to pull the bolt aside."

"You're truly a man of initiative. I have to learn from you, Uncle."

"You must warn the Old Newcomer to watch her tongue and not report any event in prison."

"Don't worry, Uncle!"

The Old Man and the First Lieutenant were the last to go to the bathroom. They tried not to make noise while bathing for fear of being heard by Buffalo King, but he was busy checking Driving Gangster's supplies. He said to the prisoner:

"Absolutely no smoking in prison. I am confiscating these five packets of Điện Biên cigarettes."

"Please, forgive me, a prisoner with a death sentence."

"Regulations must be kept. No exception! Take your stuff in!"

Driving Gangster shouted angrily:

"I am a prisoner in the stocks, waiting to be executed, not allowed to see family members. And now, some packets of cigarettes my wife has sent me, are also confiscated."

"Don't talk nonsense! Go back in!"

"I won't go if you don't give me back those packets of cigarettes."

"You want to revolt, don't you? You will know what stuff I'm made of."

Clang! After uttering those threats, Buffalo King left.

After a bath, the Old Man washed his underwear while the First Lieutenant was rubbing the pot. Suddenly, there was uproar in the yard. Driving Gangster shouted at the top of his voice:

"I'm gonna risk my life with you guys. I don't fear death. I will die, one way or another."

The two men rushed out of the bathroom. Two big trusties threw him down on the ground, and repeatedly kicked him in the stomach. Driving Gangster rolled in agony.

Buffalo King watched in anger, his eyes rolling, but did nothing. The Old Man flung his underwear and towel to the First Lieutenant and rushed over to stop them and pull them apart.

The two trusties cursed, their faces reddened with anger:

"You damn old fool! It's none of your business."

No sooner had they cursed than they hit the Old Man. An expert in Japanese martial arts, he sent the two big guys flying flat on the ground, and then said to Buffalo King:

"If they happen to kill him by accident, you are the one who is held accountable."

Buffalo King shouted at the trusties:

"Go to your room!"

The Old Man pointed his finger at them and said angrily:

"If you ever beat anybody again I will break your necks, you beasts!"

After they ran away, he said to Driving Gangster:

"Forget about cigarettes! Bring the rest in!"

He explained to Buffalo King:

"There are vulnerable spots on a human body. If you happen to hit one of them, you can become a killer. So many people did kill by accident like that. You should be careful, Sir!"

Clang! Clang! Buffalo King slammed the doors of the cells and left.

The Actress exclaimed in admiration:

"You're so wonderful, Uncle! They are two colossal beasts, and you have knocked them over in the twinkling of an eye."

Peeping Tom got excited:

"You're such an incredible judo pro, friend! You have really taught a valuable lesson to those who have been used to bullying the weak."

Bear-head added:

"We regret not having a chance to watch your performance, Uncle! Judging by appearance, I think you're weak and need my protection. But I'm wrong. From now on, I need your protection."

His lover ridiculed him:

"Weak as you are, how can you protect our uncle! Dear Uncle, you look skinny, but in reality, you're so strong!"

The Old Man stood on the stocks and answered:

"I am not as strong as you think, dear. Japanese martial arts are called 'judo' meaning 'the soft way.' It's the art of using softness against hardness, and using weakness to fight strength. I just know how to use their own strength to knock them down. The bigger and heavier they are, the more painful their fall. A woman good at judo is able to knock out two or three young men at the same time."

Sài Gòn woman joked:

"When released, please teach me judo, big brother!"

The Middle-Aged Newcomer added, just to show off:

"My husband is a senior lieutenant colonel. When young, he used to teach security agents martial arts. Without martial arts, how can they deal with reactionaries, murderers, robbers, and bad guys."

After a moment of silence, Bear-head raised his voice:

"I was arrested for robbery. And you, lady, what did they arrest you for? For smuggling, for embezzlement of public funds, or for prostitution?"

Some women giggled. Bear-head's woman chided her lover:

"Stop it! Don't talk nonsense!"

He became truculent:

"Did I talk nonsense? No, never! If you want to break off relations with me, go ahead. I don't give a damn. I only speak my mind. I do not hide my identity. I am a robber. I said what I am. Once in prison, we should reject all forms of hypocrisy. What nonsense to talk about revolution! Please, listen to me, everybody! We're all part of a family, living in a peaceful atmosphere. If anyone, male or female, young or old, newcomer or not, has the temerity to break our peace by his or her tell-tale mouth, I do not hesitate to slash his or her face. Look at the First Lieutenant's face in cell 1 as an example. He is the fifth to be slashed in the face with this razor. Who wants to be the sixth? Go ahead and be an informer, a snitch. I don't just do the talking. I act. You see what I mean."

Peeping Tom agreed:

"You're right. As a Party member in 1953, the chairman of an organizing committee, I confess I have embezzled public funds. I don't care about being ridiculed. I care more about having enough to eat. "

Bear-head's voice resounded:

"To our enemy, the day after tomorrow will be September the second, the National Feast Day of the Communist regime of Việt Nam. I hope we'll have some pork to eat. In camp, we always have buffalo meat."

Driving Gangster cursed:

"Don't talk about the damn National Day. We may be given some ounces of meat at best, just enough to whet our appetite. What a God-damned regime!"

"Do you still feel pain?"

"Why not. Their kicks are so heavy! Luckily our Uncle has come to my rescue in time. If not, some of my ribs may have been broken."

"You're too meek. Wardens are usually not rough with those who have been sentenced to death. They prefer to stay away from them. If I were sentenced to death, Buffalo King would be in danger. Sincerely speaking, I advise you to accept your fate, not to hope for an amnesty."

"This morning, I have insisted on returning my tobacco because I lost any hope. I regret not being able to manage some kind of weapon. I only need a 10 cm long nail to deal with Buffalo King."

"You're right. Mr. Trường Chinh has never granted amnesty to anybody. Let's sing a song tonight to entertain Driving Gangster and the tearful girl who just came. Where's the Actress? Please, start the show now!"

"I'm busy. I will sing later."

"Busy doing what?"

"Don't ask! It's women's business. How about the First Lieutenant? He can sing first."

The Old Man said:

"He's eating. He will sing, later."

Driving Gangster volunteered:

"My voice is too husky to sing. To replace a song, I would like to start the show by telling a joke, a dirty joke. The story has been told several times. I think some of you have heard it."

Peeping Tom encouraged him:

"No problem! Tell it again! The more we hear, the more we laugh. Order! Order! Everybody."

"Okay. Let me begin! As everyone knows, chairman Tôn Đức Thắng was a senior Revolutionary, a very honest and sincere person. His living was plain; his language coarse. In summer, he usually walked barefoot in the presidential palace. When asked why he did not wear sandals, he laughed easily, answering: 'Just to keep my feet cool.' One day, when giving a speech in front of a senior audience, he wore glasses and solemnly read from a typewritten piece of paper: 'Dear children!' The entire audience gazed at him in disbelief. He cursed: 'Damn I'm mistaken. This is a message to the children.' Everybody laughed in sympathy, because they knew he was oblivious due to old age. As a person of 90, he was to die very soon. No exception.

"When he was in death's agony, Secretary General Lê Duẩn and other members of the Politburo were urgently whisked to the presidential palace. When they arrived, he was in a coma. They told his private secretary to keep watch and to write down carefully what he said when he regained consciousness. They stepped out for deliberation. Trường Chinh gave his opinion: 'Uncle Tôn is the oldest member of the Party. When the October Revolution broke out, he was the first to hang the red flag over the Black Sea to salute the earth-shaking revolution, starting a new era of the world history. Moscow, the capital of Russia, is the heart of the Proletariat, a place the entire progressive world turns to in confidence. And you know, one of its streets was named after him to remember his brilliant achievement. Our party and the nation are very proud of him. I propose embalming his body and building a mausoleum in his remembrance, and also as a place of worship for posterity. Hồ Chí Minh's Mausoleum has been built in the capital of Hà Nội. We should build another one for Uncle Tôn in Hồ Chí Minh City. What do you think?'

"Everybody in the Politburo agreed. Just at that moment, Uncle Tôn tried to open his eyes, asking in a soft voice: 'What are they discussing out there?' His private secretary answered: 'Dear Uncle, the Politburo are talking about embalming your body as they did Uncle Hồ. What is your opinion?' Hearing this, Uncle Tôn whispered: 'Embalming what? My cock!' Then he breathed his last. The secretary rushed out to announce the news of Uncle Tôn's death. Lê

Duẩn asked: 'Did he say anything as a last recommendation?' 'Dear Secretary General, he told me to embalm his cock and exhaled his last breath.'

"All the members of the Politburo looked embarrassed, not knowing the reason why he wished to have 'it' embalmed. Considering himself the most learned, Trường Chinh explained: 'Our Uncle is so profound! What he means is that 'it' represents the reproductive power of the human race. Quite a few countries have erected statues to worship 'it.' His last wish is very sacred. We have to fully comply. The funny thing is that such a majestic mausoleum, as big as Uncle Hồ's with troops of honor guards, is just built for 'it.' Premier Phạm Văn Đồng expressed his opinion: 'We can have a crystal box made, adorned with a hammer and sickle flag and a yellow-starred red one, to hold 'it.' I will decree that historians will write about the great significance of embalming and exhibiting 'it' in public.' Minister Phạm Hùng applauded: 'It's a wonderful idea. I will apprehend and put in reeducation camps all those who maliciously distort the noble meaning of our project.' Secretary-General Lê Duẩn concluded: 'The main problem has been resolved. Now comes the location. Where are we going to place 'it' in Hồ Chí Minh City?' Phạm Văn Đồng suggested: 'According to the report of the Commerce Ministry, the General Department Store in Hồ Chí Minh City looks very colossal and imposing, but the customers often complain about the poor supply of merchandise, saying, 'There's not a cock here.'[9] To appease the public, why don't we put 'it' in the General Department Store? Agreed?' Every politburo-member gave a big round of applause."

Hearing the joke as told by Driving Gangster, all the prisoners were convulsed with laughter. They laughed and laughed until they cried. Even the Middle-Aged Newcomer could not help laughing.

The Old Man cleared his throat, and said to the group:

"We shall now have a poem that was composed by Nguyễn Chí Thiện, who was arrested four years ago outside the British Embassy on Lý-Thường-Kiệt Street.

Uncle Hồ and now we have Uncle Tôn!
Both are fond of embracing our kids
The uncles' complexion is rose-tinted

But the children's in fact is pale blue.
In between the uncles' two moonfaces
Red scarves fly around thin-necked skinnies.[10]

After a moment, the music show resumed. The Actress and Peeping Tom sang some songs individually. Then, the First Lieutenant sang a duet with the Afro-Asian girl—a song entitled: "The Pounding of a Pestle in the Village of Bom Bo," and another one with the title 'Light a fire, dear!'

"Stop!" Driving Gangster has heard someone call from outside. A girl called three times from Hàng Bông Thợ Nhuộm Street, her voice loud and clear:

"Tomorrow, I'll see you at dawn, Father!"

Driving Gangster began to sob loudly:

"It's my daughter. She calls to inform me of the hour of execution."

A disturbing silence reigned over the entire division. The Old Man said quietly to the First Lieutenant:

"His family knows, because a death notice has been posted around. How miserable he is tonight! She should rather keep silent than let her father know in advance like that."

That night, the whole division seemed to be in mourning. Nobody spoke because they did not know how to console him. The Old Man sometimes heard him sob loudly in the middle of the night. He remained silent too. Before daybreak, Driving Gangster cried more loudly.

The Old Man stood up on the stocks, saying in a sad voice:

"Farewell, dear friend! You go first! We're waiting for our turn; stop crying! We'll go the way of all flesh."

Driving Gangster then collapsed and fainted.

At about 5:00 A.M., four armed security guards rushed into the cell. They locked his hands, blindfolded him, pulled him out of the stocks and took him away. Nearly fainting from being in the stocks so long, he could hardly walk. Two of them had to take him by the arms and drag him away.

There had been no singing for days in the division before life came back to normal. One morning, during the bathroom hour, the warden on duty brought in a barefoot, saffron-robed monk and handed him over to Buffalo King. The paper-thin monk had no belongings except a used towel.

Buffalo King ordered:

"Sit down at that corner!"

The Monk stood motionless and spoke calmly with a Southern accent:

"I won't. Why do you tell me to sit on the ground while you sit on a chair?"

"What's your crime? Are you a reactionary, a monk in disguise? I will keep you here for good."

"Venerable Buddha! I am what I am. I'm not anybody in disguise. I entered a religious life when I was a child. Homeless, I live in the open air. To be in prison or anywhere else makes no difference to me. You're a disrespectful person. I don't want to talk with you."

"In! You stubborn mule! Let's see how far you can go."

Clang! He then opened the room where Driving Gangster had lived, for the monk to walk in. *Clang!* He locked the door and left.

The Middle-aged Newcomer whispered to the girl in the same cell:

"A bunch of stubborn reactionaries! They are all the same. They must be punished severely."

It's Bear-head's turn to go to the bathroom. Taking advantage of the moment when Buffalo King was conversing with the warden on duty, he opened the window of the Monk's cell and looked in. He could not believe his eyes. He saw the Monk sitting cross-legged in mid air, about half a meter above the floor, with arms folded, eyes half closed. The Monk lowered himself slowly to the floor and looked at Bear-head with a benevolent smile:

"Shut the window please! Remember not to tell anybody, son!"

Like a machine, Bear-head obeyed the Monk.

It was dinnertime. *Clink! Clank!* Buffalo King opened all the doors for prisoners to get out for food.

Sitting still on the floor, the Monk said:

"I eat only once a day. You may give my meal to others."

Then he closed his eyes.

Buffalo King said to Bear-head:

"Take this ration in! Let him starve if he wishes."

That evening, Bear-head asked the Monk:

"Master! What did they charge you with? I just don't understand why a virtuous person like you could be arrested."

"I only try to perform good deeds. Answering the call for a mystic life, I left An Giang and started the journey to Tibet. When reaching Hà Nội, I was arrested and brought here for no reason. It's a good chance for me to meet you friends, anyway. Tomorrow morning, I will leave this place. No power can stop me. Is it right that a prisoner in this cell has just been executed?"

Everybody puzzled at his words. The Old Man said to him with great respect:

"That's right! You're truly a supreme Master."

"His death is an injustice. He died just because of 28 tons of rice. His soul has come to me, imploring for liberation, and I have answered his prayer. Don't ask me anymore! Let me meditate! Goodbye everybody! Tomorrow morning, I will leave this place."

That evening, nobody cared to sing. They murmured to one another, wondering how the Monk had come to know everything about Driving Gangster when the event was still hushed up. The Monk had certainly been informed by his soul.

The First Lieutenant appeared doubtful.

"Let's wait until tomorrow and see. During long years of fighting, I have never sighted ghosts. Death is the end of everything."

The Old Man reprimanded him:

"Shut up! The supernatural is something you cannot understand. Let me practice some techniques of Qi Gong."

The next morning the Monk was still sitting, praying to Buddha when everyone was almost done with their washing and cleaning. They began to doubt. The Middle-aged Newcomer said to her cell-mate, her voice shrill with mockery:

"That Monk is a reactionary, a big liar. Yesterday, the warden threatened to keep him here for good."

No sooner had she said that when a warden came in and handed Buffalo King a piece of paper. Looking at it, he opened the door of the cell where the Monk was still sitting and said:

"Thanks to the Party's leniency, you are released now."

Stopping at Buffalo King's desk, the religious man looked at him, warning:

"Your family will be in big trouble. Try to improve yourself and accumulate good deeds!"

He followed the warden on duty and deliberately moved out of the prison. Prisoners went on talking about the mysterious Monk with much excitement from noon until nightfall. Bear-head recounted the sighting of the Monk sitting cross-legged in mid air. Nobody believed him, so he cursed:

"Damn it! If I make up stories, I will be shot like Driving Gangster."

"It's impossible! What you've said contradicts the laws of physics. Anything heavier than air cannot float."

Peeping Tom added:

"Yes! It's so hard to believe! But why did he know Driving Gangster had been executed just because of 28 tons of rice? This proves man has a soul. He also affirmed with solid certainty that he would be released this morning. He knows what will happen in the future, which cannot be explained by science."

The Old Man said to Bear-head:

"As for me, I believe you. During the harsh winter days at camp 'Heaven's Gate,' an old monk in the same cell with me remained in good health for years, although he was thinly clothed and ate only once a day. He taught me nutrition and martial arts. Regrettably, scarcely had I learned something when I was transferred to another camp. On this planet, there are countless inexplicable mysteries. Shallow knowledge of science only invites skepticism. We must believe this monk. However, if we divulge the news to others, they won't believe us, for sure. The monk has predicted disaster for Buffalo King's family. Let's wait and see!"

In prison, the inmates lived in anxiety. They waited restlessly for the unknown. But they were very friendly and sympathetic to one another, sharing feelings, and knew how to comfort and encourage one another. Songs can bring vitality to a somber place where time seems to be lying stagnant without end. The Middle-aged Newcomer harbored a grudge against Bear-head, still she tried to smile broadly in front of him. She rarely talked or shared gifts with others. One day, she offered to give him some sugar and cake, but he flatly refused. Sometimes he threatened to slash informers in the face, indirectly warning her against any bad move. As a result, prisoners kept 'driving' gifts from cell to cell, and smoking tobacco without Buffalo-King's knowing.

As he was walking out of the bathroom one morning, the Old Man saw the First Lieutenant go directly to the front yard to meet with Buffalo King. He fell to his feet in front of Buffalo King, whispering something he could not hear. After that, Buffalo King entered their cell, leaving the door open and began searching throughout the cell. He finally bent down and ran his fingers under the floor. He then pulled out from the crack of the stocks a piece of aluminum the Old Man had borrowed from Peeping Tom the day before to trim his toe nails.

He held up the metal and said:

"To keep this metal in prison is against the rule. Where did you get it?"

The Old Man answered in a calm voice:

"I don't know. It's not mine. Someone may have hidden it there before. I never care to look around in the cell."

Clang! Buffalo King locked the door and left without a word.

The First Lieutenant said quickly:

"Don't think I have reported, Dad! I just begged him for permission to write to my aunt. But he refused, as my interrogation files are not completed."

The Old Man nodded:

"You don't have to explain. I know it's not you."

His face brightened:

"How can I explain as I have given every appearance of being an informer? He started the search right after I had whispered to him. Why do you know it's not me, Dad?"

The Old Man explained:

"You know where I have kept the aluminum. If you had informed him, he would not have searched around the cell for a long time before coming to the stocks. In prison, such an unexpected search sometimes happens. You're not an informer, I know."

As a general rule, when a piece of metal is found about a prisoner or in his cell, there's no way to argue. He will certainly be put in the stocks. However, the Old Man's case is different. He knew the hidden side of Buffalo King's playing card: that he took bribes from the female prisoners. Buffalo King did not want to rock the boat. Besides, he took the Old Man for a special prisoner, especially since the day the staff officer gave him gifts.

As for Bear-head, he said emphatically that the First Lieutenant was an antenna, and threatened to slash his throat. The Old Man had to calm him down.

During the weekend, Buffalo King looked tired and depressed. He did not have a black look as usual. He did not even care to keep the peephole closed. He smoked all day, without saying a word.

Peeping Tom appeared happy. He said:

"The Monk must be right. Such a change of attitude is a clear indication that something wrong must have happened to his family."

The Actress joked:

"His wife may have cheated on him. Maybe his daughter got pregnant."

Bear-head promised:

"I will have this matter investigated, and everything will come to light in a few days."

That Saturday, Gandhi took Buffalo King's place. The Old Man made tea for him and said:

"I don't know why the warden in charge of this division looks so worried in recent days."

Gandhi heaved a deep sigh:

"His only son has just been arrested and charged with armed robbery and murder. Today young people are totally corrupt. I don't understand why even children of influential people become robbers. Their families already live in the lap of luxury."

The Old Man smiled ironically:

"Those persons are too preoccupied with their job of educating the public to have time for their own children. The nation comes first, family second, you know. How great their sacrifice for the Revolution!"

Gandhi chimed in:

"What a revolutionary spirit! They write poems to excite children of other persons 'to split the Trường Sơn Mountains for the war against the Americans,' whereas they send their own children to schools in Russia and Germany. They also say, 'A Revolutionary suffers before the masses, and enjoys after them.'"

The Old Man laughed:

"Confucius once said: 'Worry before people do! Be happy after people are!' Confucius's advice sounds reasonable because it implies something concerning the mind. Whereas the words 'suffer' and 'enjoy' used by Trường Chinh connote something concerning the body, which sounds ridiculous."

Gandhi appeared disappointed:

"Now is a hard time for straightforward people. I don't like to crawl and fawn upon my boss. Therefore, I have been a lieutenant for dozens of years and never promoted to a higher rank. By way of compensation, no prisoners hate me."

"Everyone in prison respects you. A good name is priceless. Do you think Buffalo King can ask for the mitigation of his son's sentence, thanks to his devotion to the Revolution?"

"We're just small fry. Not like big fish. Their children are released right after being arrested."

The Old Man picked up his mug of water and said:

"I have bothered you enough, sir. Now, let others out!"

When he entered the cell, the First Lieutenant asked him curiously:

"What have you said to Gandhi, Dad?"

"During the conversation, I came to know that Buffalo King's son has been charged with robbery and murder."

The young man jumped up happily:

"It serves him right! It serves him right!"

The good news spread like wildfire. It was music to the ears of all the prisoners.

Sài Gòn Woman handed the Old Man a light blue handkerchief, whispering:

"This is for you as a souvenir, dear Brother! It took me several days to make that pattern of embroidery."

He held the gift in his hand and said: "Thank you, dear Sister! My possessions are only dirty rags. I feel guilty, because I have nothing valuable to give you in return."

"Let me go find some paper for you to write a few lines to me as a souvenir." She then went back to her cell. A few minutes later, she walked out with a piece of white paper and a red ink ball pen. He unfolded the handkerchief to look. In the center was embroidered a plant with green leaves and blue flowers. The words 'Forget Me Not' were right underneath.

That night, he could not sleep. He lay wide awake, thinking. He is only a decrepit, skinny prisoner with no future. How can such a person find love? Faced with many deaths, he has been taught how to treasure life and make light of death. His body is just like a stunted tree at a somber corner of prison. His mind however gets clearer and sharper, and his heart more secure and open. Sufferings have helped him move closer to mankind and appreciate better the values of life. 'Forget Me Not,' the name of a wild flower is an explicit message of love. Don't forget me, dear! How can he forget her? His life in prison is similar to a vast expanse of wilderness, while the words 'Forget Me Not' ring loud and clear like the joyful sounds of a babbling brook. The mirage of a green oasis seems to loom in the distance. How can he forget such a tender, loving care? 'Dear, dear!' It's an intimate appellation he has never heard for a long time. It sounded so sweet, so tender, so inviting ... to the point that he became choked with emotion and fell into ecstasy. All of a sudden, his conscience was lit up as if by a flash of lightning. She is married; he said to himself, it's a bad idea. I have suffered the loss of my wife to another man. How can I nurture the dream of stealing the wife from another person? No, no! Definitely not! It's so shameful, so unfair!

He sat up, made a roll of tobacco to smoke. After smoking, he became fully awake to reality. Why don't I take her for my younger sister? He asked himself. Oh, no! I don't want to be a hypocrite. How can sexual love turn into brotherly love? I'd better keep the status quo. Again, he smiled to himself. What a damn fool I am! As a prisoner, how can I go further? Better keep it as a happy memory of a lifetime. Happy with the idea, he took another puff.

The quiet of the night reigned over the prison. The First Lieutenant was sleeping soundly when he took out the pen and paper. He became too emotional to write. Any phrase he could think of was only an old cliché, not suitable to his current state of mind. "As a military man," he mused, "I have never written a poem in my life. In this case, any love poem will be acceptable." He racked his brain, trying to remember some romantic poems he had learned when he was young. None of them could express his true feelings. He smoked one more time and watched the smoke curling lazily upwards. Suddenly, some verses of a fellow prisoner came to his mind. He found them perfect for this situation. Overcome with joy, he hastened to copy them down. His clear handwriting looked beautiful. The red color of ink on the white paper gave him the feeling he was writing in the blood from his own heart:

"These verses are for you, my dear, to remember the days we were together in the Hanoi Hilton prison":

My life, there's nothing worth to tell,
My body, imprisoned, decrepit,
I only have a tearful heart.
With sincerity, I give it all to you.[11]

He suddenly sympathized with the cadre and his wife. That guy had come to his family's rescue while his wife was being pushed to the wall. She lost hope of ever seeing her imprisoned husband again.

All night, the Old Man could hardly get to sleep. Buffalo King opened the door for him to go to the bathroom first. The warden appeared haggard. His eyes reddened. His water pipe was bubbling continuously. Seeing the Old Man drying the laundry in the yard, he told the First Lieutenant to go. He invited the Old Man to smoke tobacco and drink tea and asked:

"As a longtime prisoner, how do you find the situation in camp?"

"Over there, food is the same. Lodging is better with more space; but we have to labor harder. Criminals, most of them; young people die more easily than political prisoners."

"Why?"

"Young people often starve to death. They eat dirty stuff and die in great number from infection in the digestive system. They also die from stab wounds because they often come to blows. Permanent hunger pushes them to borrow food from those who have plenty of supplies, with 'compound interest.' Some of them have three or four 'creditors' at the same time, and their 'food debt' sometimes amounts to 3,000 rations. Being too hungry, they keep borrowing until they can't afford to pay back, and their 'creditors' have to collect their daily rations, leaving them nothing to eat. As a result, they starve to death easily in a few weeks."

"Why does the supervising board not intervene?"

"Sometimes, they do. But there are too many cases for them to solve. So they just ignore them. Death sentences in the entire nation are about 60 or 70 a year on average, whereas the number of deaths in camps is at least 100 times greater."

Buffalo King sighed:

"I ask just for information. Now you can go."

One day later, wondering why Buffalo King had been replaced for several days in a row, the Old Man asked Gandhi:

"Why have you been here every day?"

"The warden in charge is sick. I am temporarily taking his place."

At the news, every prisoner heaved a sigh of relief. Many wished that Buffalo King would go to hell soon. Good signs began to show among the prisoners. The First Lieutenant, the one who had the guts to eat even human liver, began to believe in God, and wished to live a better life in order to get His blessings and protection. The Middle-aged Newcomer began to distribute, out of charity, some food to the hungry.

One morning, the Sài Gòn Woman was called for interrogation. She came back half an hour later, telling everyone that she and her son would be set free the following day. She asked Gandhi's permission to make tea and serve refreshments to all prisoners as a farewell party. Gandhi agreed with pleasure. She stood at the table full of cups of tea and boxes of candy, inviting all those who passed by on the way to the bathroom. Gandhi let tobacco addicts have a puff.

After distributing her food to the needy, she handed the Old Man a sizable bag of gifts and said to him in a voice choked with emotion:

"My ring is in the bag, dear Brother. Feel free to use it in case you're transferred and need money."

He could hardly answer her when she turned away with tearful eyes. At night, a singing party was held to celebrate Sài Gòn

Woman's release. Everyone volunteered to sing. The Singer began the program with a song entitled: 'A Day of Return.'

Like a bird spreading wings,
back to its old nest,
I'm on my way home,
My home, sweet home.
How painful the moment of separation!
How sad the homebound journey, dear!
The music I used to hear,
Is only a hush, now.
Without your sweet voice calling,
I'm like a boat losing its way.

She sang five songs in a row, all of them romantic and sentimental. Then came Peeping Tom's turn. He sang 'One Day' with some phrases slightly altered to fit the occasion:

Away from you, my dear!
Alone in a room, I silently cry,
My napkin soaked in hot tears.
The words 'I love you' still ring in my ears.
Don't ever forget me, dear!
Far away … but we're always near.

When the song came to an end, Bear-head shouted out loud:

"Uncle! Why are you so quiet? Sing something to bid farewell to her!"

"That's right! Cell 1 must sing."

"Okay! Okay! It's my duty to sing a song, by way of saying 'goodbye' to our good friend."

Peeping Tom laughed without reservation:

"It's not right. You'd better say: 'To my special friend.'"

Bear-head shouted at the top of his lungs:

"Who has the right to beat the drum in the pagoda? Who is clever at making her 'his own'?"

Waiting for the uproar to die down, the Old Man said:

"As the old saying goes: 'Acquaintance is made in a single boat trip,' so we are now in the same boat, the boat of misfortune. Our friendship should be deeper and deeper. By way of saying 'goodbye' to a sentimental friend, a woman of great compassion, I would like to sing a song called 'Separation.' The song is as follows:

I miss the minute we separate.
The feeling moment we met, you know
Just like a leaf in the wind.
Your silhouette blurred in the distance,
The whole universe sinks in gloomy darkness.
And time like water, flowing on and on ...
With clouds drifting along.

Overcome with emotion, he repeated the song three times. The entire audience gave him a big round of applause. The singer praised him:

"Uncle, tonight you sing very well, much better than other nights. Your voice sounds to me so melancholy, so emotional!"

Peeping Tom grinned mischievously:

"As a matter of fact, he did sing well. It's real feeling. It has a soul. It's inspiring."

Bear-head asked Sài Gòn Woman:

"What's your opinion, Auntie!"

She did not answer. The Actress stood up, joking:

"Auntie must be too moved to speak out. Let me sing some merry songs for her listening pleasure."

She then sang several songs in a row, all of them with quick beats. She closed with a song entitled: 'It's Summertime!'

It's summertime, when the sun bursts with vitality;
Summertime, when the air vibrates with rhythms of life,
  everywhere;
When the wind whispers in the clouds vaguely;
When a flight of birds spans the blue sky;
When some roaming boat moves lazily,
With a couple of oars swaying in hesitancy.
Summertime, in fresh, tender bamboo bushes along the way,
In the flute music floating far away ...
Summertime, when nature looks so nice! so lovely!

When the music ended, Sài Gòn Woman simply said 'Thanks!' and wished everyone good luck.

That night, the Old Man again could not sleep. He lay fully awake, feeling the ring in his hand. Now and then he got up to have a puff of tobacco. He often thought that through long years of suffering in prison, his heart had become badly bruised and stone-hardened, leaving no room for love, that so much time devoted to Zen meditation had turned him into a person free from all attachments to life. But now he found he was wrong, completely wrong. Only an amorous look, an attractive smile, a small gesture of tender loving care has enough power to turn him into an optimistic person and revive in him all the burning desires of a young man. He thought if the iron gate of the prison had not been shut tight, no hurdles set up by any code of ethics could stop him from taking into her cell, holding her tight, and passionately murmuring to her, sweet words of love.

In the morning, the warden on duty came with the decree of release for the Sài Gòn Woman. With Gandhi's permission, she carried her belongings along the hallway and stopped at every cell to say goodbye. At the Old Man's cell she slipped her finger through the window bars. He held her finger and squeezed it for a long time.

She spoke, her eyes filled with tears:

"Goodbye, dear Brother! I'll pray for your safe return. I can never forget you. When released, please, let me know right away. I'm waiting for you, dear."

He was choked with emotion:

"If I'm alive, I will look for you, by all means. Bon voyage, dear!"

When letting her finger go, he had the feeling that a brief moment of happiness had just passed like a flash. As in a dream, he followed her with his eyes for a few seconds before she was out of sight at the corner where Gandhi was sitting.

The warden spoke in surprise:

"How strange! She cries on her way home!"

Life went on smoothly in the division, thanks to easygoing Gandhi. Peeping Tom and the Dollar-Goddess, as well as Bear-head and his lover, felt closer and closer to each other. Peeping Tom gave half his amount of gifts to the Dollar-Goddess. So did Bear-head's lover. They did it openly. They did not have to stealthily drive gifts to each other as before.

One morning, the Dollar-Trafficker looked into the Old Man's cell and complained:

"The interrogators are so cruel! They don't let me take supplies to press me for confession. Without the Sài Gòn Woman's help, the Afro-Asian girl and I would not have sanitary napkins."

He was enraged:

"Those dirty beasts! When you are called for interrogation on the day you have your period, go ahead and shove your blood right in their faces! Don't be ashamed! At that time, they will yield to you for sure. These are my two pieces of underwear. Use them for the time being!"

She hesitated:

"Don't you need them, Uncle?"

"No, I don't need them, now. In summer, I stay naked. In winter I have warm clothes."

"Thanks, uncle! It's very kind of you."

One day, the Singer confessed privately to the Old Man:

"Uncle, I will be transferred to camp soon. The supervising board entrusted me with the job of an antenna. I have done nothing to help them. I don't have the heart to inform them of others' private affairs or such violations as smoking tobacco, sharing gifts."

"You work for the supervisors, not for the interrogators, don't you?"

"Yes! But remember there are two kinds of surveillants. 'Antennas' for the interrogators are those who help them conduct an investigation or complete an interrogation."

"You look visibly thin. Try to maintain a good heart! You will receive many other good hearts in return, and God will protect you. I've just received some supplies from my family. I will ask permission to share with you."

The day before, the Old Man had received some supplies of sugar, milk, candy, meat, glutinous rice, vitamin C, even a cotton coat, a felt hat, and various items of clothing. He knew right away they were from the Sài Gòn Woman, because he knew his sister could never afford those valuable gifts. He looked at these gifts with tears in his eyes. His heart had never been so deeply touched! He distributed them to those who had no supplies. As for others, he just gave some only as a diplomatic move.

When receiving the gifts, Peeping Tom asked him: "Are these from 'her'?"

He nodded. Peeping Tom looked at him with a triumphant smile:

"What a good guess I've made! I knew right at the very beginning you'd hit the jackpot."

The Old Man smiled again: "I have to admit you're a great expert in love."

"My 'Dollar-Goddess' has been completely conquered. We both won big, friend."

Smart Bear-head also knew it. He came to talk with the Old Man in private: "Congratulations! Uncle, you have won big. You deserve it. From now on, you're no longer lonesome."

Nothing stands still in an ever-changing world. Neither does life in prison. Reunion alternates with separation. Bear-head was sentenced to life-imprisonment and would move to camp. His lover was transferred too. The Actress was released. Three or four other prisoners took their places. Peeping Tom would be released soon.

On a bleak midwinter morning, when it was still dark, Gandhi opened the cell doors and told the Old Man and the Singer to move out. The First Lieutenant appeared sad. He helped him pack up. The Old Man left him three kilograms of roasted glutinous rice and some pieces of cake.

The young man said in tears:

"Dad, I sincerely wish you good health. Thank you for everything. Being with you for three months, I have learned a lot."

During the painful moment of separation, he felt somewhat relieved. He knew the young man shed thankful tears not for the gifts he had received but for his nice treatment of him.

The Old Man and the Singer bade farewell to Gandhi. He looked into Peeping Tom's cell saying:

"I hope we'll meet again outside prison."

Peeping Tom was moved:

"Bon voyage, friend! My home address is 28 Hàng-chiếu Street. We must certainly meet again. I firmly believe, as a man of strong character, you will overcome every difficulty."

Beyond the vineyard, two trucks were ready. About forty prisoners were sitting in line in the yard. Male and female prisoners were kept apart. Female prisoners sometimes sobbed audibly. The Old Man had the feeling he was attending a funeral service. The Singer said goodbye to him in a tearful voice. Each prisoner was given a handful of steamed rice wrapped with banana leaves and a little bit of salt. Armed guards fastened every two prisoners in one manacle. Poorly-dressed prisoners stood in groups, trembling. All women were squeezed into one truck; all men into another. They were muttering obscene curses when the two vehicles started moving slowly. Hỏa Lò's iron gate flung wide open. *Clang!* And shut again. *Clang!*

It was the beginning of December; Hà Nội's weather was getting chillier. Streets were still deserted in the early morning. The Old Man wore a coat and a felt hat. He sat in silence between two armed guards with an AK-47 between their thighs. The trucks were rattling along Long Biện bridge. Underneath, the friendly looking Red River appeared blurry and motionless in the dim glow of dawn. Away from Hà Nội once again, he did not know what the future would hold for him. Wherever he goes, it's the same with him, because this is the land of foes. He is a stranger right in the heart of his homeland. The country is crisscrossed with prisons and concentration camps like a gigantic spider web. People around him are always on the alert, living in permanent doubt and gripped with fear.

Looking up at the sky covered with mist, he felt sorrow for his people and his country. He hummed under his breath a verse he had learned from time long ago:

How sad!
Mountains and rivers shrouded in dense mist.

G. Mist in the mountains of the Ha Giang region in northern Vietnam

"Re-education camps," where dissident Vietnamese were expected to learn to become obedient Communist citizens, were placed in the mountains and jungles to prevent escape. Nguyễn Chí Thiện spent his earlier prison years in these mountainous regional areas. The primary jobs in labor prison camps were cultivation of bamboo for the weaving of mats and husbandry of pigs, which were marketed by the government. (Photo by Jenny Dỗ, Vietnamese American attorney and artist.)

STORY 5

Milk Cows

For giving some yucca to a friend
She was put in shackles.
She soon got infected
Tetanus killed her.
A simple story like that
Costs the Party just a piece of paper!
At the reception of the news
Her mother went mad with suffering.
She raised an outcry through the street
The authorities soon caught up with her:
'You have no right to blacken the regime,' they said.
'If you don't stop right away
You will end up in jail as well!
What's the big deal, anyway?'[1]

IT IS BARELY NINE IN THE MORNING but the sun is already out full blast. It's going to be one of those sultry days. Dozens of women prisoners are emptying five gunny sacks filled with nylon bags next to the water tank facing their room. These bags were used by the families to send in extra supplies for the prisoners. The women's job was to clean them, one at a time, and spread them all over the yard for drying. Beside the nylon bags there are also the Japanese sandals. Prisoners in the collective rooms have to go barefoot. The prison normally collects their footwear and throws them into a warehouse. The Hỏa Lò supervising team, however, confiscates both items and

---

"Milk Cows" was translated by Nguyễn Ngọc Bích from the original Vietnamese "Đàn Bò Sữa" in *Hỏa Lò* (2001).

sells them for money. Then they buy pigs and raise them next to the kitchen.

The kitchen crew is assigned the job of feeding the pigs, using part of the prisoners' rice and vegetables. In the sty there are always seven or eight such well-fed 'Mr. Pigs.' Once in a while, the prison wardens and armed security guards find some pretext for festivities by felling one such 'Mr. Pig.' Of course, the prisoners are not entitled to anything, not even a bite. The time is summer, and the courtyard, made up of refractory bricks, is burning hot. The prisoners, who are without footwear, sit there gulping down their snacks or meals as their soles of their feet get searing hot. In the winter it is no better, the bricks are ice-cold, and one's feet freeze, becoming all purple, as if standing on a bed of sharp needles.

It's not often that a prisoner gets to sit in the open air right next to the water tank. She can get as much water as she wishes to freshen up her face or pour it on her arms to feel delightfully fresh. The women take time doing their task while gossiping:

"What a pity, the poor baby!" one laments. "He's like a stick and is covered with scabs."

"Remember the day he came? What a cute little one! He was smiling all the time."

"He's just like his mother. Oh how I hunger for a baby of my own!"

"You mean to have one so you can take him to jail with you?"

"Poor little thing, he is only ten months old and already in jail."

"His mom does not even have enough milk to let him nurse."

"What do you expect? How can you have milk with so little food? There are no rations for him."

"Yet we don't even have canned milk to feed him."

"These days he's underfed and cries all the time. His cries are getting weaker. It is heartbreaking!"

"His father, I understand, was fighting in Cambodia when he stepped on a mine. All she's left is an older sister, but the sister is even worse off than she. Having a large family to feed herself, the sister dared not offer to take care of him."

"As for his father's side, they come all the way from Quảng Bình. Apparently they are also a hunger-stricken bunch. Besides, it's quite a distance from Quảng Bình to the city. Where would they have the money for a train or bus ticket to come out here to Hà Nội to take back the baby?"

"Come to think about it, she was quite a daredevil. An elementary school teacher. How did she have the guts to criticize the Party policy of carrying out one's 'international duty' by fighting in Cambodia and tell them to go to hell. She deserves to be arrested."

"What you mean? She was no daredevil. When she learned about her husband's death, it was too much, so she went crazy, and that was how it happened. Apparently, they were much in love."

Suddenly, the female warden's voice is heard, loud and sharp:

"Hey, bitches! Hurry up and get back in your room. Don't you take advantage of the occasion to shoot the breeze. Next time, I'll get others to do the task. And you won't even get your turn. Just a couple of nylon bags, and you took the whole morning to do it! It's clear your lazy bones are not used to work!"

The heat of the communal room hits them like an oven as they come in after enjoying the fresh air outside. The women's room is not as crowded as the men's, but it is still overcrowded. An odor that is hard to describe pervades, which is a mixture of toilet smells mingled with sweat, blood and pus coming from lesions and scabs, syphilis and chancre, as well as the women's menstruation discharges. In this respect the women's room is much worse than the men's. And the women themselves are starved, with crinkled skin and dirt all over them, and their heads like so many birds nests. Their women's curves have now become straight lines. Some exceptions to the rule include the trusties, those thrown into jail for corruption or traffickers, and a few 'phenom's' who have had a track record of stripping others of their possessions by force. Only those can be said to have some meat and fat left on them.

In late afternoon, after she is finished counting the prisoners, the women's warden locks up the room. In the heat, nearly two hundred women, some having taken off their pants while other have gotten rid of their blouses, sit and lie in a thoroughly disorganized fashion. Some using tiny pieces of material are drying the blood and pus off one another's scabs. Nearer the door, some phenoms are leaving their breasts exposed as they talk.

The room's headwoman, who is well over 40 but still sporting a slim figure, is holding the baby in her arms. She is trying to soothe him: "How I feel for you! An infant like you and already in jail! All because your mother spoke against the Regime for the draining of our best manpower to kill Cambodians! Be good, baby, I'll try to find you some milk. Smile, child! Such a pitiful kid, expected to live on nothing but thin gruel! Do you still have some sugar for your baby? Remember not to eat his share, OK?"

"Thank you, thank you for giving him your love. How can I have the heart to eat his share? I still have enough sugar for him for the next few days. He's just got so much scabies. And now he runs a fever. I'm so worried about him. The medic gave him some aspirin but he kept throwing up. As for the scabies medicine, it's still not available after all these days. He cried all night and did not go to sleep. He's lost so much weight! I wonder what crime he and I committed in a previous life to have such a rotten life this time around. His father has left his bones in a foreign land, Kampuchea. He and I, we have been in jail for five months now."

The Schoolteacher covers her face with her hands, sobbing uncontrollably.

Headwoman consoles her:

"Come on, don't you cry. They'll just have to let you go. Up there they will examine your case, take pity and consider your case with some leniency. You were none too smart, you know. You're not the only one with a dead husband or son; there are many wives and mothers in your situation. Did anybody dare to call them names as you did? You just have to write a petition admitting to all your shortcomings. Then ask the Party to forgive you."

"I have done all that, admitting my fault. I have written two petitions. Nothing came of it. In actuality I never did call names. I only cried that their 'international duty' had killed my husband. Right away, I was taken into custody."

"But you said it at school, which was taboo because such a statement would be heard by your students. You see, you must realize how serious an offense that was."

A young phenom, quite shapely with her oval face and straight nose, a baby-soft, white complexion, pouts:

"So what? Such a declaration doesn't deserve jail! Me too, I did not do anything that harms the system, and yet I'm still in here. I slept with Europeans from the embassies. Now what harm does that do to the regime? I am not strong enough to go to work building roads and carrying rocks. So I make a living by 'the oldest profession.' I have my goods and there are buyers. I didn't steal from anyone."

"Well, you serve the Europeans and get paid handsomely. In our case, we sweat by day working on various projects, and we just moonlight a bit at night, so we don't ever have enough. But that doesn't stop our going in and out of jail. One time I ran into a real rascal. He took me on his bike and went all the way to the suburbs. Not only did he fuck me without paying—he even took my pants as he fled on his Honda. I was lucky to meet a kind old man who saved me. He gave me his pants, just wore his shorts and took me home on his bike. I will be grateful to him the rest of my life. Too bad I never ran into him again."

"So you think that it's not dangerous serving the Europeans? Each time I go into an embassy I have to lie down on the car floor. This last time, I had just stepped out of the car, I had hardly hit the pavement when they nabbed me right away. They even suspected me of being a spy!"

Headwoman sighed a long sigh, thinking back to old days:

"To be honest, let me tell you, I also went with quite a few westerners. They were all quite distinguished, and they had manners. They gave me money, radios, watches, a bicycle. For a while I lived like a queen. And I did not have to do it on the sly as you do nowadays. I was living in Hải Phòng. My parents owned a pharmacy. I was educated and could handle myself in French quite fluently. I was quite active so I got recruited into the Youth League. They assigned me to work at the Beijing Hotel near the Hạ Lý Bridge. This was where the Czech medical team was lodged. Before I started work there, I was introduced to a comrade member of the city Party secretariat who told me that I should do my utmost to keep our expert guests happy. He raised his index finger to stress his point: 'Remember to serve them unconditionally. You must satisfy their every demand. You understand what I mean, don't you? For this is revolutionary work that requires sacrifices. You see, numberless comrades have laid down their lives for the Revolution. Your task therefore is a most glorious task.'

"Just seeing the Czechs at their table, I could not but feel pity for our cadres. They had fish and meat and seafood galore. There was not a meal in which I didn't see them dispose of mounds of leftovers. They said that the lotus seed preserve that was presented to them as a gift, was too sweet, so they threw it in the garbage. Our cadres received 18 *đong* per month per person for their food. But the Czech experts were entitled to a monthly regime of 180 *đong*. Not only that, they paid for things at subsidized prices, so it cost them a pittance. Fruit and flowers, canned food, beer and wines, what have you. On top of that, their doctors received a salary of 2,000 *đong* per month. Even their chief cook got 600 *đong*. At the same time, our doctors got 60 *đong* per month.

"At first, I thought that I was the only one entrusted with my mission. Later on, I found out that many young and pretty ones had also been given the same task. But they were not posted at the hotel. They were only brought there in the evening or after lunch, during the siesta. Depends on the requests that came. Every one of these chicks came in dressed in long, flowing *áo dải* and redolent of all kinds of perfume. In a lifetime of service to the revolution, that was my most glorious moment. A few years later I was admitted into the Party and, with the Party's recommendation, I was later introduced to my husband. This time, however, I am in jail because of a corruption case involving 20 tons of rice. My subordinates who manned the stores, they all grew rich. They only nibble, and at the end of day they have their bags full. Their crime passed unnoticed. For instance, the people are entitled to ten kilograms of rice per person a month. They only have to measure for them nine and one-half kilos each. Just imagine how much they get considering the tons and tons that are sold every day. So they make quite a bundle. However, they also have to grease quite a few palms."

Phenom is quite upset:

"You did exactly what I was doing. Yet yours was considered a glorious mission that entitled you to Party membership. Whereas I am slandered and thrown in jail. Oh God, what's the meaning of all this, I wonder."

"I did what I did on order from the Party. In your case, you took it upon yourself to do what you did. That is the difference. But let's drop the topic. Let's see how we can find milk for the baby."

She sways the infant back and forth, cajoling: "Poor little thing! Look how thin you are! My heart goes out to you."

"You're not the only one to feel that way towards him. But the people who receive provisions from their families, none of them have canned milk. What can we do?"

Phenom grows jubilant at the thought of a possible solution:

"I've found a way. The armed guards go on rounds at night. They know that in summer we don't wear anything when we go to sleep. So they take turns climbing to where the barred windows are so they can snoop and peep from up there. They all crave us like mad. Which leads me to think: Why can't we resort to our profession and in the process get milk for the baby? Tonight I will go near the door so as to seduce them. Any guy who would want to touch me had better come up with two cans of condensed milk. The head honcho ordered everyone to be covered at night. What a prig! But one night when I had to get up to go pee, I caught him at the game. I saw him climb up and peep in from the barred window. On another occasion, I came back from an interrogation session when I ran into him; his eyes could not keep off me, so he thought of something or other to ask me—just to detain me. He then even offered me moral education. But he smelled strongly of alcohol."

"He had a stroke and died over a week ago. He blatantly courted me a couple of times. Men, they are all like that. Your idea is a good one. You can start tonight."

Schoolteacher looks hesitantly at Phenom:

"How can I express my appreciation for your kindness? I did not realize you care that much for my baby. But I don't want to put you in jeopardy, either. For if this leaks out, you can end up in stocks."

Phenom replies right away:

"For him I would do anything. I am not scared of stocks. It's better to serve him, it's certainly better than serving the Revolution."

Schoolteacher is unnerved:

"You're throwing a dart at me. But you are right. I won't take it in a bad way. Just remember, you must win. Be careful."

At night, Phenom puts herself right by the door. The whole room has gone to sleep. The mosquitoes have a field day humming as they go from one carpet of flesh to another, drawing blood from one scabbed body to another. The quiet is punctured from time to time by some delirious cries emitted in a dream or some mutterings, expressions of surprise that sound like sobs. At the approach of someone. Phenom puts her head down on her knees.

"It's late, how come you are still not sleeping. Why are you sitting here?"

She looks up and flashes one of those smiles:

"Report to you, cadre, it's just too hot. I couldn't close my eyes. I sit here just to get some air. The whole room is kind of stuffy."

She stands up, and the unbuttoned blouse all of a sudden exposes her breasts. The guys could not take their eyes off her two solid hills, which are crowned by two alluring pink tits.

"I have something to report to only one of you."

One turns to the other and says: "Why don't you go out there and guard."

When the second guard is out of sight, Phenom adopts a most seductive voice:

"We have had no rice in the last couple of days. I cannot eat sorghum. So it hurts me right here, in my chest. Could you possibly give us two cans of sweet milk?"

The guard adopts a solicitous attitude:

"You should try and eat your meals so as to keep in good health. OK, at three in the morning tomorrow night I will bring the milk. How does it hurt? It's miserable, you know, to be sick in jail."

"Thank you, cadre. It hurts me right here. It's god-awful."

She points to her chest. The guy takes advantage of the occasion, puts his hand right in through the bars and tries to knead her breasts.

She lets him do so for only a minute, then retreats:

"I'm going to sleep. Tomorrow night, I will wait up for you. Please remember, two cans of milk. And I will repay you most properly."

She turns away. The next morning, the kitchen trusty comes by to take away the water can that is left outside the door of the room. The headwoman calls out to him:

"Friend, can I ask a favor of you?"

The kitchen trusty stops and looks around with apprehension:

"What is it? Say it quick."

"There is a baby in the room, only ten months old. He cannot eat yet. We have candies and cakes, can you trade them for a can of milk so we can feed him. If possible, could you also find us some antibiotics. He has been running a fever these past few days. The medic said that there are no antibiotics left, that we'll have to wait until the next shipment. Could you do us that favor?"

"OK, I'll do my best."

He carries the water can to the kitchen and starts thinking. As part of the kitchen staff he usually is led, together with others, by a warden on duty to go and find provisions in the market. To find a can of condensed milk is no trouble. But the regulations strictly forbid any contact with the prisoners in their rooms. Furthermore, women talk, they can't keep a secret. If discovered, he would be the first one to be sent away to a reeducation camp. His wife has had to pay ten ounces of gold for him to find a slot in the kitchen crew. Sure, he also feels for the infant, but how can he put himself in jeopardy? No, he just can't take that risk. As far as the antibiotics are concerned, it's simpler. The medic just gave him 30 tetracycline tablets and told him to crush them, then spread the powder on the butt of the pig where he has been bitten by rats. The pig was an extra fat one, so fat that he could not even stand up. He just lies there. That was how at night the rats came and ate up part of his butt. The kitchen crew had to work extra fast to secure a bamboo shelter for him to tuck him in. Now if he lets the baby have some of the tetracycline, who knows, should the young one turn worse, he would be in big trouble. So why get involved in somebody else's business? It's best to stay away.

That night, Phenom is ready before the time of the appointment.

Yesterday's guard soon comes by and, with a rascally smile, he excuses himself:

"I was so busy all day and didn't have time to go downtown. Can we meet tomorrow night, at around one? That will not be my round, but for your sake, I will bring the milk. Let me see where it hurts still, OK?"

The lady is furious and about to cuss him out but she holds back. Hoping the fellow would deliver the two cans of milk the following night, she plays along and lets him touch her a minute or so. Taking advantage of the moment, he suddenly plunges his hand further down. But she eludes him and whispers:

"Somebody is awake. Tomorrow."

Phenom goes back to her place, hot-faced and furious. Her neighboring friends ask in a whisper:

"What happened? You failed?"

"You ran into a parasite, right? He only wants to take advantage of you and is unwilling to pay, right?"

"There must be a way to deal with him. How can we let him get away with that?"

Phenom whispers back as she develops a common plan of operation for the following night. Everybody agrees and swears to carry out the plan at all costs. And this time, they would harvest big.

In the morning, seeing no milk, Headwoman laments to the Phenom:

"I've asked the kitchen guy to help, but he was afraid and did not dare to. And you lost two nights for nothing. Let me ask the warden to allow me to write home. My husband, I am sure, will send in the milk. But it will take until the end of the month at the earliest."

Phenom is all smiles:

"Don't you worry. I promise you we'll get the milk tomorrow night at the latest. We might even get it tonight, who knows."

Near 1:00 A.M. she waits at the door. She has wasted two nights on the fellow, so now she has a legitimate grudge against him. She will not easily swallow failure, she tells herself. If the guy is a rascal, she will show him what a double rascal she can be, too. "A tangerine's thick skin will call for a sharp fingernail," says the proverb.

The guard who was disappointed the night before shows up empty-handed again.

Phenom is all sweetness:

"Oh how I miss you, darling. I was so afraid that you would not be coming. I wouldn't be up waiting for you, just for two milk cans, you know. By the way, where it used to hurt I feel a lot better. I think all it takes will be just another of your wonderful massages."

The guard falls right into the trap:

"If you truly love me, when you are out of here we can marry."

He puts his arm through the iron bars and feels divine, kneading her. The Phenom grips his wrist in her strong hands. A friend of hers, hidden against the wall, jumps out and in a flash robs him of his watch—a trick at which she's an expert. The whole thing happens in a few seconds.

Phenom purses her lips and tells him to his discomfited face:

"You dog tick! Each time is worth two cans. You get it? Tomorrow, at exactly 11:00 P.M. if you don't produce six cans, I will turn this Seiko over to the prison supervisors and tell them what happened. This is not an empty threat. At exactly eleven. I will not waste my time waiting."

After that, she just walks back inside, oblivious to his mumbled entreaties.

After obtaining all of her six cans, the Phenom returns the Seiko to its owner, then turns over all her booty to the Headwoman. In a victorious mood she declares:

"You hang on to this. Each day let's give the little one half a can. Once the supply is gone, I will find another cow to milk."

The women are full of admiration:

"You are something. And a real good head too. You deserve your name 'the phenomenon.' Those armed guards will die at your hands."

"From now on, I will have to play with cash only, no credit. I will not let things drag out like this time."

Now that he has milk, the baby has regained some weight. The Headwoman has also found him some medicine for the scabies so these can be taken care of. He no longer suffers from so much itching. And somehow, even without medicine, his fever also abates.

The Schoolteacher gives the baby to the Phenom and says in an emotional voice:

"From now on, you are his adoptive mother. When he grows up I will tell him, and I will teach him to consider you as a real mother."

Phenom coddles the infant in her arms and smiles a truly happy smile. She feels so good inside having done a good deed.

One day follows another, and within a month there have been three more armed guards bringing their milk tributes to her.

Headwoman praises Phenom:

"Truly, my dear, you said it right. They're just a bunch of milk cows. What a good milkmaid you are!"

The beginning of August arrives. The weather turns unseasonably hot. The sun burns brighter than ever and literally pours down fire. Everything exudes heat, the prison walls, the cement floor, the tiled roofs, just about everything oozes heat, a stifling heat that suffocates. In the overcrowded room, the awful smells become intolerable.

The warden, sitting under the ceiling fan, grumbles:

"What an oven! Hỏa Lò deserves its name. Even the fan blows nothing but heat. Turn it off, I tell you. The radio says it will be over a hundred today. And they say this heat wave will not abate until several days from now."

All the women prisoners now have rashes all over their bodies. They are itchy and scratch till they bloody themselves. None can find sleep at night. The baby again runs a high fever. He starts throwing up everything that is fed to him, whether it's aspirin or milk. His whole body is covered with red spots, and he cries to the point of suffocation. His mother is now bare bones with eyes showing deep black circles, not knowing what to do as she cradles him. Having gone without sleep night after night, she is exhausted. Early one morning she simply dozes off. When she awakes she finds her tiny baby open-mouthed, all parched with eyes showing their sockets, immobile. His two cute hands are tightly closed. Shaken with fear, she takes him to her bosom. He no longer breathes. In a panic she yells, with tears flowing down her face:

"He's dead. My baby. He's dead."

The whole room is in commotion. The Headwoman, the Phenom and some other women all rush over. He is truly dead. The Schoolteacher has her head on the baby's chest and passes out. Phenom covers her face with her hands, sobbing.

Headwoman, tears streaming, goes to the door and cries out:

"Report to you, cadres! There is a death in the women's room."

After a while, the warden comes accompanied by a male trusty. The warden opens the door and asks:

"Who is dead?"

"Report to you, the baby!"

"Take him out here."

Headwoman walks in the direction of the baby and is about to pick him up when his mother regains consciousness. She hangs on to the infant and yells in a madwoman's voice:

"He's my son. He must stay with me! No one has the right to take him anywhere."

Seeing the Schoolteacher in such state and hanging on to the little corpse, Headwoman tries to console her:

"Calm down. He's dead, your boy. Let them take him away so he can be properly buried and rest at peace down under. How can you keep him here? Now listen to me. I am like a sister to you, and I can feel your pain. Me too, I love him dearly."

Schoolteacher squeezes the body even tighter:

"No, no! I must keep him with me."

The warden who has been standing outside the door is getting impatient. She tells the trusty:

"Go in and take him out."

The latter walks in, yanks the baby from the arms of his mother and pushes her away. *Slam!* He takes the baby out of the room quickly.

Schoolteacher jumps up, runs after, and shouts:

"Give me back my baby! Give him back! I am going to kill myself!"

She knocks her head *bang bang bang* against the iron bars of the door. Headwoman and Phenom restrain her as best they can. The blood trickling from her forehead is now mixed with her tears, forming a stream of red. The two women take her back to her place and lay her down. Phenom tears a piece off her dress to cover the Schoolteacher's wound and clean the blood off her face.

As the cool cloth rubs, she regains consciousness again and screams some more:

"Give me back my child! Give him back to me! Oh darling, how I love you."

Afraid that she will commit suicide, for the next few days, whether day or night, the other women take turns sitting by her and consoling her.

After knocking her head against the iron bars, the Schoolteacher does not die. She only becomes a crazy woman. She laughs and cries, then goes into a long period of inaction. At other times she cradles a bundle of clothing as if it were a baby in her arms, kissing it. Every day she dances and sings. Her voice is guttural but she dances really well. And she sings only one song. It's a song taught at school ever since she was six or seven years old. She sings as she dances with an ethereal face

"Who loves Uncle Hồ more than we children?
Our Uncle is slim and sort of tall
And his eyes shine like stars while he sports a long goatee.
For love of the land he forgets himself
And though he is old now
He's still full of life.
How we wish He lives on forever
So that he can teach us children to become human beings."

One day, when everybody is eating in the yard, she stands up and starts her song-and-dance routine. The warden, who was reading the daily newspaper *Nhân Dân*, stops to watch. She compliments her on her beautiful singing and dancing. Noticing that the paper has a big picture of Uncle Hồ, she begs the warden to let her have it. She is crazy but rather inoffensive, not given to explosions or disruptive behavior. So the warden takes pity on her, cuts out Uncle Hồ's picture and gives it to her.

From that day on, every evening, the Schoolteacher puts up Uncle Hồ's image near where she lays her head down at night. She kneels in front of the image and cries while imploring him: "I kowtow to you, Uncle. My husband has been sacrificed in the name of the Revolution. Please take pity and forgive my child and me! Yes, we are fully aware of our offense against the Party. Please be kind and take pity on us. Please forgive us!"

Witnessing her, neither the Headwoman nor the Phenom can contain their tears.

Then one day, at the beginning of October, she is led away by the prison medic. They take her to a camp for crazy people in Châu Qũy, Gia Lam District.

Headwoman whispers to Phenom:

"I think they will take her to the Việt-Đức Hospital for treatment. Uncle Hồ is looking after her, I guess. For He has a lot of supernatural power. The day He died, remember,

People cried while the Sky also rained.[2]

STORY 6

Posing as Statues

Near six feet tall, he weighs less than ninety pounds
Qualified, I guess, to fly into space!
Seeing his white hair and beard, they call him Old Man,
A forty-six year old fellow, with a twenty-year record in jail!

The fuel—is made of thousands of laments
And the launching pad, thousands of dreams put together.
The cosmonaut driving this Poetry space ship
Is no other than the indestructible Goddess of Liberty.[1]

Clang! "Ready to pack up and move to another room!"

The Old Man stands up, silently grabs his worn, crumpled and stained clothes and throws them into a small bag. When rolled up, these clothes serve as his pillow. He also throws in his tin can, for which the lid is missing, puts his threadbare towel on his shoulder and walks out. These are all that he has.

Reaching the door of the cell, he says in a loud voice: "Bye, everybody! Those who will be released, please send my 'best regards' to my fellow countrymen nationwide!"

The whole cell row bursts out laughing. The prison warden's eyes are spitting fire:

"You're lousy! You think you're a political leader?"

He doesn't bother to reply. During his long years of imprisonment, he has used humor and sarcasm to turn events and situations into laughing matters to ease the stress. Thanks to his sense of

---

"Posing as Statues" was translated by Vann Saroyan Phan from the original Vietnamese "Tạc Tương" in *Hỏa Lò* (2001).

humor, he could survive any prison camp. The prison wardens, in fact, have named him "Nutty Old Guy."

The prison warden is walking ahead of him. Neither of them cares to talk to the other. When they are out in the open air, the Old Man looks up at the blue sky high above and takes a deep breath of the fresh morning air. A feeling of sorrow and resignation comes upon him. The immense blue sky and the fresh morning air are quite unfamiliar to him, for they are not his possession! They have been apart for a very long time. There will be no more rendezvous with nature.

Leaving the cell makes him feel that something is missing, as if the cell were a warm nest. He knows very well that staying together with criminals will double his hardship. In the past, cells were reserved for key prisoners or those who were shackled and kept there for a few months because they had broken the prison regulations. Prisoners considered the cell to be a hell abounding with human tortures. Life inside this kind of grave is like that in a concrete tomb with the summer air as suffocating as in an oven and the winter cold piercing to the marrow. Everybody was afraid.

The capacity of Hỏa Lò prison remains the same, while the number of people incarcerated keeps growing. The rooms are filled with people like sardines in tin cans. In the cells, the prisoner can lie down on a concrete platform that is sixty centimeters wide. Therefore, compared to the rooms it's like living in paradise! Except for prisoners considered to be extremely dangerous, those who have the priority to stay in the cells are friends or relatives of officials working in the Security Ministry. And a must: money! Likewise, any prisoner who wants to work as an informer to the Inquisition Committee must be a Party member.

Turning left, then right, the men come to room 14. The prison warden stops and walks into a small, open room with no walls and no doors at the front. In the middle of the room are a wooden table and a rattan chair. This is the office of the prison warden for this part of the complex. The prisoners call this place 'the Windy Inn,' for the ceiling fan is always turning furiously like a storm. The Old Man watches two prison wardens talk to each other for a while, then the one in charge of the cells walks away.

Three trusties are inspecting supplies sent to prisoners from their relatives. They pour the supplies on the yard and examine them from item to item. Sticky rice puddings of all kinds are being opened up and cut across during the inspection of food. Sugar, roasted salty sesame, meat, and fish are poured into enamel bowls. Candy and sweets are stripped of their wrapping. After the inspection, the men bring their supplies to another place, squatting in a horizontal line, each a meter apart from one another as required by the prison egulations.

A trusty gives the order: "Nobody is allowed to give out or exchange supplies with others. Violation means forfeiture of your supplies!"

Those prisoners who are almost dead of hunger begin their attack against the food supplies. Burying their faces in the heaps of food, they eat ravenously to eliminate their desire for food. Their hearts and minds are concentrated in their effort of chewing and swallowing. They forget everything in life. The ulcerous and swollen hands incessantly grasp cooked rice, cakes and meat and put them into the open mouths.

The Old Man stands there, watching and shaking his head. The prison warden is still busy drinking tea and smoking a cigarette, not bothering to look at him. He throws the rush bag on the floor and wearily sits down. The trusties supervising the prisoners who are eating are still awaiting orders.

The Old Man never pays attention to prison wardens. With years in prison, he realizes that all prison wardens—whether they are young, middle-aged, old, thin, fat, tall, short, white skinned, brown skinned, sloe-eyed, hollow-eyed, slant-eyed, small-eyed, squint-eyed—have something in common. They are all contemptuous, fanatic and hostile to prisoners.

"Who has just met his relatives?"

The imperative and harsh voice of the prison warden is heard.

A man, standing up from his meal with his mouth full, quickly replies.

"Myself, Sir!"

The warden turns to the trusties:

"Inspect him!"

Two trusties rush to the scene:

"Take off your shirt!"

The prisoner tries to unbutton his shirt with two hands soiled with scabies and full of sticky rice and fat from the food he is eating. One trusty frisks through his shirt while the other one orders the man to raise his hands, face him and turn around.

"Take off your pants!"

The prisoner, bending his back, tries to take off his pants while the trusties poke and shake them briskly.

"Report to you, Cadre. There's nothing at all."

The prison warden frowns and wrinkles his nose, looking at the body full of scabies, blood and pus. Noticing that the guy is nervous, he shouts:

"Take off your shorts!"

The prisoner bends over and takes off his shorts. His face is pale. He uses both hands to hide his testicles.

"Have him raise his buttocks upward! Look at his anus to see what's in there!"

The trusties push the prisoner into position. Then one sits down, uses his fingers to open the man's anus, and looks in. Discovering something within, he shouts:

"Contract your muscles hard to force it out!"

Working on it for a while, he pulls out a long, round plastic bag.

"Report to you, Cadre: rustic tobacco!"

The prison warden is exulted:

"How can you think you'll outwit me? A pair of mosquitoes flying by, I can tell which one is male or female. Just watching how you behave, I can be assured that you have problems. You were a reporter in the outside world. Can't you read the regulations?"

"How to deal with this case?" a trusty humbly asks the prison warden.

"Confiscate all the food supplies. Order him to swallow that portion of rustic tobacco! He puts it in his anus and thinks he can outwit me. Now I have it put into his mouth!"

The trusties quickly bring the food supplies to the warden's room. The frightened prisoner implores:

"Please forgive me just this time. It's been a very long time that my wife is able to send me such things. But I acted foolishly. I swear not to do it again. If you want to punish me by having me swallow that portion of tobacco, I'll obey and do it right away!"

"The order to confiscate his stuff remains valid. Put that amount of tobacco into his mouth!"

The Old Man stands up and says calmly:

"Report to you, Cadre. By swallowing such an amount of tobacco, the man may become intoxicated with nicotine."

The prison warden looks at the Old Man from head to toe with great anger:

"It is none of your business. Shut up! You must know where you are standing. You're just a prisoner!"

"I'm always clear with my standing. I'm the prisoner, and you're the jailer. I speak up because I'm afraid you will cause death to somebody."

Clang! "What's the matter?"

A fifty-something security agent enters the room. The man bears the rank of major and wears yellowish, well-ironed khaki along with a well-polished pair of black shoes.

The trusties greet him with bows of respect:

"Good morning, Sir! Good morning, Sir!"

The prison warden quickly changes his countenance and replies politely:

"Report to you, my Chief. This prisoner goes to meet his family, and he secretly brings rustic tobacco in!"

"Forbid him to meet his relatives for four months. For his tobacco, throw it into the gutter!"

The administrative director of the Hanoi Hilton enters the room. The prison warden quickly pushes a chair toward him:

"Please have a seat, Chief!"

The director sits in the offered chair throws a glance at the Old Man: "You come here!"

The Old Man grasps his bag, walks in, and stops when he is about three meters from the director, as required by the regulations.

The director looks at the bag of the Old Man and asks:

"Your belongings are that simple?"

The Old Man replies with deadpan humor:

"I'm a ordinary member of the International Proletariat! Besides two sets of clothes, I don't have anything else. No wife. No supplies. No date of return. Three nothings."

The director nods his head:

"You're right to say so. Do you know why you have to move from the cell out here?"

"To a prisoner, changing locations or moving from one place to another is nothing serious. I don't mind to ask why."

"I hear reports that you always urge death-row prisoners to welcome Hoàng Văn Hoan and Chinese forces to come and liberate Việt Nam. Do you know that you can be prosecuted for that crime?"

"This is quite wrong. I don't have any respect for Hoàng Văn Hoan, even when he was the fifth-ranking member of the Politburo, full of power. Before the August Revolution, he lived in China and Thailand and never spent a single day in the French prison. Now, only after fleeing to Peking, he has the courage to revolt. For the Chinese side, I don't like Chiang Kai Shek and despise Mao Tse Tung. Long before, I never gave them flowers and embraced and kissed them. Why should I urge prisoners to welcome them now? In addition, these death-row prisoners shout and make a lot of noise as they shake their shackles, making it impossible for others to sleep. All other prisoners, including myself, tell them to stop, but they don't listen. You just ask other men in the cells, and they will say the same thing."

The director looks thoughtful, then says a moment later:

"The officials in the Ministry have mentioned your case to me. In short, I advise you not to revolt once you're in here. This will benefit you. Don't force us to chastise you. The cadres report that you're very obstinate. You must know that even metal melts in the Hỏa Lò furnace!"

The Old Man replies with an unflinching voice:

"What I am against is the Marxist-Leninist doctrine and the regime based on it. This is just a disagreement on political issues. In a democracy, I cannot be detained for my viewpoints. And that is my objective. It's not to come to the Hanoi Hilton to protest against prison officials. I have been here for nearly three years, and I've never broken the rules or said disrespectful words toward the cadres. One reason may be because I am not used to calling myself 'the cadre's grandson,' so they think I am recalcitrant. Because you're here now, I can tell you frankly that the purpose of reeducation is to help people become good and regain their personality. Prisoners who call themselves 'grandsons of cadres' are losing their personality. The cadres shouldn't allow them to address them like that. That means they should tell prisoners to respect themselves and keep their own personality. Only by doing so, cadres may have a chance to improve the conduct of prisoners."

"We never force them to address anybody like that. The prison regulations have no such clause. Well, I'll talk to you on the matter on another occasion."

As he leaves, the trusties dance attendance upon their protector:

"Bye, Sir! Bye, Sir!"

The prison director huffs out angrily, and shouts to them: "Inspect his belongings and push him into his place. Have him stay in the toilet perpetually."

Stomp. Stomp-stomp.

The inspection is finished. A prisoner leads the Old Man into the communal room with more than 200 inmates. Upon entering the room, a prisoner tightly embraces the Old Man:

"Oh my God! Big Brother! It's been seven years now that I meet you! You remember me?"

"Well, you're in prison again. Prison is your home, right?"

The prisoner shakes both of the Old Man's shoulders:

"Big Brother, you look much older. Both your hair and beard are white. But your manners are the same. Deliberate and imposing. Clever in your speech. Even the administrative director respects you. Somebody else could be ruined under his hands!"

Another prisoner who has come to greet him is full of praise:

"After years in prison, I've never met anyone like you. Your words please our ears! The administrative director is well-known as a tyrant in the entire Communist prison system. He is a terror to everybody. But you don't care about him. I admire you!"

"Will everybody please go away so that Big Brother can rest! You want a bath right now? I'll ask the trusties to bring in a bucket of water for you."

The Old Man shakes his head:

"Let's do it later. Do you have rustic tobacco? I crave it. It's been a very long time since I've smoked!"

The prisoner, who now considers himself to be the Old Man's attendant, turns toward another prisoner standing aghast, looking at the new guest:

"Make a big roll. Quick!"

The guy hurries into the toilet. A moment later he brings out a cigar wrapped in newspaper sheet.

The Old Man's attendant asks the fellow prisoner:

"Come to the door and watch. If anything, inform us. And Big Brother, you follow me. This is genuine rustic tobacco, trade-marked Vĩnh Bảo!"

He ushers the Old Man into the toilet. This is a space of about three square meters with walls and without door. Even if the room has just been washed, it still stinks.

"Big Brother, please lean against the walls. Because it's been a long time since you smoked, you may fall down!"

Another prisoner comes in with a piece of plastic, cut from the handle of a tooth brush, a piece of wrapping paper serves as a spill, and a thin piece of cotton. He bends over and pulls a piece of glass from a corner. He puts the cotton in the step of the toilet bowl, scratches the piece of glass against the piece of plastic on which a flint is fixed. The flame catches fire and burns the piece of cotton. Quickly, he puts the piece of paper to the fire and brings it up to the Old Man's mouth. The latter draws a long breath and staggers from the tobacco high.

"Big Brother, let me help you up. Stand still!"

The Old Man's eyes are closed. His body is light, floating on rising waves. Sweat trickles down on his forehead. His eyes are dim and weakened. He splutters:

"Drunk … drunk … drunk …"

The two prisoners laugh in excitement:

"It's exactly *'driving your drunken mind to the end of the forgotten world.'*"

In the communal prison room, during work hours, several hundred of the prisoners sit with their arms around their knees, filling up both sides of the platform, which serves as their beds. The attendant invites the Old Man to sit next to him. The inside-duty trusty, as big as a bear, walks imposingly back and forth by the door.

The Old Man asks the attendant:

"Who is the room's headman?"

"The one who inspects you and ushers you into the room. But all the trusties are 'slaves' under my control. They call me 'Chief Prisoner.'

"How many trusties are there for a big group of prisoners like this?"

"They have a room headman who is in charge. One on duty inside. Three on duty outside to serve the prison warden and inspect prisoners going to interrogation sessions or those who are new arrivals. Two others are in charge of cooked rice distribution and dish washing. Seven in all. All these guys used to be cadres in the outside world. They were arrested and put in here, and their crimes range from corruption, bribery, public property theft, and adultery to debauchery."

"Too many people. How can they fit into this space?"

The Chief Prisoner derides:

"Because of fucking Phạm Hùng, the Minister of Security! Since the day he replaced Trần Quốc Hoàn, who lost his post because he couldn't prevent Hoàng Văn Hoan from escaping, he has declared that he would transform Hà Nội and other cities into places free of crimes and as clean as a whistle. He searched furiously, made a lot of arrests in order to put as many as he can in prisons. He has vowed not to count the numbers. I myself was arrested in this case, with no crime at all. It's impossible, even if we want to live honestly, Big Brother!"

The inside-duty trusty barks the orders:

"Be prepared to come out and eat! One by one. Take off everything, except for your shorts!"

Those prisoners who are watching already know that this morning they have both bread and sorghum, and they make it known to everybody in the room. But only those who come first have bread. So the prisoners all hurry to take off their clothes and rush out. The inside-duty trusty has to beat some of them, sending blood to their mouths to stop them. But they still jostle to advance.

"Big Brother, take off your clothes! This is an order from the Supervision Team to prevent prisoners from hiding stones, broken glass, and metal to kill each other. But, in actuality, the measure is aimed at providing security to the prison wardens."

The Old Man, the Chief Prisoner, and four bear-heads come forward while others make their way out. Six of them are the first to reach the yard. Each receives a small loaf of bread and a bowl of brine. The prisoners fall into rows, facing each other. There are tens of human rows, filling the yard. A heap of nylon bags of meat, fish, shrimp and roasted salty sesame, which belong to those having supplies, are poured down on the yard from a big jute bag.

A trusty holds up each of these nylon bags and asks aloud: "Whose is this?"

Every bag has its own sign. Whoever recognizes his bag will shout back: "It's mine!" And the trusty will throw the bag to him. The prisoners eat voraciously. Some chew bread, others scoop sorghum with aluminum spoons of which the handles are already cut short to prevent prisoners from using these as weapons against each other. Once sharpened at one end, these spoons can pierce the eyes.

Here and there, comments in low voices are heard:

"How attractive is bacon! Please give me some! Next time when I have supplies, I'll pay back twice as much!"

"Shit! Don't be too hard-fisted just for a spoon of roasted salty sesame!"

"The last time I gave you something. So, don't forget to give back to me this time!"

"If you want bacon, give me a small roll of rustic tobacco!"

"A roll of tobacco for a capsule of tetracycline for pustules!"

Suddenly the prisoners stop eating and gaze in wonder. A girl some twenty years of age is walking toward them. Following her, about ten meters away, the female prison warden has the look of a scoundrel. The pale, oval-faced girl looks fragile and sorrowful.

A trusty is supervising the men eating their food. As the girl approaches, he makes a grimace:

"Do you sell your under hole to feed your upper hole?"

Another prisoner blinks and says aloud:

" Looks sweet-smelling! Can I fuck you?"

The girl walks past the place where the Old Man is sitting. A terrible smell from her pants, worse than that of a dead rat, pierces his nose and makes him spew out some bread he is chewing.

The prisoner on duty inside laughs in delight: "This kind of 'public girls,' once lifted up by the armpits and shaken for a while, will certainly drop down a basket of sticks."

The girl silently walks away. Seeing that there are some grains of rice on the four-cornered, sticky rice pudding wrapping thrown in the gutter, she throws herself down on the water stream and picks up the grains. She puts them in her mouth and begins to lick.

The shrill voice of the female prison warden is heard throughout the court-yard:

"Bitch! I'll have you locked up!"

She seizes the girl, grabs her tangled hair, pulls it harshly and slaps her furiously. Almost in a whisper, the girl begs to be spared. The exhausted and hunger-stricken prisoners are busy, crouched down eating without paying attention to anything around them. They raise their heads and look around as they hear the piercing sound of the female prison warden.

The meal lasts about ten minutes. The prisoners are pushed to their pen like pigs. Without washing their mouths or drinking water, they sit in order on the cement floor.

During the day, three waves of prisoners have been sent to Hỏa Lò from the jails in Hai Bà, Đồng Đa, Hoàn Kiếm, and Ba Đình districts. Almost thirty men. All of them have swollen faces, cut noses and black eyes, walking with unbalanced steps. They had all been beaten well at the district jails.

The room's headman, embarrassed, reports to the prison warden:

"Sir, the room is full to its capacity and people have to lie down in the toilets. How can it accommodate more people?"

The prison warden clicks his tongue:

"All rooms are the same. Just push them in! In a couple of days some will be moving out."

After dinner the prisoners sit wherever they can in the room. The day is over. The hallway of three meters wide is also packed with people. The noise of several hundred men talking makes up an indescribable and mingled sound. The smell of blood and pus is nauseating. The smell of dripping sweat is sour and like a spoiled pie, which makes the mouths of hunger-ravaged prisoners water.

They ask each other:

"God damn it! Where did they get these pies?"

The group of trusties, the Chief Prisoner and his attendants stretch mats on the floor at the end of the room. Each has a mat of 70 centimeters wide, which occupies a big area. They sit together as a separate group. At the center is a big canteen of hot tea.

The chief prisoner puts a hand on the thigh of the Old Man:

"Why are you limping with your left leg?"

"I was in stocks in the cell for eight months. How can I walk straight right now?"

"Why don't you change your legs. Isn't it better if each leg takes a turn being shackled?"

The Old Man taps on his shoulder:

"You're wrong. If one leg is shackled, its size is reduced by time and is no more tightened by the shackles. This will reduce the pain. But don't worry about this. My legs will be back to normal after a few months. Here is a verse about leg irons that was published in Hồ Chí Minh's 'Prison Diary':

> *They clench the right leg in their jaws,*
> *leaving the left to bend and stretch.*[2]

"How can he shackle and starve you when he was himself jailed in over thirty prisons by Chiang Kai Shek?"

The Old Man replied:

"Perhaps it is because he learned from Joseph Stalin and Mao Tse Tung that the only way to control those with our own thoughts and ideas is to starve us into submission. Uncle Hồ had no new ideas for national reform, only to kill as many as possible who might oppose his dictatorship. In reality, many of the poems in 'Prison Diary' were not written by Hồ; he stole them from his Chinese cellmate."

The Chief Prisoner pours the tea into a plastic mug:

"Big brother, please drink it. It's the real Tân Cương fish-hook tea!"

The Old Man sips once:

"It tastes really good. But it's not hot enough to make it taste better."

Headman explains:

"It boiled half an hour ago. It has cooled down after being wrapped in the blanket."

One by one, in seniority order, the Chief Prisoner and then the Headman hold up the mug and drink. Then come the bear-heads and the trusties. One man opens a big roll of rustic tobacco and makes a cigarette and respectfully gives it to the Chief Prisoner.

The Chief Prisoner is all smiles:

"A saying goes, 'respect the elderly and you'll live longer.' This is for you. Enjoy it with all your pleasure!"

The Old Man takes a long drag. The tip of the cigarette is red with flame, burning quickly. He slowly breathes out the smoke and drinks a gulp of tea. The cigarette also goes around in seniority order. The cigarette is sweet smelling. More than two hundred eyes look attentively at the cigarette. Some mung bean cakes are peeled and shared.

The Old Man touches his hoary beard:

"In the cell, sometimes those who come out for interrogation pick up a few cigarette butts and bring them back home to enjoy. They must be sparing by 'holding back smoke,' that is, they never let a curl of smoke out of their noses!"

The Chief Prisoner laughs:

"In time of scarcity, we ourselves also do the 'holding-back-smoke' thing. This evening, we invite Big Brother to a dinner of shrimp noodles and boiled chicken. You just stay here, and we'll feed you to help you recover fully so that you can continue with your 'protracted war of resistance.'"

The Old Man frowns slightly: "Perhaps you and your bear-heads will beat and rob others of their food, won't you?"

"No. We use other tactics. They all volunteer to hand in their stuff to us!"

"Volunteer the same way as the bourgeoisie 'volunteer' to offer their house and property, farmers 'volunteer' to join the agricultural cooperatives, and young men 'volunteer' to join the army?"

The Chief Prisoner laughs joyfully:

"We never let it happen! We use the method of exchanging things, which benefits both sides. Our commodity is rustic tobacco. Tobacco is more precious than blood in the Hanoi Hilton! Those who want to smoke four times a day: One in the morning, one after lunch, one after dinner, and one at night time have to give us meat, sugar, and shrimp noodles. As you know, rustic tobacco is something very strange. Just smell its smoke and you feel dizzy right away. Especially when you're already full with fat meat and candies, you feel quite unsteady from smoking. All the guys come and beg us to exchange something for tobacco. We have the statistics. In this room, there are about 40 prisoners with criminal records on money issues who receive big supplies from their families. The other two dozen are medium range. The rest are extremely poor or have no families, hungry all the time. He who wants to have a roomier space to lie down or water to clean up his body every day will have to give us half of his supplies. They have wealth. It's quite reasonable for them to use wealth to save their lives!"

The Old Man commends:

"Your scheme is rather humanitarian. Not so bad as those in other rooms where they beat up people and at the same time rob them of their wealth."

Headman, who was a Party member when he was outside, politely says to the Old Man:

"We've heard that you've been constantly imprisoned because you're against the regime. Please tell us about your life and work!"

The Chief Prisoner intervenes:

"Save it for another day. Today Big Brother is still tired. What I'd like to tell you is that, while I fear nobody in this world, I have good reasons to honor him as my leader. When he was at Phố Lu Camp in Lào Cai, our Big Brother was put in shackles many times with both arms stretching around the waist, which left him unconscious for some time. But he just bore it and didn't say anything!

Remember those fierce VC, the Killing-American Heroes who have killed Americans on the battlefields in the South? After they got their medals they visited the North and were welcomed by Uncle Hồ. Then they went out on the town, got drunk, and fought with policemen. Then they were arrested and sent to concentration camps. Once imprisoned, these guys were so fearful of this type of shackling that they all went crazy. Some fell down on their knees and asked for mercy. Others yelled at cadres and cursed both Uncle Hồ and the Party. I've learned to respect Big Brother since then. Here, let me put you in shackles with both of your arms stretching around the waist to see whether you can bear it."

The Chief Prisoner orders the robust inside-duty trusty to stand up. He holds his wrists, twists the palm of his hands upward, and stretches his arms around his waist. The trusty utters a loud, painful shriek before he can successfully shake himself loose.

The Chief Prisoner laughs loudly:

"Just a slight twist on your arms and you start yelling that way! This way of shackling requires two men to make both ends of the arms meet while the third man locks the handcuffs. They don't lock it at the wrist but some 10 centimeters from it. I still remember a winter when the temperature was at zero degrees Centigrade, our Big Brother was stripped naked and shackled that way out in the yard. Two of his fingers were tied up with copper wire while he was hung upside down with barbed wire. His body was sweating heavily. His beard and his hair were all wet. Looking at the scene, everybody was scared to death."

The whole group, with full respect, looks at the Old Man with hoary hair, bony face, bare chest, and bare ribs like ocean waves.

The Old Man sips some tea, gives out a sigh:

"It's an old story. We must be prepared to suffer more."

Headman, pulling a piece of white paper, an envelope, and a ballpoint pen secreted under his bed mat, says in a soft voice to the Chief Prisoner:

"The prison warden has the Vietnamese resident from France write a letter. He'll be here shortly to take it."

"Finish it quickly, once and for all!"

Headman waves across the room to an elderly man with disheveled hair and bristling beard who is scratching his scabies:

"Come over here, Frog-lover!"

The tall and lanky overseas Vietnamese stands up and walks through the group of prisoners who are sitting and wiping pus on their bodies with pieces of cloth as small as the size of a match-box. Coming nearer the Headman, he squats down.

Headman instructs him:

"You must write letters to your family. Don't forget one kilogram of tea buds, one kilogram of rustic tobacco, two cartons of Điện Biên cigarettes, one kilogram of MSG, and three hundred piasters. Tell your relatives to give all these things to the letter carrier. Never tell anybody about this or your life will be ruined!"

The overseas Vietnamese is not happy:

"That costs a year's salary of my wife!"

Headman responds sternly:

"You're already favored. We have to pay much more than you do for that kind of favor! If you feel it's too expensive, give the pen and the paper back to me! You don't want to pay to be a trusty prisoner, do you?"

"I just want to express my feeling and never feel reluctant to pay."

"If you think so, it's good. Just sit here and write. Be concise!"

The Old Man, having pity on him, says to the Headman: "

"He's kind of slow. Let him sip some tea before writing so that he can be wide awake."

The Headman pours out the remaining tea from the canteen:

"Take it!"

The Old Man says to him in a soft and friendly voice:

"Please sit down at ease. How long since your have been back home in France? What did you do outside? Why were you sent here?"

Perhaps because this is the first time he has been asked about his life in a kind voice, the man is willing to tell his story:

"Sir, I was an engineer working in Montpellier. Four years after Việt Nam's reunification, my wife and I returned home. I had gone to study and work in France in 1964. I thought the goal of my return to Việt Nam was to help the country rebuild after many years of war. I was assigned to work at the Trần Hủng Đạo Factory while my wife was working as an accountant there. Although the salary was low, both of us never complained about it. I just made some comments on the way the leadership of the factory was conducting the work there, suggesting ways to improve its operation. They didn't listen to me but had me write notes admitting my faults. Then they brought me to staff meetings and criticized me of having been spoiled by capitalism.

"A French woman from the Embassy, who had been a friend of mine in France, invited me to a dance party at the Embassy. After the party, we were accused of indulging in debauchery. Feeling hurt and depressed, I asked my brother, who is a high-ranking Party member, to help us return to France. But my brother got angry and called me a fool.

"Before my return, in a letter to me, my brother had advised me to think twice before coming back home. But I didn't understand what he meant and decided to go back home anyway. This time, he told me that he has no right to petition for my return to France, and I must do it myself. After I submitted my petition six months ago, I was arrested and sent in here. The interrogator who questioned me accused me of everything in life. One thing was the intentional destruction of the prestige of the factory's leadership. The other thing was urging workers to make protests. The last one was spying for foreigners. I replied that never in my life could I do such things. He banged on the desk and said that I was obstinate, asking me the reason why I returned home when I was enjoying a good life in France. I explained to him that patriotism was the real motive, adding that I was encouraged by many cadres coming to France to mobilize people back home for the rebuilding of our country. He chided me, saying that such an explanation was nonsense, and even dogs and children couldn't digest my reasoning. How can I cheat the Revolutionary government with that?"

Listening to the story of the overseas Vietnamese, the Chief Prisoner, bear-heads, and the trusties chuckled. Then they bent over laughing as if they were listening to a joke.

"Why on earth is there anyone who is so stupid?"

"His head is full of residue. It's a waste for him to spend time learning!"

"It's like refusing to eat rice and eat human waste instead!"

The Old Man waits for the laughter to stop and says in a compassionate voice:

"Perhaps now you can understand what is socialism and communism. You're not the first one to do so. And you won't be the last one."

The earnest man looks up, his voice becoming serious:

"This terrible society is not the one Karl Marx would like to have created. Marxism-Leninism has been betrayed! Had President Hồ been alive, certainly these things wouldn't have happened!"

There is another peal of laughter. This time, even the Old Man, who rarely laughs, bursts out laughing while swaying his head:

"Okay. Continue with your letter! Try your best and be patient. There is no other way."

The Chief Prisoner waves a piece of cardboard as if he were using a fan:

"It's a waste giving him tea to drink. Finish your writing quickly and get lost!"

Headman wipes off his sweat while looking at the ceiling fan turning slowly high above his head, and pants:

" What's the use of this ceiling fan? God damn it! What a cheat! Fans of all kinds are the same in the Hanoi Hilton. But those in the room of prison wardens run like hell!"

The Chief Prisoner laughs with his lips tight:

"Wait until winter to see the fans run like windstorms! What a pity for those who lie under them without mats and blankets!"

A minute later the letter is finished. The French Vietnamese puts it in an envelope and gives it to Headman.

Suddenly the booming voice of the prison warden is heard:

"Where's the Headman of this room?"

"Your grandson is here, Sir!"

Headman runs out and hands the letter to him through the iron-barred door:

"The letter is written the way you have requested."

The warden thrusts a package of rustic tobacco into his hand:

"Don't forget to keep it top secret. I have to leave now."

"Thank you. Don't worry. He's quite lucky to have you help him this way!"

Headman gives the package of rustic tobacco to the Chief Prisoner to be put away.

In the toilet, a bear-head from the group has made a fire and heated a pan of boiling water. Fuel is from small pieces of torn-away blankets and nylon. The smell of burning disperses all over the room. The 'noodle battle' is brief. Ten minutes later more than ten bowls of shrimp noodles are ready. The whole group of bear-heads, bullies, and trusties, sitting in a circle, is eating out of these bowls. A prisoner stands watching at the door.

The Chief Prisoner grasps a boiled chicken thigh with his chopsticks and puts it into the Old Man's bowl:

"A dinner like this every night plus a canteen of lemonade can provide more than enough calories for the 'protracted war of resistance'!"

"For a very long time I have had nothing but the regime set up by the prison camp. Eating this way may give us diarrhea!"

"Don't worry! We have medicine for it."

Headman sounds joyful:

"Tonight, the mail will arrive. In a few days, we'll have a kilo of rustic tobacco available for exchange whenever we like to do so! Among those who have just arrived today, some wear jeans. The Chief told me to collect these jeans. A tiny amount of tobacco is enough."

The Chief Prisoner shows his frustration:

"This warden is really a vampire and villain. Let's press him to give us some packs of Điện Biên cigarettes!"

"Cigarettes are tasteless. Once inhaled, it just makes us feel sour in the mouth. If we like it, we can have it. I don't know why tobacco is so important that they forbid people to smoke. When addiction is high, people may gouge each other in the eyes, cut another's tendon, or kill each other just for a puff of tobacco smoke!"

The Old Man is thoughtful:

"It's understandable. The Hanoi Hilton is a temporary detention camp for interrogation. In an interrogation session, it's a kindness and a favor to people to be treated with a cigarette, which may have influence on the prisoner's psychology. This can help the interrogation process. For this reason, smoking is forbidden only in temporary detention camps. That way, cigarette smoking becomes a measure used in interrogation."

Headman nods his head and says,

"Ah! Thanks to your explanation, we now understand something. How dark is their scheme!"

A prisoner comes out from the toilet. After a few staggering steps, he slumps down like a falling tree, unconscious. More laughter is heard:

"He's simply knocked out by the ghost of hunger!"

"This ghost is Superman! He knocks out some guys each day."

The Old Man stands up:

"Let me come and see what is going on with him!"

The Chief Prisoner voices his protest:

"It's normal here when someone suddenly falls down like that. But, after a while, these men will simply recover. For the first few months, all of them are like that. Later on, when they get accustomed to hunger and their stomachs become smaller, everything is okay. You don't have to worry about them any more."

"Anyhow, let me see what happened to him. I can't just let him alone in this situation."

The Old Man walks to the place where the unconscious man is lying. He sits down, feels his pulse, calls him by shaking him. A moment later, he opens his eyes.

The Old Man helps him stand up:

"How do you feel right now?"

The man speaks with tiredness:

"I used to feel darkness in my eyes and fall down unconscious like this."

"Did your family send you supplies?"

"My parents are dead. When I am imprisoned, my wife has to bring up our two kids. She cannot feed me."

Seeing that he's too weak, the Old Man helps him sit against the wall:

"Please take a rest and don't get up until your dizziness stops."

The Old Man comes back to his place and tells the chief prisoner:

"You're right. He is only sick because he's hungry! I suggest you give him a can of sugar and water."

"Oh yes! It's easy."

The Old Man comes to the place where the prisoner is sitting against the wall, his face pale with hunger:

"Stand up and I'll help you to walk."

The prisoner leans on his knees with his hands and stands up. The Old Man leads him to the Chief Prisoner, whereupon he finishes the can of sugar and water:

"I feel much better."

The Old Man takes pity on him:

"How long have you been imprisoned here?"

"Eight months, Mister."

"What crime did you commit?"

With tears in his eyes, he begins his story:

"I'm not guilty of any thing. I am a young man with the skill to repair watches. But I don't have my own shop. I have to move along on my bicycle to serve clients in the wards. I used to hawk my service this way: 'I'm here for those who need to repair fast, slow, and broken watches ….' One day, perhaps destiny has frowned on me. I shortened the wording into 'repair inoperative watches, broken watches ….' After hawking through some wards, I was arrested by security agents from a police station. They condemned me for showing irreverence to President Hồ whose name in speech is the same as 'watches.' Afterwards, I was sent to the Hanoi Hilton. The interrogator compelled me to admit having reactionary thoughts by deriding the nation's leader with my hawking. He said that the words 'repair inoperative watches, broken watches' meant a bad wish for President Hồ. I explained that I had to shorten my hawking to save energy since I was coughing a lot those days, and I never hawked that way before. Anyhow, I begged him to spare me because I really didn't mean that. I had two kids to raise and dared not insult President Hồ. He told me if I admitted to my crime, the Party would be lenient with me and release me to my wife and children back home. Because I believed in him, I admitted to committing the crime and signed the report. But I don't know why I'm still locked up here. And I really don't know how my wife and my children are doing right now."

With this, he starts crying bitterly.

Headman chirps with his lips:

"We deserve to be imprisoned for what we did, which is spending the government's money irresponsibly. This used to benefit my wife and my children. And it's fair to go to prison. It doesn't make sense for you to be sent into prison for what you did! But I don't know why you admitted to this sort of crime, which is so deadly?"

The Old Man gives a sigh:

"With this crime, it doesn't matter if you admit it or not. If you're not sentenced to something, you'll end up being sent to a concentration camp."

"So, is it true that you don't have any acquaintance in this room?"

"I got acquainted with only the old man next to me who used to be a *cyclo* driver. It's only because I am sent here and we lie next to each other."

"Where are you lying?"

"We've been lying in the toilet for three days."

Headman chides him:

"You're telling lies! The toilet is reserved only for new arrivals to replace those who have been there for a long time. You're not new in here. Why do you have to be there?"

"My brother, I dare not concoct the story. My place and that of the *cyclo* driver are far from the toilet, near the center. Three days ago, there were two guys who coerced us to go to sleep in the toilet in their place. They threatened to kill us if we let the headman of the room know."

Headman's face is red with anger:

"Who are these two guys? Just tell me. Could they eat tiger's liver or drink bear's bladder to be so dare-devil? Don't be afraid of them! Just tell me who they are!"

The prisoner leads Headman to the place of the two in military uniforms who had broken into the French embassy for burglary. They were caught just a few days ago, so they are still healthy and sharp.

Headman yells at them: "Follow me, both of you!"

They slowly walk after him and then sit down on the floor.

The Chief Prisoner gives a grimace: "You took this place from the old *cyclo* driver, didn't you?"

"No, sir. What that guy says isn't true."

Headman says in a loud voice: "Where's the *cyclo* driver? Come here!"

From the toilet room, a man of sixty-something with tangled hair, bristling beard, and eyes full of rheum, walks slowly toward him, coughing.

"Is it true that these two guys pressed you to go to sleep in the toilet?"

The old *cyclo* driver trembles and says: "Yes. That's right, sir!"

The Chief Prisoner stands up abruptly and gives a side kick to their faces. Both of them fall down, their heads hitting the floor.

"Kneel down!"

The two men try to stand up, then kneel on the floor.

"Those on duty, give them ten kicks to the backbone!"

The order is given, the Chief Prisoner comes back and sits next to the Old Man, the anger still in his face. The inside-duty trusty stands up:

"Both of you lie face down here! Let your dad serve you the 'pig feet' dish!"

The two prisoners hesitate, then comply.

The inside-duty trusty holds up the sole of his big foot and pounds it on the back of each guy. The whole room keeps a breathless silence to witness the punishment. The sound of them groaning with pain is heard. Two backs rise and fall.

After three times, the Old Man stops him:

"Enough! Spare them."

He whispers into the Chief Prisoner's ear:

"With more beating, they may fall down dead and you will be sentenced to death."

The inside-duty trusty stops and laughs:

"Remember that you still have seven 'pig feet' pending!"

Both rise with enmity still filling their eyes. The Chief Prisoner jumps forward as quick as a flash and pumps them heavily on the chest. Both fall down headlong.

"Why do you show resistance? Your dad will beat you until you lose all your will to retaliate!"

The two bear-heads clumsily stand up and plead:

"We dare not hate you. Please spare us."

"Remember that here I can beat an idiot into a sage, and a sage into an idiot. Under my hands, he who is quick will become slow, and he who is slow will be quick."

"We already know your power. Please spare us!"

Headman gives the order:

"As a punishment, you must come and stay in the toilet for a week! Now, disappear!"

Both walk toward the toilet at the end of the room, their faces hanging down.

The old *cyclo* driver looks at the Old Man and says hesitantly:

"Sir, please tell me what to do."

"If you have anything you want to say, please speak out. You're old, just speak to me as friends."

"Yes, sir. I simply violated a traffic law and was fined 20 piasters. I didn't have enough money for the fine. They kept my *cyclo* at the police station for several days. My wife and my children were hungry. I begged them to give back my *cyclo* so that I could go to work. If I had money, I would pay the fine. For several days, I came to the station and implored them. Instead of giving back my *cyclo,* they kicked me out. With deep resentment, I stood in front of the station, called for God, and called the names of Party leaders Lê Duẩn and Trường Chinh, telling them how my family was suffering. As a result, I was sent here. I am already here 14 months. I'm illiterate. Please write a petition for me, asking the Party to spare me."

"What crime did the interrogator charge you with? Did you disrespect the leaders?"

"How can I dare disrespect them? I just called for God and called the Party leaders' names. But the interrogator said that I had insulted the leaders. I had to tell lies that I was drunk at that time and that was why I did this. The interrogator asked why I didn't call the names of my parents. I cried and implored him. He told me to put my fingerprints on the document to admit that I have insulted our leaders. I didn't accept it. For eight months they haven't called me in for further interrogation. Do you think that I will be released?"

"Had you been related to the French previously?"

"No. Originally I had been a rickshaw man on the Hà Nội–Hà Đông route. And I've been driving *cyclo* for decades."

The Old Man pondered: "I'm not sure. But if you're lucky, you'll be released. For your petition to be released, you must ask the prison warden. If possible, I'll help in writing the petition. Does your family send you supplies regularly?"

"My wife and my children are poor. They do it once every six months."

"Well, don't worry too much. Be patient and keep waiting. Maybe there's still hope."

Outside in the yard, the security guard's loud voice is heard:

"It's nine o'clock already. Go to sleep!"

The inside-duty trusty stands up and shouts:

"Those who just arrived today, come and stand in that corner! The rest of you lie in place!"

Thirty new prisoners elbow each other in a space some three square meters next to the door. This is a vacant space where nobody is allowed to lie down, sit or walk past except when someone needs to go to drink from a water can outside the steel bars. The rest of the prisoners compete to lie down on two platforms on the walkway in the middle of the room. Not a small opening. All have to lie in the style of a spoon upside down, with their legs bending. In the toilet, ten people are lying and sitting.

The inside-duty trusty gives the orders:

"Those who just arrived, listen carefully! Spitting on the floor is prohibited. Those who disobey will be given five kicks on the chest, forced to swallow their own sputum and stay in the toilet for a whole week. Those who scoop water to drink but put their hands with scabies in to wash will be punished the same way! This is to keep sanitation for all of you. We already brought water in for us to drink. Going to the place where the trusties lie is strictly forbidden. Those who violate this will be given ten kicks on the chest and put in the toilet for one month! Among you, those who have gonorrhea and syphilis will be kept separate. Tomorrow you'll learn 36 prison regulations. Look at the slogan on the wall: 'Three cleans: Eat clean. Stay clean. Everything clean.' You must obey. Room 14 is the most advanced unit of Hanoi Hilton Prison."

The orders given, the trusty turns to Headman:

"Where will we keep more than 30 persons now?"

"We should try to squeeze them into one place, no matter what."

The trusty calls their names one by one and squeezes them into the crowd:

"Jostle up! Jostle up!"

While shouting, he kicks the prisoners on their abdomens and chests, trying to secure a space 15 cm wide for another man. There is only room for seven more men.

The inside-duty trusty wipes his sweat and laughs:

"Squeezing people by using kicks only got to this point. What to do with the rest of them?"

Headman thinks about it for a while but cannot decide anything. Finally, he says:

"At first, put 10 men into the toilet to replace those who have been there for many days and nights."

The inside-duty trusty orders those in the toilet to go out and pushes eight new men in along with the two guys who were punished with kicks before. Headman discusses with the other trusties the way to solve the problem concerning the 20 persons remaining outside. Nobody can find a solution.

The Chief Prisoner taps on his forehead and says:

"I have a solution! Let them 'pose as statues,' which means tonight they will stand up against the wall and tomorrow night, another group will replace them."

Everybody is pleased with the good idea, their faces reflect a great joy.

"A good initiative! A great initiative!"

Pretty soon, more than twenty 'statues' are squeezed along the wall after a lot of moving and jostling among the men.

The Chief Prisoner turns to the Old Man:

"That's good! In a moment, I'll lower the mosquito net, and Big Brother will come and sleep with me. Lots of mosquitoes and bed bugs. But we have so many people for them to suck the blood till satiety!"

"The prison warden presses me to lie in the toilet. If we disobey him, will the trusties get into trouble?"

Headman laughs:

"By night he has to sleep with his wife. How can he know? About secret reports to him, this room has no record of such things. We apply fascist rules to snitches. I think even Hitler must have called us his forefathers! No doubt that the jailer is on our side. We rely on each other for survival."

The inside-duty trusty stands up and straightens his shoulders:

"The 'president of the bank,' where are you? Give me some dollars!"

A skinhead trusty with bulging eyes and bushy eyebrows is chanting while lying with his hands on his belly:

Love for her who has a big tummy to beat melodiously so
that it grows bigger and bigger …

Hearing the voice of the inside-duty trusty, he awkwardly sits up and takes a bulk of newspaper sheets and cement papers from under the mat. They are glued with sticky rice, stained with oil from roasted salty sesame.

He gives the trusty four pieces of paper the size of a hand, and says in a loud voice:

"The bank closes at 11 pm. Those who need strong currency must know that."

The Chief Prisoner laughs:

"Big Brother, do you know that toilet paper in the Hanoi Hilton is more precious than U.S. dollars? To prevent prisoners from exchanging information, the prison regulations strictly forbid them to use any kind of paper. The prisoners on duty outside steal paper sheets used to wrap supplies and open a paper bank here. Those who want paper have to give something for it. The bank is doing very well with this kind of business. Those without families on the outside are contemptuous of this. They reason that buffaloes and cows don't need to clean their anus, and they still live well and healthy. 'Stay dirty and stay long' is their slogan."

The Old Man sighs:

"The knowledge of our people is so low that it leads to this situation! After the feudal lords and the colonialists are the communists! Nobody knows the day when we will see the light at the end of the tunnel. I'm old and feel very disappointed. Most people of the younger generation who have been brought up under the current regime are ignorant and spoiled. "

"Everything has its own time, Big Brother. When the night ends there will be daylight. It needs men from only one-tenth of the population like you and me to prevent both the fascists and the autocratic communists from ruling over us! Using violence and power, the communists rule over the nation like me ruling over this room. But experience tells bear-heads like us that ruling based on violence does not last long. In other rooms, *coups-d'etat* and stabbings among prisoners happen frequently. The reason why seven months ago I could seize power here without any riot is that I have limited the use of violence and oppression. I don't rob, deceive, repress anyone unreasonably. I just punish violators when they are proven guilty. Many times I protect and help the desperate, creating conditions for them to live in safety. When I have rustic tobacco I share it with the whole room to smoke. Those who are sick are exempt from sleeping in the toilet. I don't let people oppress people. Therefore, they fear me but do not resent me. This is why I think I'm superior to the communists! The communists merely use tricks, oppression and violence. They openly cheat and use excess violence. They won't last long, and I'm sure about that!"

"I'm surprised that you're so intelligent. Your perception is quite right. But what is 'not long' in history sometimes equals what is 'too long' in a man's life. Hope that your generation will be able to see the happiness of tomorrow. The younger generation will be saved."

"It's thanks to your advice to me. By nature, I'm not an evildoer. I have never stolen anything from common people. I just steal government properties. They rob people, and I rob them in return. It's no big deal, after all! However, since the day I met Big Brother, I have become a serious person. All things considered, I'm still a hundred times more honest than many Party leaders!"

"In normal society, you might become a talent because you're so intelligent. Anyhow, the reality of this society also gives you the precious knowledge many intellectuals don't have. In the last analysis, life is the greatest book. All other books are just copies of it. But I'd like to talk to you about a practical matter. I see that the room is so narrow because each of you occupies a mat, which takes up too much room. Can you make a little sacrifice by having two persons lie on only one mat?"

"Big Brother, you always think of others. Yet a good man like you must go to jail for his whole life, which proves that this society is so bad. I quite agree with you, Big Brother. Tomorrow, I'll have the room's headman rearrange everything. It's late now. Let's smoke once and lower the mosquito net for sleep."

The Chief Prisoner rises and gives the order:

"Be ready to fire the last shot!"

The trusties and the bear-heads gather and form a circle. The trusty in charge of smoke and fire opens the pack of tobacco and makes a big roll. He shakes his legs and sings a tune:

Very long and very far away are the days I miss you ...
I am on the military operation amidst artillery fire
throughout the campaign.

He tears up some cotton into small pieces, pulls out the brush on which there is a fire stone and gets ready for striking. But the piece of glass has disappeared. He turns up all the mats in search of the piece but can't find it.

Headman chides him:

"How can you make a fire without it? You really come to nowhere! For tomorrow also, how can we stay awake without a smoke?"

Everybody stares at the person in charge of smoke and fire with indignation.

The guy grumbles:

"Nobody likes this! No doubt I put it under the mat, right here. I don't know why it disappeared!"

The Old Man makes a gesture with his hand:

"This is no big deal. We'll have a way out."

So saying, he holds a pair of near-sighted glasses and beats it against the floor. The lens break into hundreds of small pieces. The Chief Prisoner isn't quick enough to stop him.

"Without glasses, how can you read?"

The Old Man speaks calmly:

"We don't have anything to read. Seeing things clearly or dimly, it's the same! Why do we need glasses when day or night we have to stay in this room?"

Headman's eyes brighten with admiration:

"What chivalry! This is truly real knighthood! From now on, please allow everybody to call you 'Big Brother'!"

The whole group shouts tumultuously:

"Right! From now on, we will all call you 'Big Brother'"

The Old Man is easygoing:

"Within the four seas, all are brothers. Here we're all in a mishap. It's a predestined union that we meet here altogether."

"Where are you going? Back to your places!" shouts the inside-duty trusty at four or five guys making their way out of the morass of people.

"We are walking out for drinking water."

"No way! There is no water to drink now. Step back!"

The Chief Prisoner shakes his head:

"With winter, comes hunger and cold. With summer, comes hunger and thirst. From 5 in the evening to 7 in the morning, there is only a bucket of water of about one hundred liters for 250 prisoners. Hỏa Lò is as hot as an oven or a boiling pan. Everybody sweats like hell. With brine and sorghum for food, all are thirsty to the utmost. It's better to leave for the concentration camp as soon as possible!"

The Old Man is thoughtful:

"The concentration camp has its own hardship. Everywhere in our country is the same. There is no happiness in the outside world, either! It may be just a little bit different!"

Headman sounds sorrowful:

"Anyhow, staying at the Hanoi Hilton is better because we're close to our families. My wife has to offer 8 ounces of gold in bribery so that I can stay here. It takes three more ounces of gold to be chosen as a trusty. I'm lucky that I'm smart enough not to reveal everything. There are many big fish involved in my case, and I'm just a tiny one. Thanks to their help, I was sentenced to only four years in prison. But one day in prison equals a thousand years outside. Four years is enough for me to suffer a great deal!"

The Chief Prisoner laughs:

"Four years equals the time we spend peeling off four sticky rice puddings at Tết. Compared with Big Brother, it's just a siesta!"

The Old Man makes a calculation:

"Four years is not worth half a 'well' from Tố Hữu the poet of the Party:

> *Well, it's been nine years. Our resistance has been going on*
> *for three thousand days without a rest.*

The whole group laughs and coughs: "You have a very good sense of humor, Big Brother!"

"Following the example set by Tố Hữu, we just *"go on with our resistance until the day we are victorious!"*

From the toilet echoes the sound of people cursing and fighting. The inside-duty trusty angrily rises to his feet:

"Shut up! Those who cause disorder are punished with kicks that will break their jaws!"

Silence.

Headman says to the Old Man:

"The room is crowded and it's too hot. Without iron-fisted discipline, prisoners would bite each other to death or quarrel every night. They have already transferred a number of prisoners to Xuân Hỏa, 20 kilometers from here. There is rumor that the government is planning a huge prison in the suburban area. The Hanoi Hilton, first built by the French nearly a hundred years ago, is very out of date!"

The Old Man speaks haltingly:

"My opinion is this. The Chief Prisoner has a very good idea to have men pose as statues. Those who have to stand as statues at night are allowed to sleep in compensation and don't have to line up during the day. And nobody is allowed to lie down in the toilet. Along both sides of the walls there is a lot of space. We're up here, close to the door, but still we cannot bear the foul-smelling odor. It's disgusting to lie in the toilet. The situation of these people is the same as ours, and we must be understanding. There is only a small toilet for a huge number of people like this!"

The Chief Prisoner agrees:

"You're right, Big Brother. But it's late now. Many of them are tired and are already asleep. We shouldn't interfere with their sleep. Tomorrow night, we'll rearrange things. It's quite inconvenient to let a dozen of people lie in the toilet while people are using the facility. We're still lucky that these poor people take only the prison's regime of a little sorghum and salt water. Having almost no vegetables for their meals, they only use the toilet for defecation once a week. Because they sweat often and do not have enough water to drink, fewer of them go to piss. Otherwise, the toilet would overflow!"

Headman feels a bit worried:

"It's a rule that during office hours everybody should remain sitting and keep order. If the prison warden knows that we allow those who pose as statues to lie down …"

The Old Man disagrees:

"Don't worry. You don't have to be afraid of the prison warden. He should be afraid of you instead. You have all the proof, both in witnesses and in material, to send him into prison so that he can lie down on the same place with you! If he is knowledgeable, you must explain everything to him. And he should listen to you and understand. If the Supervisory Team comes in, let me deal with them!"

The inside-duty trusty chides:

"God damn it! They never dare come in here because they're so afraid of the stink in our room. They really don't care! When it's time to count prisoners in the room, although it takes just one minute, they have to wear a gauze mask!"

The Chief Prisoner shows his admiration:

"Big Brother is so formidable. Now that we already know his weakness, we must make him afraid of us! Why should we be afraid of him when we bring pans or cauldrons to the room? Thanks to us, he can afford to buy his watch, a bicycle and a radio. But he's only obliged to give us some tobacco. We must press him to give more!"

Headman doesn't agree:

"He already ignores what we're doing. But he's so crafty. How can we hide things from him? If we create tension, our relationship with him could be broken, and that's not good."

The Old Man agrees:

"Yes. We'd better not to be so tense with him. If need be, just give him a warning and this will make him understand. You know, the reason why all of them are kind to me, from the prison wardens to the head administrator, is that, after three years living here, I know some of their secrets. I just hint that I know their problems. Besides, men from the Ministry often meet with me, and this makes them scared. Just keep the situation as is, and we will benefit from it."

The Chief Prisoner poses a question:

"But, Big Brother, if so, why were you shackled for eight months?"

"This punishment is by order of the Security Ministry. That I was transferred here from the cell was also by order of the Ministry. Their scheme is to let me live with the criminals so that robbers and murderers may inflict great harm on me and make me half-dead, half alive. This is not related to the Supervision Team at the Hanoi Hilton. To me, life or death does not matter. But as long as I'm still alive, I must fight. And when we take up the fight, we must be smart, conscious and know how to deal with the situation."

The Chief Prisoner chief shakes his head: "If you don't explain, how can I understand? When you have time, please tell me the whole story of your life. I think it must be very interesting!"

The Old Man stands up:

"Of course, I'll tell you my story. But there is nothing interesting or strange in it. Mine is not a detective novel. Let me go to the toilet. It's already late."

The inside-duty trusty is eager:

"I'll go with you. I'll lead you in there. You must have the skill of a Kung Fu master or a circus artist to get through without tramping or falling on these piles of human bodies!"

The inside-duty trusty holds the Old Man's hands and leads him away. Before stepping in, they must find some openings between the men lying close to each other so that their feet don't touch them. There are places too far away, and they have to jump and stand on one foot. They could easily step on the faces, necks, chests, arms, or legs of the men lying there and then fall down on them. After a while, the Old Man gives up and cannot walk. The inside-duty trusty has to wake people up so that he can lead him to the toilet's door.

In the toilet, a man squats on the surface of the toilet bowl, his head dropping down on his knees. Another guy sits on the step leading to the bowl. These are the two who were given kicks in the evening. They have already secured two of the best places. Some prisoners lie curled up on the urinal, others sit against the wall. The place is so overcrowded that the inside-duty trusty has to use kicks to force them to stand up, thus making room for him and the Old Man to urinate. As soon as they leave, these prisoners immediately lie down. The nauseating odor makes their eyes sore and their noses run.

Back in his place, the Old Man shakes his head:

"Everything must be rearranged so that there will be a passage in the center of the house, some ten centimeters wide, enough for a foot. It only requires five or six more men 'posing as statues' to make such a passage. If we let things continue this way, it's inevitable that we will step and fall down on those lying there!"

The inside-duty trusty acknowledges:

"This way, even I myself cannot get through. Tonight, it's my turn to sit up and keep watch. Hi! The banker! Go to sleep! At two thirty it will be your turn!"

"Why? Is it true that people should sit up and take turns keeping watch?"

The Chief Prisoner, already inside his mosquito net, sticks out his head for a reply:

"Big Brother, get into your net and sleep. Let me tell you this. In this room, besides those evildoers and petty thieves who make up the majority, there are still many who are fierce bullyboys who used to rob others in the outside world. There are also those who committed major crimes. They are cruel and fierce. Many of them used to be sabotage specialists against the U.S. Army. Seizing power is what they want, especially in such a desperate situation! I have taken all measures possible to prevent or divide them so that they cannot unite into one block. A slight indication of insurgence is enough for me to destroy them. Even though I may have conquered their hearts and minds and may get respect from many of them, we must take preventive measures. If nobody is watching while we are asleep and they come to attack, it's very dangerous! Just a needle or a nail could pierce our eyes or slit our throat. How can we know that they are concealing their weapons? If someone with these weapons is caught, they should be struck hard with deadly blows. There have been some nightly raids in other rooms. 'Revolutionary vigilance' is the best policy. Whoever sneaks beyond that line at night will be knocked down. It's proper punishment. During watch time, the man who keeps watch is not allowed to leave the post, even to go to piss. Those lying around me here have been carefully selected, and they are my followers. It's not an easy task to maintain this kind of government, Big Brother. I have also established a system of shadow spies to monitor the situation and promptly inform me of the situation. What I have organized is similar to that in an autocratic state. I must confess that I've learned a lot from the Communists."

"It's OK so long as you don't oppress the innocent or beat people without good reason. In this hideous life, this is truly an arena for struggling and competing. What else can we do? Because I was shackled for a long time, all my bones and muscles ache!"

"Let me call a man in to do a massage for you. It's very effective. I am addicted to it. It's a must for me every night to have him massage me. In recent days, because it is too hot, I stopped it. This guy is a professional. It cracks wherever his fingers touch. For each session, I give him two balls of rustic tobacco. Let me call him."

"It's late now. Tomorrow is better. Let's go to sleep. Westerners have this saying, 'He who sleeps, dines.' With sleeping, we forget hunger, sorrow, hatred, and everything else. Sleep!"

Regardless of what he says, the Old Man cannot sleep. Lying still, he closes his eyes and tries to liberate his mind from his thoughts by breathing slightly, expecting to sleep for some hours. But night after night, as though he were obsessed, images appear and disappear in his mind from the early days of his manhood. He was then a man with eagerness and passion, and his life was like a sweet fairy tale with beautiful and glorious pages open before him! It was the dreamy and passionate time when one does not drink but still feels intoxicated—the time when one's eyes are still clear and one's heart is boiling, the time when the horizon is immense and the dream is visible. All has withered away, faded and died a long time ago after so many tragic events. Why do they reappear? His wounded heart can no longer shed blood at every happening in life, past, present or future. He tries to temper himself to better cope with catastrophic situations that have unfolded in his life and in his country. A life full of colors and rapture, like flowers and wine, is something far away. He wishes that it would fade and he doesn't want it to return. After decades of being incarcerated, he has merged his soul and his body into the world of prisoners, a world without time and space. It's a hole so deep and so dark into which human suffering is heaped!

Beside him, the Chief Prisoner is already asleep. The trusties and the bear-heads are also asleep. Perhaps everybody is asleep. The room is so quiet that only the buzz of mosquitoes is heard. From afar echoes the sound of the shoes of the armed guards on duty. With his body still aching, the Old Man knows that once again he cannot sleep. So, he gets up, comes out of the mosquito net, and sits on the edge of the platform.

The inside-duty trusty is sitting with his legs crossed and both hands resting on his thighs. Seeing the Old Man, he opens his eyes:

"It's too hot for you to sleep, isn't it?"

The Old Man taps on his back with his hands and says:

"Very often I cannot sleep. Now you can go to sleep and I'll stand watch for you."

The inside-duty trusty smiles:

"Big Brother, let me alone. I'm practicing yoga. It helps. After the session, I will just lie down and fall asleep right away."

"Well, go on with your practice."

So saying, the Old Man also sits with his legs crossed and his body straight. He uses his hands to caress his head, face and chest. This practice, named 'Cốc Đại Phong,' was created by a Chinese man who taught him the method. He sits and caresses rhythmically according to the rules. The blood in his body seems to circulate better. His chest aches less, his backbone is less cramped. His mind gradually becomes unconscious. He keeps caressing regularly, without using his mind to think in order to make his brain relax and settle down.

Late into the night, the Hanoi Hilton is like a silent tomb. Far away in Cell 3, a female voice is falling, then rising, echoing a haunting melody. Well, it was long ago, when he was still very young, he had a chance to listen to and fall in love with this song. But tonight, after thirty years in jail and in the stillness and darkness of the prison place, he is touched to hear the song and he feels his heart is melting! Why is the melody so heart-rending and sorrowful? The girl in the cell seems to confide all her feelings to the lyric. His heart and mind seem to follow her voice back to the early days of his life when human love was still sweet, life was still rosy, and the moon and the water were still dreamy and fictitious …

The night of yesteryear, I missed the boat boy singer
I tenderly raised my paper fan
And kissed the wind toward someone …

The song drifts in the wind, floating above the river and the water, fraught with a sorrowful and remorseful feeling …

From the bottom of the cup of tea emerges the image of
Trương the young man.
And around the cup, the boat is floating to the melody of a
zither.
Yet life begins to wither, nevermore knowing Springtime.

The Old Man suddenly feels the emergence of a long chain of months and years that blackens and buries his life. He sits there stupefied, holding his hoary beard. Yes, it's right that *'life begins to wither, nevermore knowing Springtime.'* His throat is choked and his eyes are hot. He trembles. No! He cannot let weakness penetrate his mind! He must be strong to deal with reality! He tries to stand upright, and stares grimly into the whole room. On the floor, a couple hundred sets of human skeletons and skin, all ulcerous, are tightly embracing each other. The nauseating odor of blood, pus and sweat mingled with the smell of the toilet soars up and spreads out …. A comparison comes to his mind. Yes. The prison place is really a collective open grave not yet covered with earth! He stands at the bottom of this huge grave, with both hands drooping. He stares at the corpses, looking into his skeleton that is silhouetted on those underneath it and thinks of the supernatural and endless vitality of human beings. Human beings are indeed creatures that fit all circumstances! How could water buffalos, cows, chicken, and pigs survive if left to die of hunger and penned in like this? Certainly they would not! They would stomp each other, bite each other and then die. The worms, though credited with swarming up against each other, still are fed up and have a space to crawl across and along! He thinks of 10 people sitting and lying, half asleep, half awake in a toilet of three square meters, filled with suffocating excrement and urine. He thinks it's better to die than live like that!

Several days ago, the prison administrative director tried to remind people of the achievement of the Soviet cosmonaut who has lived and worked for three months in the space ship going around the earth. A world record! He smiles ironically, wryly laughs at his own thought, wondering whether the space hero would be able to live three days in this prison toilet. Absolutely not! How can this cosmonaut compete with 10 Vietnamese "cosmonauts" asleep in the toilet, which is the spaceship of the Socialist Republic of Việt Nam! He thinks these 10 'cosmonauts' should have won medals as 'Space Heroes'!"

"Get up! Get up! It's two-thirty am. It's your turn to stand watch!"

The inside-duty trusty calls aloud while pulling the leg of the prisoner 'banker,' who awakens and comes out of his mosquito net. He opens his mouth and yawns as if his jaws would jump out, then says in a sleep-filled voice:

"Why are you so noisy! You have a watch to prove that it's about time?"

He looks at the old-fashioned pocket watch given to him by the prisoner on duty inside, mumbling to himself:

"It's only 2:25. Why are you cheating with 5 minutes?"

"The watch is 5 minutes slow. Why is it cheating?"

The inside-duty trusty takes back his watch and throws himself into his mosquito-net again.

The Old Man wants to urinate. But as he realizes that he cannot pass by the heap of human bodies. He gives up and returns to his net. The Chief Prisoner still sleeps soundly. Youth is truly awesome! He thinks of the months and years he has spent in hardship and ill treatment. If it were not for the resourcefulness of youth and willingness to live, how could he have survived for decades, leading such a buffalo's life?

Now he is getting old. His body and his soul are wearing out, stunted, slack and losing vigor. It's frightening to think of the long way ahead! Knowing that he is nearing the end, he has practiced yoga for the last several years. He doesn't mind if things are not right or unfair. In the face of all the treachery, brutality, humiliation, he just sighs a long sigh and does not raise his voice in protest, which he used to do in the old days. He stops working with his mind. Death is swinging his scythe in a menacing manner. He is not afraid of death. Death to him is an escape. The brown earth is his eternal bed. With both hands drooping, the eyes shut, he can feel that lying dead will be the end of all the sorrows and misery of the world. But he just wants to live, even with a sea of bitterness, torture, hunger, humiliation, and rancor in every minute of his existence. He tries to live. He doesn't have the right to fear life! His work is half done. He must live on. And to live is to open wide his red eyes to watch the wretched life that is encircling his country and his fellowmen. Many times, too depressed and on the verge of succumbing, he used to derive strength and vitality from God and Buddha to stay firm. Still surviving, he has begun to believe in God and in his destiny. This belief has contributed a considerable part to his willingness to live. Deep in thought, the old man is soon carried away by a sound sleep.

"Give me a cup of orange juice .... Please do me a favor by giving me a bowl of gruel—huh huh—a bowl of chicken gruel—huh huh ...!"

The sound of a repeated lamenting awakens him:

"Why don't you send me supplies—huh huh ...huh—lemonade, ice, gruel—huh?"

The Old Man gets up, opens the mosquito net and crawls out to look at the toilet.

A prisoner who is lying close by stands up and slowly goes to piss. Approaching the toilet, he stops and uses his leg to kick a man lying nearby:

"Fuck you! You're a fool! Orange juice and chicken gruel. You keep shouting and I can't go to sleep. If you don't shut up, I'll stomp you to death!"

The Old Man makes his way past the row of mosquito nets and finds the big water can of the trusties. He lifts the 20-liter plastic can and shakes it. Not a drop of water left.

"Big Brother, you want some water to drink?" the Chief Prisoner, just awakening, asks.

"No. I want to see whether water is still available and give it to the moaning man for a gulp. But water is completely gone."

"Big Brother, please go to sleep. It's only 5 am. Two more hours, when the door is open for everybody to wash his face, the guy will have a chance to drink. We can't find a night without somebody moaning in his dream!"

Again, the moaning is echoed indistinctly from the toilet:

"Dear God! Give me orange juice, sticky rice, banana, meat—huh … huh—boiled pork—huh … huh …, my God!"

The Chief Prisoner shakes his head:

"Too hungry and too thirsty make men delirious and they just ask for food!"

The inside-duty trusty shouts:

"Whoever continues to murmur will be kicked five times in the stomach!"

The moaning stops right away. Perhaps the guy is afraid of being kicked.

The Old Man uses a handkerchief to wipe away his sweat:

"It's just 5 in the morning and it's hot like this! Seems today is hotter than yesterday. It's already been hot for a whole week. No doubt there will be thunder and a storm. If you think that you cannot sleep any more, open up your mosquito net to get more fresh air!"

The Chief Prisoner rises and unhooks his net:

"I have had enough sleep now. With the net down, it's less stinky, but hotter. I feel cooped up here and just want to be sent out to the concentration camp."

The Old Man replies:

"I know that many from the camp are longing to come back to the Hanoi Hilton. Graves are everywhere on the hills around the camps, which shows how harsh life is there. You must have peace in your mind to live. Don't stand on this mountain and look over to the other mountain. It doesn't matter because it's the game of destiny!"

"But living in one place forever is depressing. It's a joy for me to meet you, Big Brother. I don't know whether prison life in imperialist countries is better or not?"

The Old Man is thoughtful:

"Prisons in colonial and imperialist countries are less effective. The communists are never afraid of prisons. They consider prison to be a school. And it really was a school! Many men came in without knowing French. When released, they could read books and newspapers in French. They even founded Party committees and recruited members. They opened training courses on politics and cultural issues. Food was sufficient, and books and newspapers were everywhere. You will know more when you read the diaries of communist leaders who tell of their days in prison. Hồ Chí Minh wrote his 'Prison Diary' on paper—so he forbids paper to people in his prisons. During the reign of the Russian Tsar, Lenin was deported to Siberia for three years. He read, wrote, fished, hunted, and even married a wife! So, it doesn't matter if people are in or out of prison. They even became famous as revolutionary heroes!

"With this experience, the communists build up horrifying systems of prisons to destroy all the vitality and will of prisoners. In reality, these are execution grounds without the sound of guns; or holocausts without electricity and fire. Ten years later, those who survive these communist prisons still have nightmares when they are sleeping with their wives!"

The Chief Prisoner rolls his eyes in agreement:

"I must admit that the communists play a very wicked game! But once they can no longer hold on to power and disintegrate, the population will chop them into pieces! Now, let's smoke and pray for their quick downfall! Where is the man in charge of 'smoke and fire'? Be ready to fire a shot and start a new day!"

All the trusties and the bear-heads unhook their nets and fold them in unison.

After a good shot, the inside-duty trusty gives an order:

"Everybody wake up! Those in the toilet walk out!"

Ten people from the toilet slowly walk out. Dozens of prisoners get in line waiting for their turn to pass water or empty their bowels.

Suddenly, a terrified voice is heard:

"Report to the headman of the room, one man has died!"

"The man lying next to me. He's dead!"

The disturbed noise resounds here and there.

Headman stands up and shouts:

"Everybody clear off both sides! Be quiet and keep order!"

Headman, the inside-duty trusty, the Chief Prisoner, and the Old Man all walk to the door of the toilet. A young man with a bald head, wearing only slacks and no sweater, is lying with his eyes wide open and his head turned to the other side.

The Old Man sits down and puts one hand on his nose. He crawls out and puts his ears on the chest of the dead man.

He stands up and says to Headman:

"In fact, his dying moment was when he was delirious, babbling and moaning. We'd better carry him to another place ourselves."

Two trusties carry the dead body and put it on the platform, close to the wall of the toilet.

The inside-duty trusty runs to the door and shouts: "Report to the Cadre! There is a death in Room 14!"

He calls for help a dozen times. Nobody answers.

From the end of the room, people are noisily discussing the situation:

"He was only in for one week!"

"His hometown is Bất Bạt, Sởn Tây Province."

"He was discharged from the army."

"He told everybody he was taken into custody because he accused the agricultural cooperative leadership of corruption."

"Is he married?"

"The day before yesterday, when he said he was sick, the prison medic slapped him, saying that he was just pretending to be ill."

As morning breaks, a kitchen helper is walking in the yard to take back the water can as usual. The inside-duty trusty runs outside and asks the kitchen guy for help:

"Please inform the cadre that there is a dead man in Room 14."

The kitchen guy is calm:

"I've not seen anyone yet. If I see someone, I'll inform him."

For a while, the Old Man sits silently, as his memory returns. He says to Headman:

"Check and see if he has clothes and tell someone to put the clothes on for him."

Walking toward the end of the room, Headman breaks the silence:

"Where are the clothes of the dead man?"

A lame man shakily stands up:

"Report to you. He has only a shirt. For pants, he has torn them up to clean his anus after emptying his bowels. All that remains is here."

The lame man holds up the shirt and the pants that have only one leg left.

"Put the shirt on him."

The lame man walks to the corpse and sets it upright. The 'inoperative watches, broken watches' guy is eager to lend a helping hand.

"I want to put my own pants on him. Is this okay?"

"You have extra pants? You're an acquaintance of him outside?"

The lame man looks sorrowful:

"I'm not. But he lay next to me for more than one week and we were neighboring friends."

"Okay. Put them on him."

Click-click! The sound of someone unlocking the door is heard.

Headman quickly runs to the door:

"Report to Cadre, one man has died."

Two prison wardens, wearing gauze masks, enter the room:

"Where's he lying?"

"Report to you. He lies over there."

All the prisoners give way and keep utmost quiet. A cadre holds up a camera and takes picture of the dead man. Three shots in a row.

"Carry him out to the yard!"

Two trusties, one grasping the shoulders while the other holding both legs, carry the dead man outside. The 'inoperative-watches, broken-watches' guy takes off his shirt while running after them:

"Take this shirt and cover his face!"

The Chief Prisoner chides him:

"You have only one shirt. When you have to go to the camp, are you going without your shirt? Here, take this mosquito net and cover him."

The Chief Prisoner throws the net to one of the trusties. The corpse is put in the middle of the yard. The yellowish net covers the whole dead body.

"Run in quickly!"

The trusties hurriedly run into the room, pulling the door shut. *Click-click!* A prison warden clicks the key. Then both of them take off their masks before walking away.

The Old Man says to the Chief Prisoner in a broken voice:

"Well, human love still exists and does not quite disappear in this wretched and brutal life. From now on, let's pay more attention to the 'inoperative-watches, broken-watches' guy and the lame man."

"We honor your order, Big Brother! Where is the 'smoke and fire' man? Fire a smoke to chase the coldness of death out of this room!"

Again, the group makes a circle. The ceremony of firing shots solemnly starts.

"Hey, lame and 'inoperative watches, broken watches' guys, you come here!"

Realizing that they are called by the Chief Prisoner, both men come closer, shaking with fear:

"What's our fault?"

"Sit down on the floor. Today we must punish you!"

The two prisoners, still trembling, sit down on the floor and implore:

"Please forgive us if we did something wrong!"

The Chief Prisoner bursts out laughing:

"Can't forgive you! Today we must punish you. Each should draw on his pipe, get high in tobacco and then fall down!"

The men's faces break into smiles:

"Thank you! Thank you!"

The 'smoke and fire' man puts a small-sized cigarette into the mouth of each man, and gives the order:

"Breathe in and draw it to the end!"

All the prisoners in the room stare at the guys and the two red-hot cigarettes, which are burning strongly and spreading rapidly. Upon finishing a long drag, the two guys fall flat on the floor. Their eyes are dimming and their mouths are drooling with water. Seeing that the whole room is staring, the Chief Prisoner declares:

"Tonight, each of you is allowed a free smoke!"

All the prisoners are shouting with joy:

"Hooray for the Chief Prisoner! Hooray for the Chief Prisoner!"

One man, too excited, shouts:

"Long live the Chief Prisoner of Room 14!"

The Chief Prisoner protests:

"Long live for me to end my life here this way! What the hell are you wishing me?" The whole room bursts out laughing

Clang. Seven o'clock. The door of the room is opened. Another day begins like hundreds of other days. The inside-duty trusty orders groups of 20 prisoners to go and wash their faces at the small water tank. Each gets just two bowls of water. Two trusties fetch a stretcher, put the corpse on it, and carry it outside. When they pass the watch officer's room under the grapevine trellis, they put the stretcher close to another dead body. In the watch officer's room, beneath the portrait of Chairman Hồ, large, dark red words read: TREAT THE DISEASE AND CURE THE PATIENT.

A female nurse of the security force smiles amorously to the guard on duty:

"When did they die, my dear?"

"They're like a group of hogs piled up on each other. Who knows when they will die?"

Two trusties are given the order to carry the corpses onto the penitentiary truck.

The administrative director is merry in his sky-blue sleeveless shirt. Throwing his cigarette stub into the brick yard, he asks the medic:

"The day before yesterday, which hospital did you bring these dead men to?"

"Report to you, the Chief. To the Saint Paul Hospital, Hospital 108."

"Today, bring them to Bạch Mai and Vietnamese-German Hospitals. Remember to scatter them to hospitals throughout the city. Keep the number of the dead secret!"

"Report to you, the Chief. I have been scattering them that way."

The prison medic climbs onto the truck and sits next to the driver. He puts the files of the two deceased on his knees. The trusties are dismissed.

The truck slowly drives away, carrying two prisoners who have been "cured of all diseases" out of the Hanoi Hilton …

They confiscate everything, shoes and sandals
forcing one to go barefoot
Toilet paper, no, throw everything away!
The Hanoi Hilton being the closest to Communist leaders
Men are the closest to beasts!
At the Hanoi Hilton toilet paper is hard to come by
So many prisoners dispense with it, living like dogs,
Like buffaloes
For it takes lots of tactful diplomacy and gifts
Before one can secure some—it's harder even than
securing a plane ticket![3]

STORY 7

A Choice

Dear Uncle,

Reading a book I borrowed from you about Nazi concentration camps reminds me of my sick days in the winter of 1985 at the clinic at Hỏa Lò Prison, better known to the outside world as the Hanoi Hilton.

Though we call it a clinic, it is just 5 meters long and 3 meters wide. No windows. Completely closed. The main door to the yard is open only during office hours. Patients are strictly forbidden to look outside. The floor of the house, covered with rough layers of cement, has a nauseous stench. Of course, no medic or nurse likes to enter the room.

The ward has six single beds, two and one-half feet wide, each for two patients. Three of us who have tuberculosis and another patient with heart failure occupy two beds at the end of the room. There are no electric lights, so it is always dark, damp, and cold. We have the feeling of lying in a temporary grave, waiting perpetually to be buried.

At about eight o'clock one morning, I still remember clearly, the sky is as dark as our skin. It is winter. The floor, the roof, the walls, the beds, all exude coldness. Twelve patients are all evildoers and thieves. No one gets supplies or has warm clothes. Everyone is covered with only a thin blanket, so we curl together and tremble.

A trusty calls people out to receive medicine. We go, leaning against one another. The medic, sitting near a bowl of red-hot coal,

---

"A Choice" was translated by Vann Saroyan Phan from the original Vietnamese "Một Lựa Chọn" in *Hỏa Lò* (2001).

is chit-chatting with his young nurse. Seeing us, the nurse smiles and says to the medic:

"Look at them! The dying one is helping the one about to die."

The patient who has heart failure gets a shot of Ouabain. Those who have dysentery get a shot of Emitine. Those of us with tuberculosis get pills to swallow on the spot, each with five INH pills. Plain water makes us cold as it goes down the throat. The patients avidly look at the pot of hot coals at the medic's feet.

I believe that if that pot of coal were a brazier, I would jump onto it to burn myself. That would burn away my hunger, my coldness, my illness, and my incarceration. It would end my misery and everything else.

Among the patients is a man with severe diarrhea. His pants are dirtied with excrement. He is too weak to live. His eyes are dull. He sits flatly on the yard, bending his head over his knees. When I help him to his feet and walk him into the medication room, the medic holds his nose and says to the trusty:

"Bring him out to take a bath and wash his clothes!"

I help walk the patient to the round water tank and pull down his pants. The trusty dips the pants into the tank, shakes them and throws them to me so that I can squeeze them to dry. He fills a bucket with water and splashes the man on his belly and buttocks, which makes his clothes wet. Each time the water is poured on him, the man moans and trembles with his body in a spasm.

I put his clothes on for him, take him back to the clinic ward and have him drink three Ganidan tablets. He falls down on his bed, The patient who shares the bed with him puts a blanket over his body. We are so cold, we have to huddle in pairs and curl ourselves in blankets.

At about ten o'clock, the kitchen helper (a trusty prisoner) brings a pot of cooked rice and a pot of brine to our place. We bring out our bowls. The trusty distributes the rice. He counts the bowls and finds out there are only eleven. That means one bowl is missing. I shake the man with diarrhea under the blanket to wake him up. He is motionless; his body is stiff.

I take his share of rice and divide it into eleven equal parts. A moment later, the medic and two trusties come in with a stretcher to carry the dead man away. How can we still feel hungry even though we are very ill? A meal of half a bowl of cooked rice is emptied right away. Nobody dares ask for gruel, which is merely liquid and very thin. If they take gruel, they will simply empty it through urination.

A few days later, three men with dysentery fall down dead. That evening, when one of the men with dysentery breathes his last breath, his five friends—too afraid to utter a word—lie down together. Two hours later two more are dead. The three men who survive are consoled that living or dying is just a game of destiny.

For nearly one month, I witnessed many people dying or being sent to the clinic. Most of them had dysentery or diarrhea. One man got syphilis. His hair fell out, leaving his head completely bare. This man was a country lad who, out of hunger, went to town to earn his living. Not knowing how to work as a thief, he frequented restaurants to lick at dishes to satisfy his hunger. Actually, there was nothing left for him to lick out there. Only a little bit leftover from bowls of noodle soups, Hà Nội or Huế style. Rarely were there those who intentionally left something for him or anyone else to lick!

He told everyone about his first days in Hà Nội. One night, he sat alone in the Botany Garden with nothing to eat. A girl who came and sat near him showed her love to him. This was the first and only time he knew a woman. And he got the disease. He was caught and sent to the Hanoi Hilton in a government campaign to rout all the homeless and those without identification papers. He did not have a chance to go to a concentration camp before he died. The night he was dying, everybody took pity on him. He murmured a song his mother used to chant to him when he was a child:

> *Leaving behind the boat, the oars and the river, the boat girl went away for marriage.*

Do you think he died of syphilis? No. He died of dysentery. He caught the disease from other people. The toilet is at the end of the room where those of us with tuberculosis are lying. Men with dysentery or diarrhea often dirty their pants with excrement because they cannot wait for their turn. They ask for a chamber pot, but the medic says no. Even in a cell shared by two men, there is only a pot made of iron or rubber. Later on, the trusty brings in a bucket made of metal sheet to avoid the tough task of cleaning up after the men.

All of us stood aghast at the sight of three or four men competing for one toilet bucket with their bony buttocks aiming at the target.

In fact, it was not very cold that winter. It was only eleven or twelve degrees centigrade on the coldest days. But we felt terribly cold. In the morning when we went out to receive medication, while looking at the weak sunshine on the tropical almond trees with their rusty-colored branches and leaves, we thought of our decayed bodies as withering like these leaves. They might fall down from the branches at any time!

One Saturday night, the man with heart failure lying next to me began to confide his secrets to me. Choked with tears, he tried to speak, and I believed that he had been wrongly accused. Everyone thinks that, having raped an old lady, he is a man who never spares a child or an elder. He said that was completely not true. He used to be a history teacher at a junior high school, a bachelor who had never married. His parents were working at the Hòn gai coal mine. Both were Party members. The principal and Party secretary of his school was a woman over fifty, short and fat, with grey hair. Her husband was an army colonel stationed in Cambodia for what they called an international duty. The old lady used to offer him cigarettes, tea and MSG, and sometimes coupons for sugar and meat. She told everybody she just cared for him as a younger brother. Because she was kind to him, so was he to her.

That morning, all the teachers were bringing school children to a visit at Uncle Hồ's Mausoleum. She told him to stay at school so that they could discuss his promotion to Party membership. To become a Party member was his life-long dream. He was overjoyed. She led him to her office and locked the door carefully. She made tea and prepared some cakes for him. When he was drinking, she went behind him to embrace him, putting his head against her breasts. And she tried to kiss him several times. Overwhelmed with fear, he begged her not to do so. A Party secretary like her should not set a bad example. Anyhow, if they were caught doing this, it would be a disaster. She giggled and chided him. "What's the use of being a role model?" she asked him. "Even such big bosses as Lê Duẩn, Võ Nguyên Giáp, Nguyễn Thị Bình, and Nguyễn Thị Định were changing bed partners! Revolutionary figures were human, too."

At last, he yielded to her. From that time on, she took care of him. She even gave him money to buy a bicycle and a watch. One day at noontime, when the two were making love, they were caught in the act by the students looking through the window while climbing a ladder to whitewash the walls. Afraid, she begged him to confess that he had raped her, otherwise her husband would shoot him and then shoot her. Then there were her children. They were all Party members, and she could not dishonor her family with such a horrible act. He was alone, so he should take pity on her and say that he had just attempted to rape her.

Thinking of her good feelings toward him, he reluctantly admitted his 'crime.' And he was sent to the Hanoi Hilton. He said his crime was adultery, not rape. He was quite passive. He complained that since the day he was put into prison, his parents had denied him. The old lady he loved did not send him supplies. As long-term inmates with much experience, we explained to him that she was not his relative and could not send him supplies. How could she, on behalf of a rape victim, feed a man who had raped her? So, even though he was charged with adultery only, he had to serve time in prison. He was right to confess that he had raped her. Bringing her into this case wouldn't help him but would harm her because she was really in love with him. And he understood what we explained to him. But he remained lying on his belly, sobbing.

All three of us who have tuberculosis are sitting together wrapped in a blanket. All the patients in the clinic sit in the same manner, except for the one with heart failure and others who are too weak. All of us tremble as if attacked by malaria. The blankets are foul. Once a year, after hundreds of patients have used them, these blankets are briefly doused instead of being washed. We have to put these filthy blankets over our faces and our heads. The cold comes though to the marrow of our bones. It is like a needle pushed in to ulcerous skin. It would be better if we could have some logs to burn away the cold as well as the smell of death. Then the living air would hold on and warm up everything. Such a wish is like dreaming of summer in the middle of winter, or sunshine in the middle of the dark night!

At about midnight, the man who is leaning against my back suddenly coughs and spits blood on my shoulder. We come out of the blanket and help him to the toilet bucket. He spits out nearly half a liter of blood. The blood is fresh and red and looks like broken pieces of lung. We call for help. After a while, the trusty in charge of the clinic arrives. He stands outside and keeps complaining that Vitamin K, which is good at stopping bleeding, has run out. He suggests that we wait until Monday when he can inform the medic. We have no choice but to lead him back to his bed. I sit with my back against the wall. He is leaning against my chest, with both hands tightly grasping the man sitting in front of him. His fever grows higher. His body is so hot that we feel warmer. All of us sit this way for the whole night. Someone is lucky enough to be able to take a nap.

Once in a while, those with dysentery and diarrhea stand up and go to the sheet metal bucket to defecate. The smell of excrement dominates the room. Then there are some who fall down and cry because they happen to sit on a broken bed. The armed guards patrolling outside never look into the clinic. They understand that these dying men will never have enough strength to climb up to the roof and flee by jumping down. From time to time we ask ourselves whether dawn has broken or not. Everybody wishes it would soon be sunrise. When you have the sun, you'll feel warmer. And then you'll have a bowl of cooked rice.

Thinking of rice, we feel our stomachs tortured by hunger. We're always hungry. In fact, swallowing a cold bowl of rice often makes us feel colder, and the cold seems to be increasing. The stomach is stimulated, and we're even hungrier. We are tortured more and feel more miserable. During the winter, when we don't have to face the danger of being attacked by bedbugs, we have to deal with body lice. They bite and we feel itchy, and we scratch all the time. The rashes break out. Our fingernails are filled with blood.

The next morning is Sunday, and we cannot go out to get medication. I leave the prisoner who spat blood against the wall so that I can go to the toilet to evacuate my bowels. I do this only once a week because there is not much to eat. Afterwards, I come to the bed of the man with heart failure. I intend to advise him to write home and ask his parents to sell his bicycle so that they can have money to buy him food and supplies. He had a watch and a fountain pen, but he already surrendered them to the jailer upon his arrival in prison.

These things are considered lost because nobody could ever take back what they have given to jailers! Now he is lying there with the blanket over his body. I lift the blanket and find that he is dead. His eyes are wide open and white, his mouth out of shape.

As I am about to go to inform the guards, one of my tubercular friends stands up and stops me, whispering into my ears:

"If we inform them about his death now, the kitchen will certainly cut his meal. Let's wait until after meal time!"

I agree with him about the good idea. Those who have dysentery and diarrhea are still sitting with blankets over their bodies and don't know anything. So, three of us who have tuberculosis can have four portions of a meal. Anyhow, it's not a big deal if we let them know about the death some hours later. Once in a while, to make sure no one becomes suspicious of anything, my friend comes near the corpse and says some encouraging words to the dead person:

"Very tired, huh? Try to get some sleep. Tomorrow, you'll have some medicine. Don't worry!"

When the feeding trusty brings the meals to the room, the dead man's bowl is placed in the waiting line:

"Just stay there and take a rest. I'll help put your bowl in line!"

Those with dysentery and diarrhea eat and quickly finish their meals, not forgetting to drink a lot of water so that their stomachs fill. This is the only way we can overcome hunger. The water is so cold, we shiver while sitting against one another waiting for dinner.

Three of us sit around the dead body with four portions of breakfast in front of us. As I strongly believe in the human soul, I silently pray and invite the deceased to come back, forgive us and have lunch with us. The additional portion of meal is evenly divided among three of us, and we feel a little bit warmer in our stomachs. If you have never been tortured by hunger in prison, you can't know the importance of just a spoonful of rice in life. Some may break their friends' skulls for just that.

At noon, I plan to report the death. My friend, too greedy, insists on waiting until nightfall so that we can have another portion of food for dinner. I decide not to follow his advice because I'm afraid of being shackled when the truth is finally revealed. At the clinic, anyone found violating regulations—smoking, for example—will be in stocks for a week, even though he or she is seriously ill. Some have died while in stocks that way. So, I fake panic and shout as I walk out of the door. The trusty in charge of the clinic goes to inform the medic. One hour later, the warden on duty leads in two trusties with a stretcher, and they take the dead man away. I don't see the medic or the nurse.

My friend gets mad at me. His face is red with anger. But he dares not speak because he is afraid that our cheating could be revealed to the outside. To me, the plan to get an extra portion of meal like that is a success.

I believe in destiny. If I had had to stay longer at the clinic, I would have died, either of tuberculosis or of dysentery. But in the early hours of the following day, the man who coughed up blood and I are ordered to move to another prison. We share the same shackles. The truck packed with prisoners leaves Hà Nội and heads south.

When the truck arrives at Phù Lí, my friend spits nearly a liter of blood and dies right on the truck. Perhaps it is because the truck jolts too much on the way. Yet the armed guards don't bother to unlock the handcuffs. The dead body is wedged between the men for three hours. At Camp Thanh Phong, they finally unlock the shackles and carry the dead man away.

There are captive former South Vietnamese officers at this camp who have been continually shuffled from camp to camp so that they will not organize escape. These men give me medicine and food from supplies their families have brought during their visits to the prison camps. Some of them are put in stocks simply because they are caught throwing me sorghum to eat. Thanks to their love and care, I survive once again.

Prison has taught me to be patient and well-prepared to suffer. I treasure life. In the last analysis, it's better to live than die. But, to be sincere, if I were to serve another twelve years prison time with a life full of misery and shame and worse than that of an ox or a pig, I definitely would choose death.

Please remember me to the family,

Affectionately,
Your Nephew

Poet, my friend,
You must know how to keep your soul always unsullied
Like that proverbial pink lotus that spreads fragrance even in the midst of slime,
Like a lone star shining in the pristine night sky
Twinkling far, far away, and glistening with dew …
You must also know, friend,
How to live in this world as if you were deathless
Despite all its misery and cold, dangers and tragedies
And though your body may be ravaged by illnesses and shrinking by the day.
Your spirit must still be stronger than rock or steel
Standing firm in the midst of destructive time.
Only then can you let your poetic mind roam free
Flying high and wide even in an iron trap.
As for dying or getting out of here
That's heaven's decision, not one that is up to you![1]

H. In prison—Nguyễn Chí Thiện at Ba Sao Prison Camp, 13 July 1991

Photo was taken during a conversation with the Chief of Security (hand visible) three months before his release. At the time Thiện weighed less than ninety pounds. Thiện requested a copy of the photo as a souvenir and later used it for the cover for a book of his poetry, *Hoa Địa Ngục, Tạp 2*, prepared in 1996 in the United States. The photograph was part of the Vietnamese/American Heritage Project exhibition at the Smithsonian Institution in early 2007. (Security agent at Ba Sao Prison Camp.)

I. At work on the Hỏa Lò stories, Paris, 2000

Writing the *Hỏa Lò/Hanoi Hilton Stories* was supported by a fellowship from the International Parliament of Writers in 1998. The photograph, taken in 2000, shows the ministrations of villagers in rural France who brought him goats' milk to increase his strength. (Courtesy of the International Parliament of Writers)

Notes

STORY 1

A Short Ride

Phong Quang name of a village in Lào Cai Province. There was a huge prison here, right next to the Chinese border.

Phú Thọ a province in the mid-region of North Vietnam.

Yên Bái a province in the highlands of North Vietnam.

Concentration camps Some prison camps were established by the French during colonization and others as border security outposts for the Japanese Army occupation in World War II. They were expanded when the Gulag system was imposed by Hồ Chí Minh and the Vietnamese Communist Party (VCP) following the Revolution of August, 1945. Prisoners were shuffled between camps in order to keep them from forming associations for escape. See Nghia M. Vo, *The Bamboo Gulag; Political Imprisonment in Communist Vietnam* (McFarland 2004) for an excellent map of the concentration prison labor camps throughout North Vietnam and South Vietnam.

Hải Phòng second largest city and major port of North Vietnam

Hỏa Lò a furnace or kiln with extreme interior heat. The Vietnamese name for the Hà Nội Central Prison, built by the French in 1898.

Vũ Thư Hiên Vietnamese writer, author of *Miền Thơ Ấu* [Land of Childhood] and *Đêm Giữa Ban Ngày* [Night in the Middle of Day]. Imprisoned for nine years (1967–1976) for supposed involvement in the 'anti-Party revisionist plot.' Currently living in Paris.

Lê Quang Dũng poet, imprisoned for 16 years. Currently living in Hà Nội.

Captain Kiều Duy Vĩnh a captain in Bảo Đại's National Army of Việt Nam, he was imprisoned for 15 years. A writer, he now lives in Hà Nội.

Hồ Chí Minh (1890–1969) supreme leader of the Communist Party Việt, President of the Democratic Republic of Việt Nam (1945–69).

Kim Bông name of war-horse in Phùng Cung's short story, "Con ngựa già của Chúa Trịnh" [Lord Trịnh's Old War-horse], 1956.

Sơn Nam Thượng ancient name of present-day Sơn Tây Province.

Phùng Cung poet (1928–1997) living in Hà Nội, author of the short story "Con ngựa già của Chúa Trịnh" [Lord Trịnh's Old War-horse], first published in *Nhân Văn* No. 4 (1956). He is also the author of two other poetry collections, *Xem Đêm* ('Watching the Night') and *Trăng Ngục* ('Prison Moon'), which are recently published together with his other posthumous writings in California and Canada.

Nguyễn Công Giân brother of the author Nguyễn Chí Thiện, lieutenant colonel in the Army of the Republic of Viêt Nam (South Vietnam). Because of his strong linguistic skills, he was involved with training South Vietnamese officers in the United States in the 1950s. He served in the military delegation representing the government of South Vietnam during the Paris Peace Accords of 1972. Imprisoned by the Communists for thirteen years beginning in 1975, he emigrated to the United States with his family in 1993 and assisted with the author's immigration in 1995.

1 Nguyễn Chí Thiện, "A Sudden Train Whistle" (1985). Translated by Nguyễn Ngọc Bích in *Blood Seeds Become Poetry*, p. 15.

2 Resolution No. 49, dated June 29, 1961, was voted into law by the Vietnamese National Assembly under the orders of Hồ Chí Minh., the president of the Democratic Republic of Việt Nam. The resolution allowed security police to send 'bad, dangerous elements' to concentration camps for reeducation for up to three years without any trial. In reality, this three-year term would be repeated indefinitely, which is why many lived in concentration camps three, four, and even five times three years. After this infamous Resolution, North Vietnam became a huge prison.

3 *History of the August Revolution* ('Cách Mạng Tháng Tám 1945', Sự Thật Publishing House) was republished in English by the Foreign Languages Publishing House in Hà Nội in 1972. The pages that credit the Soviet Union with the surrender of Japan are 110–12.

4 *Nhân Văn* [Humanities Magazine] was published in Hà Nội in 1956. Writers such as Phan Khôi, Nguyễn Hữu Đang, Hoàng Cầm, Lê Đạt, Trần Dần, Phùng Cung, Phùng Quán, wrote short stories, poems, and

essays demanding freedom for artists and stopping the brutal intervention of the Party into literary matters. Hồ Chí Minh forbade the magazine after five issues. Many writers and poets were sentenced to hard labor and after that were not allowed to write for three decades. The magazine was very popular among city people, especially among students and intellectuals. The controversy of the relationship of Vietnamese writers to Marxist-Leninism is analyzed in 1982 by Nhử Phong, "Intellectuals, Writers and Artists"; in *North Vietnam Today*, edited by P.J. Honey, 70–92, New York: Praeger; and in 1992 by Hirohide Kuihara, in "Changes in the Literary Policy of the Vietnamese Workers' Party, 1956-1958"; in *Indochina in the 1940s and 1950, Volume II*, edited by Takahashi Shiraishi and Motoo Furuta, 165–93. Ithaca: Southeast Asia Program Cornell University, 1992.

5 Nguyễn Chí Thiện, "Winter Rushed In," (1970), translated by Hằng T. Nguyễn, in *The Will of a Vietnamese*, p. 45.

6 Several references to recent histories in English that contain conclusions that Vietnamese Communists deliberately practiced starvation as genocide:

Anne Applebaum, *Gulag; A History* (Doubleday, 2003). Winner of the Pulitzer Prize for nonfiction in 2004. The prison camps of North Vietnam were created from the Soviet system.

Quang X. Phạm. *A Sense of Duty; My Father, My American Journey* (Ballantine, 2005). Details of prison reeducation camps in Việt Nam after 1975.

Cao Ngọc Phượng, "A Form of Torture: Food Deprivation" from *The Indochina Newsletter* (Burlingame, California: Feb.–March, 1982.) . The author recites the poetry of Nguyễn Chí Thiện which was, at that moment, becoming known to the world while he was imprisoned at Hỏa Lò.

Stuart Rochester, Richard I. Kiley. *Honor Bound; American Prisoners of War in Southeast Asia, 1961–1973*. (History Dept., U.S. Secretary of Defense, 1998). Best succinct definitions of security and police practice of deliberate starvation and torture as policy in North Vietnamese prisons.

Richard H. Schultz, Jr. *The Secret War Against Hanoi; Kennedy's and Johnson's Use of Spies, Saboteurs, and Covert Warriors in North Vietnam.* (HarperCollins, 1999). Schultz calls Vietnam "a counterintelligence state" based on the Soviet model.

Nghia M. Vo. *The Bamboo Gulag: Political Imprisonment in Communist Vietnam* (McFarland, 2004). Nguyễn Chí Thiện is regularly mentioned and quoted and thanked by the author for his contributions.

Martin Windrow. *The Last Valley: Dien Bien Phu and the French Defeat in Vietnam* (Da Capo Press, 2004). Windrow, a British historian, writes of development of the security state by Hồ Chí Minh; very detailed chapter on the fate of 36,979 prisoners of war between 1946 and 1954 (71% were unaccounted for, including 91% of all Vietnamese POWS).

7 Nguyễn Chí Thiện and his brother, Nguyễn Công Giân, did not see each other for forty-three years. The poet was met by his brother and his family at the Dulles Airport when he flew from Vietnam to immigrate to the United States in November 1995.

8 Testimony of Nguyễn Chí Thiện to the U. S. House Committee on International Relations, November 8, 1995. The full text of these remarks, translated by Nguyễn Ngọc Bích, is on page 272.

9 Peter Zinoman. *The Colonial Bastille: A History of Imprisonment in Vietnam 1862–1940.* (Berkeley: University of California Press, 2001), p. 52. This excellent history is the source of many historical comments in this volume.

10 English language version: *A Heroic People: Memoirs from the Revolution.* 2nd edition. (Hanoi: Foreign Languages Publishing House, 1965).

11 *I Chose Freedom* was written by Kravtchenko who fled from Russia to the United States. *The Devil in Paradise* and *Back from Russia* were written by André Gide, a French writer who told of his disillusion after a three-month visit to Russia.

12 The poems of Nguyễn Chí Thiện were first published in a Vietnamese language journal in the United States, *Văn Nghệ Tiền Phong*, in May 1980. The first, in book form, was anonymous under the name *Tiếng Vọng Từ Đáy Vực* ('Echo From an Abyss'), Nguyễn Hữu Hiệụ, ed. (Arlington, VA.: Thời Tập, 1980). A second edition in Vietnamese came out in 1981 under the title *Bản Chúc Thư Của Một Người Việt Nam* (Arlington, VA: Văn Nghệ Tiền Phong). A few poems from the first collection were translated and published by Nguyễn Ngọc Bích in *AsiaWeek* in 1982, entitled "A Voice from the Hanoi Underground." The manuscript inscription was first published in English in June 1982, translated by the *Index on Censorship London*, vol. 11 (3). The author's original title, *Flowers from Hell/Hoa Địa-Ngục*, was adopted in 1984 by the Council on Southeast Asia Studies at Yale University for its bilingual edition of the poems translated by Huỳnh Sanh Thông. A book-length English translation of the poems by Hằng T. Nguyễn, entitled *The Will of a Vietnamese, the Poetry of Nguyen Chi*

Thien (New York: Carlton Press) was published in 1984. In 1996, three new collections were published: *Hoa Địa Ngục, tập 2 (Hạt Máu Thơ)* by the author (in Vietnamese), soon after his immigration to the United States. These were the poems composed and committed to memory at the Hỏa Lò prison between 1979 and 1985 and in the prison camps from 1985 to 1991 (although none were composed after 1988 due to the author's extreme debilitation from starvation). This collection was translated and published by Nguyễn Ngọc Bích, as *Flowers of Hell II/Hoa Địa Ngục II; Blood Seeds Become Poetry.* A complete English translation of the poetry of Nguyễn Chí Thiện by Nguyễn Ngọc Bích under the title *The Flowers of Hell/Hoa Địa Ngục*, in which the original inscription in French is printed in facsimile and in English translation was published in Arlington, VA by Tổ Hợp Xuất Bản Miền Đông Hoa Kỳ, 1996. The first complete edition of the poems, in Vietnamese only, *Hoa Địa-Ngục*, was published by Nguyễn Ngọc Bích in Arlington, VA in 2006.

STORY 2

Revolutionary Songs

Guan Yunzhang Chinese general of the Three Kingdoms period (220–280), known for his loyalty, later worshipped as a protective saint.

Nguyễn Xuân Sanh hermetic Vietnamese poet, born in 1920, now living in Hà Nội.

Đoàn Phú Tứ poet and playwright (1909–1989), and a representative to the first National Assembly of Vietnam (elected in 1946).

Huỳnh Tấn Phát Secretary General of the NFL, short for National Liberation Front for South Vietnam, which was set up in 1960 to disguise the aggression from the North.

Professor Vũ Văn Canh taught at the University of Hà Nội.

Hoàng Văn Thụ Politburo member, ICP. Sentenced to death, he was executed by the French in 1944. While in Hỏa Lò, he was kept in cell no. 1.

Trần Đăng Ninh Central Committee member, ICP, who shared a cell with Hoàng Văn Thụ in Hỏa Lò and who later wrote an article recalling the last days of Hoàng Văn Thụ.

Tố Hữu Politburo member, CPV, and the poet laureate of Communist Vietnam (1920–2002).

1 "Tết, the Lunar New Year" by Nguyễn Chí Thiện (1984), translated by Nguyễn Ngọc Bích in *Blood Seeds Become Poetry*, p. 63

2 'The Lunar New Year in Viêtnam and among Vietnamese people in the diaspora of three million people since 1975. Tết, when followed by the name of the event it celebrates, means 'festival' in Vietnamese. Thus, Tết Trung-Thu is the Mid-Autumn Festival of the Children in Vietnam, or Tết Đoan-ngọ is the Insect Festival. When it stands alone, however, Tết is an abbreviated form for Tết Nguyên Đán, New Year Festival.' Nguyễn Ngọc Bích, *Tết! The Vietnamese New Year* (East Coast U.S.A. Vietnamese Publishing Consortium, 2004).

3 The name of a coterie of poets known by their publication, *Xuân Thu Nhã Tập* (*The Spring and Autumn Elegant Collection*). They advocated a kind of hermetic poetry.

4 Peter Zinoman, *The Colonial Bastille: A History of Imprisonment in Vietnam 1862–1940* (University of California Press, 2001) is an excellent source for the building of the prison system under French colonization and the experience of the Communist revolutionaries. Although many prisoners were beaten and executed by the French, the policy of starvation in the Gulag model was not adopted until the Vietnamese Communists took control in 1954.

5 Lyrics of a famous song by Trịnh Công Sơn, the antiwar composer of South Vietnam.

6 The revolutionary songs: The national anthem of North Vietnam, known as "Forward Soldiers" ('*Tiến Quân Ca*' in Vietnamese), by the composer Văn Cao. The signal song of Radio Hà Nội, '*Diệt Phát Xít*' ("Let's Kill the Fascists") by Nguyễn Đình Thi. Refrain from another song by Văn Cao, '*Chiến Sĩ Lục Quân Việt Nam*' ("Vietnamese Infantry Song").

7 "From Ape to Man," by Nguyễn Chí Thiện (1967), translated by Nguyễn Ngọc Bích, in *Flowers of Hell II*, 219.

STORY 3

The Moon and Waters of the Red River

Trường Chinh (1907–1988) Secretary-General, CVP (1943–1956), Politburo member, Chairman of the DRV (then SRV) National Assembly.

Hoàng Văn Thụ Politburo member, ICP. Sentenced to death, he was executed by the French in 1944. While in Hỏa Lò, he was kept in cell no. 1.

Trần Đăng Ninh Central Committee member, ICP, he shared a cell with Hoàng Văn Thụ in Hỏa Lò and later wrote an article recalling the last days of Hoàng Văn Thụ.

Phạm Hùng Politburo member, CPV, he once held the prime minister's position and was Minister of Public Security.

Phan Bội Châu Probably the most illustrious revolutionary of early twentieth-century Vietnam (1867–1940). In 1925 while being kept in cell no. 1 in Hỏa Lò, he was sentenced to death. This brought a nationwide uproar that forced the French colonialists to commute his sentence to life. Thereafter he was kept under surveillance in Huế until his death in 1940. Hồ Chí Minh, whom he considered like a nephew, was the one who sold him to the French: using a third person, Hồ had informed the French police so they could arrest him while he was passing through Shanghai in the French concession.

Hoàng Văn Hoan Pro-Chinese Politburo member, CPV; fled to Beijing in 1979.

Red Flag Youths groups of young people whose duty was to maintain the socialist life-style. If your hair was too long, your trousers too large or too tight, they carried scissors to cut them. If you and your lover sat on a bench in a park, kissing each other, they chased you away and blamed you severely.

1 "Once a Death Sentence is Pronounced" by Nguyễn Chí Thiện (1981), translated by Nguyễn Ngọc Bích, in *Blood Seeds Become Poetry,* 43–44.

2 *Our People are Very Heroic* was popular in North Vietnam in the 1950s and 1960s. It is the memoirs of Communist leaders who narrated their prison lives before 1945, under French domination. It was published in English in 1965.

3 Under the Communist regime, 'bad elements' were sent to New Economic Zones in the highlands. Their living conditions were horrible. They had to work very hard, suffered malnutrition, and often died.

Because of food scarcity, many fled back to the cities to find their property had been confiscated by the regime. Therefore they were homeless and became beggers. This policy was enforced especially against women and children in South Vietnam following the fall of Sài Gòn in 1975. With their husbands, brothers, and fathers in the concentration camps for enforced 'reeducation' for many years, the young, elderly, and female were powerless to stop their banishment to New Economic Zones, and they lost their very small homes or subsistence farms to the invaders from the North.

4 From the Introduction of *The Will of a Vietnamese: the Poetry of Nguyễn Chí Thiện,* translated by Hằng T. Nguyễn (1984): 'At the beginning of May, 1981, by chance, I knew about this magnificent book of poems through some articles in the *Van Nghe Tien Phong* magazine. I was quite excited and ordered this book right away .... I gradually read the whole book; the more I read, the more I saw different faces of the Communist and that in this world we didn't have enough words to describe this barbaric Party .... I hope when this book of poems is widely known all over the world, the poet will find that his prediction was not wrong—his poems still have a surplus supply of ammunitions and are shaking the whole universe.'

STORY 4

The Mist

Yên Đổ name of a village in Hà Nam Province. Because he was a native of this village, the famous poet Nguyễn Khuyến, was called the 'Three-time Laureate of Yên Đổ.'

Nghệ An name of a province of Central Vietnam that contained the numbered Camp Z-Eight, considered to be reserved for Chinese spies.

Phố Lu district in Lào Cai province, which held a large prison.

Văn Điển township six kilometers from Hà Nội.

Ninh Bình–Quảng Bình Road the road from Ninh Bình, which is about 80 kilometers south of Hà Nội, and Quảng Bình, the province immediately north of the 17th parallel.

Điện Biên short for Điện Biên Phủ, site of the great French defeat in 1954.

Bắc Ninh Province province immediately to the north of Hà Nội, famed for its Quan Họ tradition of folksinging.

Từ Sơn district in the province of Bắc Ninh.

Lạng Sơn a province next to China's border.

Sông Cầu Cầu River, which flows to the north of Hà Nội.

Pắc Bó cavern in Cao Bằng Province near the Chinese border, where Hồ Chí Minh took as his shelter in 1941; considered thereafter to be a historic site.

Phú Thọ a province in the mid-region of North Vietnam.

Khe Sanh site of a battle near the seventeenth parallel between American troops and the NVA (North Vietnamese Army) in January 1968, precursor to the Tết Offensive in which the ancient capitol at Huế was occupied by the Communists for one month (February 1968), but retaken by South Vietnamese and American forces in early March. The Communists massacred at least 4,000 civilians in Huế at the end of February, burying them (often alive) in pits outside the city.

Việt Minh short name for the Communist front that operated in Vietnam until 1946.

Nhân Dân *People's Daily:* official organ of the Central Committee, CPV.

Buffalo King name of a demon in the famed Chinese novel *Xi You Ji* ('Journey to the West'—or 'Monkey' as translated by Arthur Waley).

General Lê Hữu Qua former director of the Labor Reeducation Department, which was in charge of the whole prison system of North, then of all Vietnam. This means that he oversaw both facilities meant for regular criminals sentenced in court and those who did not have the benefit of a clearcut court sentence (and could therefore remain indefinitely).

Trần Hoàn musician, a former director of the Hải Phòng Bureau of Cultural Affairs.

Liu Bei king of the Western Shu during the Three Kingdoms period (220–285), known for his benevolence and kindness.

Kong Ming famous strategist of the Three Kingdoms period who helped Liu Bei to establish his reign.

Hoàng Công Khanh writer and playwright living in Hà Nội. He was sent to a reeducation camp in Yên Bái near the Chinese border.

Dương Khuê famous poet of the second half of the nineteenth century, a native of Vân Đình village near Hà Nội. He took his doctorate while relatively young under the old imperial examination system.

Vũ Đình Huỳnh private secretary to Hồ Chí Minh, then Protocol Chief at the Ministry of Foreign Affairs. The father of the writer Vũ Thư Hiên, he was imprisoned for six years (1967–1973) because of alleged involvement in the so-called "anti-Party revisionist plot."

Vũ Hoàng Chương Vietnamese poet (1916–1976). Very weak when he was imprisoned by the Communists, he was released after four months only to die almost immediately when he got home.

Simonov Konstantin Simonov, Russian poet.

Voltaire eighteenth-century French writer of the Age of Enlightenment.

Franz Liszt Hungarian composer of the nineteenth century.

George Sand French woman writer of the nineteenth century who used a male pseudonym. Chopin's lover.

Reneù Char twentieth-century French writer.

Tolstoy Leo Tolstoy, Russian novelist of the nineteenth century.

Dostoevski Russian writer and novelist.

Victor Hugo French writer and poet of the nineteenth century who was exiled by France to the island of Guernsey in the English Channel for his political activities. Victor Hugo is considered a saint in an expatriate Vietnamese religious movement that began in the 1920s, the Cao Đài.

Balzac Honoré de Balzac, French writer of the nineteenth century.

Deng Xiaoping Chinese Communist leader, who launched the modernization drive in China.

Brezhnev Leonid Brezhnev, Secretary General of the Communist Party of the Soviet Union.

Gandhi Mahatma Gandhi, Indian politician and leader, who advocated nonviolence and was assassinated in 1948.

Chế Lan Viên famous poet, one of the 'corporals' used by the regime to keep writers and poets in line.

Tô Thị legendary woman in Vietnam who is said to have waited for her husband to come back from a war until she and her infant turned into rock.

Tôn Đức Thắng Central Committee member, CPV (1988–1979); succeeded Hồ Chí Minh as president of Vietnam.

Phạm Văn Đồng Politburo member, CPV (1905–2001); the longest serving prime minister of communist Vietnam, having sat at the post some 33 years.

Lê Duẩn (1907–1986) first secretary of the PCV from 1960–1986.

Qi Gong a Chinese method of deep breathing to keep oneself in good health, to give one's mind tranquility.

1 "My Poetry's Not Mere Poetry, No" by Nguyễn Chí Thiện (1970), translated by Huỳnh Sanh Thông, in *Flowers from Hell*, 63.

2 "The Nghệ An camps were located near the Laotian border. Built a long time ago by the French for the detention of Vietnamese nationalists and now run by guards from the Public Security Agency, they were considered to be the worst camps in the North." Nghia M. Vo, *The Bamboo Gulag; Political Imprisonment in Communist Vietnam* (McFarland, 2004), 104.

3 All the incidents in these stories are true. The Chinese editor whose ankle was broken was chained to the author. His name was Thái Nhũ Siẽu, and the paper, published in Hà Nội, was *Tân Việt Hoa.*

4 "From Apes to Man" by Nguyễn Chí Thiện, translated by Nguyễn Ngọc Bích, in *The Flowers of Hell II*, 219.

5 The scholar Huỳnh Sanh Thông, editor and translator of *To Be Made Over: Tales of Socialist Reeducation in Vietnam* (Yale University Press, 1988) explains the process: "The term 'reeducation' with its pedagogical overtones, does not quite convey the quasi-mystical resonance of *cải-tạo* in Vietnamese. *Cải* [to transform] and *tạo* [to create] combine to literally mean an attempt at 'recreation,' at 'making over' sinful or incomplete individuals." (p. x)

6 "The Game of Mankind" by Nguyễn Chí Thiện (1975) by Nguyễn Ngọc Bích, in *Flowers of Hell II*, 393.

7 According to the Southeast Asian Resource Center, refugee arrivals to the United States from Vietnam following passage of the Refugee Act in 1980 totaled 95,200 for that year alone.

8 "The Swampland" by Nguyễn Chí Thiện (1972), translated by Huỳnh Sanh Thông, in *Flowers from Hell*, 97. The poet predicted the Vietnamese Diaspora that had been caused by Communist rule. That Diaspora is now at least three million people.

9 An American equivalent to the saying 'There's no cock' is 'Where's the beef?'

10 "Uncle Hồ and Uncle Tôn" by Nguyễn Chí Thiện (1970), translated by Nguyễn Ngọc Bích, in *The Flowers of Hell II*, 299.

11 Verse 83 of "A Silent Love" by Nguyễn Chí Thiện, translated by Hằng T. Nguyễn, in *The Will of a Vietnamese*, 82.

STORY 5

Milk Cows

Tố Hữu Politburo member, CPV, and the poet laureate of Communist Vietnam (1920–2002).

1 "For Giving" by Nguyễn Chí Thiện (1981), translated by Nguyễn Ngọc Bích. *Blood Seeds Become Poetry*, 39.

2 A verse from Tố Hữu's poem mourning Hồ Chí Minh when he died in 1969. The poem was printed in *Nhân Dân* [The People's Journal] in September 1969.

STORY 6

Posing as Statues

1 "Scribblings: Quatrains that Occurred to Me over the Years" by Nguyễn Chí Thiện, translated by Nguyễn Ngọc Bích, in *Blood Seeds Become Poetry*, 87.

2 "Leg Irons" from *Prison Diary* by Hồ Chí Minh (1943) translated by Huỳnh Sanh Thông in *Reflections from Captivity*, David G. Marr, editor (Ohio University Press, 1978), 72.

3 "Scribblings," by Nguyễn Chí Thiện, 93.

STORY 7

A Choice

Lê Duẩn (1907–1986) First Secretary of the CPV, from 1960 to 1986.

Võ Nguyễn Giáp General, former Politburo member, CPV, commander of the Điện Biên Phủ battle (1954); born in 1911.

Nguyễn Thị Bình Central Committee member, CPV; head of the Provisional Government of South Việt Nam delegation to the Paris Peace Talks (1968–73).

Nguyễn Thị Định Central Committee member, CPV; Deputy Commander-in-Chief, Liberation Army of South Việt Nam.

1 "Poet, My Friend" by Nguyễn Chí Thiện (1988), translated by Nguyễn Ngọc Bích, in *Blood Seeds Become Poetry*, 49.

Glossary of Prison Language

antenna A surveillant for the prison system

armed guard A soldier who watches prisoners, preventing their escape

bear-head A bully; dominant male prisoner

bloodhound An informer

cadre Any official in the Communist regime

camps Concentration camps; prison labor camps

cells Small room about 3 meters square that imprisons two persons; dark at daytime, but lit by electricity for surveillance at night

driving Sending items from cell to cell by means of string thrown and pulled

dungeon A dark room without light, day and night, used for punishment; contains leg stocks that break prisoner's ankles

handcuffs A fetter to lock two prisoners by their wrists

headman, headwoman Chief prisoner of a communal room (about 200 inmates; one who communicates between jailers and prisoners

informer A prisoner who secretly reports everything to inquirer or prison warden

irons Shackles, fetters

inside Inside the Communal Prison Room; also prisons generally

mỹ-kim Dagger or bayonet made from materials available in prison, such as nails

Old Man Counterrevolutionary inmate; political prisoner

outside Outside the Communal Prison Room; also general society

phenom A female bear-head; dominant female prisoner

rooms A large room where many prisoners live together, separated by gender

rustic tobacco Very heavy tobacco smoked through a water pipe

shackle A fetter for a prisoner's ankles

supervisor The chief administrative official of a prison, or concentration camp

trusty A privileged prisoner, often with policing duties, chosen by the jailers. Vietnamese name: *tu giac;* French name for Vietnamese trusties: *caplans*; Nazi prisoners' name: *Kapos*. All carry the stigma of cooperation with captors and the reputation of brutality toward other inmates.

warden A jailer

Translators

Nguyễn Ngọc Bích is considered one of the foremost interpreters of Vietnamese culture and civilization to the English-speaking world. Contacted by UNESCO in 1959, he produced fifteen years later the first major anthology of Vietnamese poetry in English, entitled *A Thousand Years of Vietnamese Poetry* (Alfred A. Knopf, 1975).

Since then he has devoted much of his time to producing either translations from the Vietnamese or works on various aspects of Vietnamese culture. Among his translations are: *Mother's Lullaby* (a translation of Trương Anh Thuy's *Trường Ca Lời Mẹ Ru*, Cành Nam Publishers, 1989), *War & Exile: A Vietnamese Anthology* (contemporary prose, fiction and poetry, East Coast U.S.A. Vietnamese Abroad PEN Center, 1989), *The Flowers of Hell* (a near complete translation and bilingual edition of Nguyễn Chí Thiện's Hoa *Địa Ngục*, Tổ Hợp XBMĐ Hoa Kỳ, 1996) and *Blood Seeds Become Poetry* (selected poems from Nguyễn Chí Thiện's *Hạt Máu Thơ*, Tổ Hợp XBMĐ Hoa Kỳ, 1996). He also translated from the original French, *Vietnamese Architecture*, by Nguyễn Quang Nhạc and Nguyễn Năng Đắc (Washington, DC: Embassy of Vietnam, and Saigon: Council on Foreign Relations, 1972) and produced a bilingual catalogue on contemporary Vietnamese art, *An Ocean Apart*, for the Smithsonian Institution Traveling Exhibit Service (SITES, 1995).

Among his original writings on Vietnamese culture, the best-known work is *Tet, the Vietnamese New Year* (a fully illustrated work on the best-known festival of Vietnam, Vietnamese Publishers Consortium, 2004). Bích has also appeared in many video presentations on Vietnamese culture, language and education (starring with Charlton Heston and Dick Van Dyke, among others). He consulted with several Smithsonian projects, from the American Folk Life Festivals of 1979 and 1980, to the Museum of Natural History's Southeast Asian Festivals (1987 and 1988), the Kids' Bridge (1989), and SITES' traveling exhibit, "An Ocean Apart" (1995–1998), not excluding Vietnamese cooking. Nguyễn Ngọc Bích was a member of the steering committee of the Vietnamese American Heritage Project for the Smithsonian Institution exhibit, which opened in January 2007.

Trần Văn Điền, born in 1934 in Bùi Chu, North Vietnam, was a teacher of English as a second language for several well-known public and private high schools in Sài-Gòn, such as Gia Long, Hồ ngọc Cẩn, Nguyễn Bá Tòng, Hưng Đạo, from 1956 to 1975. During that time he authored a number of English textbooks, grammars, and English-Vietnamese dictionaries.

Mr. Trần left Viêt-Nam for the United States when Sài-Gòn fell to the communists in April 1975. He resettled with his family in Grand Rapids, Michigan, where he served the Grand Rapids Public Schools as a resource teacher and later as an instructional English teacher for bilingual children from 1975 to 1980. Meanwhile, he authored a series of bilingual folktales of Viêt-Nam and translated many other selected texts from Vietnamese into English. They were published under titles such as *Childhood Memories of Viêt-Nam* and *The Taste of Viêt-Nam*. His purpose is to help Vietnamese students maintain their own language and culture and also to promote the learning of English.

In summer 1980, Mr. Trần moved with his family to California and served the Santa Ana Unified School District as a resource teacher at Valley High School for several years before retiring in the city of Westminster, Orange County. Before translating "The Mist" in Nguyễn Chí Thiện's *Hỏa Lò Tập Truyện* into English, he translated the work of two other authors from the Vietnamese: Đinh Ngọc Quê's *Memoirs of a Priest in the Communist Reeducation Camp* and Minh Vô's *Ngo Dinh Diem: Praise and Blame.*

Mr. Trần graduated from the Faculty of Letters, University of Sài-Gòn in 1957, and from the University of Maryland in 1959. He also earned a Master of Education degree at Grand Valley State Colleges, Allendale, Michigan, in 1977. His son, Trần Thai Văn, is an assemblyman for the 68th District in the state of California, the first Vietnamese-American to be elected to the California legislature and only the second Vietnamese-American to be elected to public office in the United States.

Vann Saroyan Phan, a journalist, writer and author, holds a B.A. in journalism and an M.A. in English from Minnesota State University, Mankato.

Back home in Vietnam, Phan was an English teacher in Đà Nẵng and Sài-Gòn before he was mobilized into the Army of the Republic of Vietnam (ARVN) to become an army officer during the last phases of the Vietnam War (1959–1975).

After a terrible experience in the Vietnamese gulags in postwar Vietnam, Phan immigrated to the United States in 1988, where he became a U.S. citizen who was trained and educated in an American college.

Vann Saroyan Phan's translation career started in 1992 with Agnew Tech II, a multilingual translation company in Westlake Village, California, where he worked until 1996. From 1999 to 2003, he joined KJ International Resources, another multilingual translation company in Minneapolis, Minneosta. Since 2004, Phan has been a translator for IW Group, Inc. in Los Angeles, California.

In public life, from 1999 to 2004, Phan was a member of the board of directors and Secretary General of the Vietnam Center in St. Paul, Minnesota, and from 2001 to 2004, was assistant director of the Vietnamese Social Services of Minnesota in St. Paul.

Vann Saroyan Phan is a popular figure in literacy circles. For more than six years, Phan was editor of the *East Wind, West Wind Quarterly* and *Cultural Diversity News* at Minnesota State University, Mankato (1991–1997). His writings in English and Vietnamese are published in various newpapers and magazines from Mankato and St. Paul to Westminster and San Jose in California. Since 1998, Mr. Phan has been a contributing writer of *Tinh Hoa Magazine* in St. Paul and *Suối Văn Magazine* in San Jose. Vann Saroyan Phan is the author of a collection of short stories in Vietnamese, *Nằm Trong Cơn Gió Vô Tình (Gone with the Merciless Wind)*, published by Tạp Chí Tinh Hoa Publisher in St. Paul in 2001.

Vann Saroyan Phan is now working as a staff writer for the *Người Viêt Daily News* of Westminster in southern California. It is the biggest Vietnamese-language newspaper overseas and has a weekly English edition, *Người Viêt 2*, for which Mr. Phan is a news writer.

Nguyễn Kiếm Phong is a graduate in economics and social work. He has been working in the field of social research and community development in Canada. His personal interests are language learning and evolutionary anthropology. Vietnamese Canadian author and activist Lê Duy Cấn, was instrumental in involving Mr. Phong in the translation of "Phùng Cung," which is excerpted in Chí Thiện's autobiographical "Story One, A Short Ride."

Bibliography

Works by Nguyễn Chí Thiện in English (and bilingual)

Chants de Prison/Prison Songs/Ngục Ca. Poems of Nguyễn Chí Thiện set to music by Phạm Duy, translated to French by Phương Anh and English by Penelope Faulkner. English song versions by Nguyễn Ngọc Bích, with an introduction by Võ Văn Ại and a preface by Pierre Emmanuel. Quê Mẹ (Motherland), Gennevilliers, 1982.

Flowers from Hell (Hoa Địa Ngục). A bilingual edition of poems selected and translated from the Vietnamese by Huỳnh Sanh Thông. Yale University Council on Southeast Asia Studies, New Haven, 1984.

The Will of a Vietnamese: The Poetry of Nguyễn Chí Thiện, translated by Hằng T. Nguyễn. Carleton Press, New York, 1984.

Ngục Ca: Prison Songs. The poems of Nguyễn Chí Thiện set to music by Phạm Duy, with English singing versions by Nguyễn Ngọc Bích. Hội Văn-Hóa VN tại Bắc-Mỹ (Association for Vietnamese Culture in North America), Philadelphia, 1982, reprinted 1995.

Nguyễn Chí Thiện's testimony to the Congress of the United States, November 8, 1995, in English. www.danchu.net/ArticlesChinhLuan/CollectionVN/NguyenCThien30ENG.htm.

A Selection of Flowers From Hell, translated by Nguyễn Ngọc Phách. Hoa Niên, Melbourne ,1996.

Compiled by Dan Duffy for the Viet Nam Literature Project, April 2005. Additions by Jean Libby, editor, *VietAm Review,* 2006–2007. Vietnamese translation and editing by Nguyễn Thi and Trương Anh Thụy.

Hoa Địa Ngục. The Flowers of Hell. Original Vietnamese by Nguyễn Chí Thiện. English versions by Nguyễn Ngọc Bích. Tổ Hợp Xuất Bản Miền Đông Hoa Kỳ (East Coast USA Vietnamese Publishers Consortium), Arlington, VA, 1996.

Hạt máu thơ: Hoa Địa Ngục II/Bloods Seeds Become Poetry. A selection from the *Flowers of Hell II* translated into English by Nguyễn Ngọc Bích. Tổ Hợp Xuất Bản Miền Đông Hoa Kỳ (East Coast USA Vietnamese Publishers Consortium), Arlington, VA, 1996.

"Autobiography" in Viet Nam Literature Project, with Jean Libby. www.vietnamlit.org, 2005.

"An Autobiography" in *Beyond Words, Asian Writers on Their Work.* University of Hawaii Press, *Manoa, a Pacific Journal of International Writing* 18:(1). Summer 2006:85–92.

Life, Poetry, and Prison—Cuộc Sống, Thi Văn, và Tù Đày. Nguyễn Chí Thiện's poetry translated by Nguyễn Thi. Allies for Freedom Publishers, Palo Alto, CA, 2007.

Anthologies in English with poems by Nguyễn Chí Thiện

War and Exile: A Vietnamese Anthology. Edited by Nguyễn Ngọc Bích. Vietnamese PEN Abroad East Coast USA, Springfield, VA, 1989: 167–97.

Another Way to Dance: Contemporary Asian Poetry from Canada and the United States. Edited by Cyril Dabydeen. TSAR Publications, Toronto, 1996.

This Prison Where I Live: the PEN Anthology of Imprisoned Writers. Edited by Siobhan Dowd with a Foreword by Joseph Brodsky. Cassell: London, 1996:129.

An Anthology of Vietnamese Poems from the Eleventh through the Twentieth Centuries, edited and translated by Huỳnh Sanh Thông. Yale University Press, New Haven, 1996:162, 239, 287.

The Vintage Book of Contemporary World Poetry, John D. McClatchy, editor. "Nguyen Chi Thien." Random House, New York, 1996:421–24.

Works by Nguyễn Chí Thiện in Vietnamese

Bản Chúc Thư Của Một Người Việt Nam:192 Bài Thơ Bi Hùng. Written by Khuyết Danh (anonymous). Tú Quỳnh, Westminster, CA, 1980, 1981.

Tiếng Vọng Tù-Đày Vực. Introduced by Nguyễn Hữu Hiệu. Thời Tập, Arlington, VA, 1980.

Tiếng Vọng Tù-Đày Vực Ủy Ban Tranh Đấu Cho Tù Nhàn Chính Trị Tại Việt Nam (Committee to Fight for Political Prisoners in Viet Nam), Washington, DC, 1980.

Bản Chúc Thư Của Một Người Việt Nam. Văn Nghệ Tiền Phong, Arlington, VA, 1981.

Hoa Địa Ngục. Đông Tiến, San Jose, CA, 1995.

Thơ Nguyễn Chí Thiện. Nhóm phát huy tinh thần Nguyễn Chí Thiện, San Jose, CA, 1991.

"Bài tham-luận của nhà thơ Nguyễn Chí-Thiện, Đại-Hội Paris 2000."

Hỏa Lò: Tập Truyện. Tổ Hợp Xuất Bản Miền Đông Hoa Kỳ, Arlington, VA, 2001. Reprinted Hội Cựu Tù Nhân Chính Trị & Nạn Nhân Cộng Sản VN-NSW-Ức Châu Hội Ái Hữu Trướng Bưởi-Chu Văn An-NSW-Ức Châu. Xuất Bản, 30/4/2006.

"Thi Sĩ Nguyễn Chí Thiện viết về nhà thơ Phùng Cung," in *Phùng Cung. Truyện và Thơ chưa hề xuất Bản.* Edited by *Lâm Thu Văn.* Văn Nghệ, Westminster, CA, 2003:397–423.

Hoa Địa Ngục; first complete poems edition. Tổ Hợp Xuất Bản Miền Đông Hoa Kỳ, Arlington, VA, 2006.

Xin quý vị nghe ông Nguyễn Chí Thiện nội về hai du sinh trong Tập Hợp Thanh Niên Dân Chủ September 6, 2006. http://anhduong.net/LinhTinh/Sept06/NCT-TNDC.htm broadcast speech online.

Works by Nguyễn Chí Thiện in other languages

Echo aus dem Abgrund: Gedichte aus zwanzig Jahren politischer Gefangenschaft = Tiếng Vọng Từ Đáy Vực. Bilingual edition translated by Bùi

Hạnh Nghi. R.G. Fischer, Frankfurt, 1988. Also Munich, 1993. Introduction in English by Peter Gabriel for Amnesty International.

Fleurs de l'Enfer. Translated by Nguyễn Ngọc Quỳ and Dominique Delaunay. Institute de l'Asie du Sud-Est, Paris, 2000.

Ecrivains en Prison. French version of the PEN anthology. Labor et Fides, Geneva, 1996.

Works about Nguyễn Chí Thiện in English (and bilingual)

"A Voice from the Hanoi Underground." Nguyễn Ngọc Bích, in *Asiaweek*, July 30, 1982. In Nguyễn Ngọc Bích's *Ngục Ca: Prison Songs,* 1995.

"Verses Carry 'Sound of Sobbing' from Vietnam." Colin Campbell, in *New York Times*, June 12, 1985.

"Hoa dia-nguc/The Flowers of Hell" (book review). Nguyễn Đình-Hòa in *World Literature Today*, March 22, 1997.

"Nguyễn Chí Thiện." NNB (Nguyễn Ngọc Bích). Entry in *Who's Who in Twentieth-Century World Poetry,* edited by Mark Willhardt and Alan Michael Parker. Routledge, 2000.

"The Solzhenitzyn of Viet Nam." Michael Lind. *The New Leader*, February 1, 2001. www.newamerica.net/index.cfm?pg=article&DocID=43.

"Nguyen Chi Thien: Beyond Poetry" (Part One). Nataly Teplinsky. *The Epoch Times* (International) May 03, 2006. (Part Two) May 06, 2006. http://www.theepochtimes.com/news/6-5-3/41077.html (English); http://www.theepochtimes.com/news/6-5-6/41113.html (English); http://www.epochtimes.ru/content/view/5675/34/ (Russian); http://www.epochtimes.ru/content/view/5676/34/ (Russian).

"The Journey of a Thousand Autumns of Nguyễn Chí Thiện." Jean Libby. 2006. For the Vietnamese American Heritage Project exhibition at Smithsonian Institution opening January 19, 2007. http://www.vietamreview.net/Nguyen_Chi_Thien_authorbio.html.

"Blood Seeds Become Poetry: The Life of Nguyen Chi Thien." Jonathan David Hanh Vu Hill, in *Literature News* (VNLP Newsletter), Summer

2006. Sequential art (cartoon) by a young Vietnamese American artist, assisted by Dan Duffy, Jean Libby, and Nguyễn Chí Thiện.

"Còn ai dám nói ông Nguyễn Chí Thiện là giả sẽ phải ra tòa để trả lời tội vu cáo!" Đỗ Thị Thuấn (Golden Pen) in *ánh dương online*, July 2006. http://anhduong.net/nhanvat/NguyenChiThien/JeanLibby-pressRelease.htm.

Works with significant entries about Nguyễn Chí Thiện, in English

"Vietnam Grants Access to Prisoners." *The Washington Post*, December 4, 1991. Reports release of NCT "arrested more than a decade ago."

Understanding Vietnam. Neil L. Jameson. University of California Press, Berkeley, 1993:372–73.

Vietnam, the Necessary War: A Reinterpretation of America's Most Disastrous Military Conflict. Michael Lind. The Free Press, New York, 1999:244.

The Bamboo Gulag: Political Imprisonment in Communist Vietnam. Nghĩa M. Võ. McFarland, Jefferson, NC, 2004.

"The Lies and Hypocrisy of the America-Hating John Pilger" by Gerard Jackson, April 17, 2006. Conclusion based on the speech by Nguyễn Chí Thiện to the Australia Parliament in 1998.

"Writers on writing aim for the heart" (book review). Mark Panek in *Daily Yomiuri Online*, December 23, 2006. *Beyond Words: Asian Writers on their Work:* "When writers get it right, the particular becomes the familiar, and suddenly we find ourselves, say, locked in a dark prison cell somewhere in Vietnam secretly composing an anthology of poems in our heads along with the political prisoner-poet Nguyen Chi Thien."

Recent Works about Nguyễn Chí Thiện in Vietnamese (partial list)

Chỗ Đứng của Nguyễn Chí Thiện trong Văn Học Việt Nam. Trần Nhu. Văn Nghệ, Westminster, CA, 1992.

"Nguyễn Chí Thiện hay Lý Đông A?" in *Phản Tỉnh Phản Kháng, Thực hay Hư?* Minh Võ. Thông Vũ, Vista, CA, 2004:259–90.

"Nhà thơ Nguyễn Chí Thiện thăm nhật báo Người Việt." Nguyễn Huy in *Người Việt Online*, December 23, 2005. http://nguoi-viet.com/absolutenm/anmviewer.asp?a=37425&z=3.

Giáo Già; Thư Cho Con Tập 5. Trần Minh Xuân and Mêkông-Tỵ-Nạn. Tiếng Đàn, Newark, CA, 2006.

"Trái Tim Hồng, thi sĩ Nguyễn Chí Thiện" Ngọc Thủy. Lên Đường International Vietnamese Youth Network, June 8, 2006. http://www.lenduong.net/print.php3?ID_article=17441.

Other Languages

"Pour Nguyen Chi Thien." Michel Deville. A three-minute film in *Contre l'oubli* (Against Oblivion), a compilation of thirty French filmmakers commissioned by Amnesty International in 1991.

Écrire Contre L'Oubli, Photographies de Martine Voyeaux pour Amnesty International. Avant-Propos de Philippe Sollers. Societé Nouvelle Editions Balland, Paris, 1991:40–43.

Nguyễn Chí Thiện's Testimony on Human Rights before the U.S. Congress 8 November 1995

Mr. Chairman, Honorable Members of the House Committee on International Relations,

I am Nguyễn Chí Thiện, author of the poetry collection *Hoa Địa Ngục (The Flowers of Hell).* First of all, I would like to thank the honorable members of the House Committee on International Relations, especially the Subcommittee on International Operations and Human Rights and the Subcommittee on Asia and the Pacific, for allowing me to be here today to speak to the question of human rights in Việt Nam.

Since time does not permit a long elaboration of the egregious situation of human rights in my country, I would like to summarize and give you only the barest outlines of the gross violations of human rights that have been going on since at least 1954 when the Communists first came to full power in the northern half of Việt-Nam. Tens of thousands of people have been executed during the time of Land Reform (1953–1956), many tens of thousands of so-called landlords were sent into prison and exile, and the number of landlords perishing in jail came to many times the number of those directly executed on the public denunciation grounds. Let me clarify here that we are not talking about real landlords by the standards of other countries. In Việt-Nam during those years, you only had to be the owner of a half a hectare of land to qualify as a "landlord." And the proportion of landlords to the general population was specified to be between 5 and 7 percent.

In 1961 Hồ Chí Minh himself signed a decree ordering the concentration and reeducation of several hundred thousand people consisting

---

This address was made in English, translated from the Vietnamese by Nguyễn Ngọc Bích.

of those who had served in the military or government of the Bảo Đại regime, those in the general population who may have been discontented with the regime, including Buddhist monks, Catholic priests, lay Catholics, bourgeois capitalists and intellectuals. They were all corralled in hard labor camps. These were called "political prisoners" although the term is not quite appropriate since most of them have never engaged in politics as such. On top of these, there were many more ruffians arrested at the same time and put in the same camps. The vast majority of these people were never brought to trial, and their fate depended entirely on the dispositions made by the public security cadres.

Millions of people also lost their lives in the so-called war to liberate the South. In actuality, this 'war of liberation' was nothing more than a struggle to impose Communism, or its Marxist-Leninist brand, on the whole of Vietnam as a stepping stone to the domination of the rest of Southeast Asia. After the fall of South Vietnam in 1975, hundreds of thousands of people went to fill up the Vietnamese gulags. There was no need for a blood bath since that would be too obvious. Instead, under the new regime, hundreds of thousands of people died of hunger and cold or simply died without notice in god-forsaken corners of the jungle. Your life or death was entirely in the hands of the Vietnamese Communist Party (VCP).

Since the collapse of the socialist bloc and the evaporation of the Marxist-Leninist paradise, the Vietnamese government has had to adjust through its *'Doi Moi' ('Renovation')* policy, which consisted of a certain amount of economic liberalization and "untying the chains" of cultural activities accompanied by some minimal political reforms. But in reality, what is the true nature of these reforms? Economically speaking, it meant that the common people are allowed to engage in petty business, while the country opens itself up to dollars coming from abroad. Thanks to these incoming dollars, the government has been able to double and triple the salaries of the military, the public security personnel, giving them houses and land as a means to bribe them into keeping the people under wraps, ordering them to shoot at any dissident element—to prove their loyalty to the VCP!

In Việt-Nam nowadays the dollar supremely rules. Corruption is rampant and reaches every echelon of society. A class of *noveaux riches* has formed, made up for the most part by the children of high-ranking VCP officers. The overwhelming, crushing majority, on the other hand, lives in utmost poverty.

How about the so-called unchaining of literature, culture and the arts? Culture, the literature and the arts are the very soul of a nation. Who ever gave the VCP the right to chain them in the first place? The so-called "untying of the chains" was simply a relaxation of controls that did not last more than a few years, from 1978 to 1991. The monopoly of the media, printing presses and the publishing business, has always been in the hands of the Party. To become a newspaper publisher, the director of a publishing house or a printing press, one must always be a high-ranking and trusted member of the VCP. Even so, the Party is far from feeling reassured; it makes certain that public security officers are always in charge. The people simply have no voice in society except when they choose to sing of Uncle Hồ or the Party.

What about the so-called political reforms? They simply don't exist. The National Assembly is an instrument of the Party, and so are the labor unions and the various administrative units of the government—everything belongs to the Party. Buddha and Christ, too, must belong to the Party if they are to survive! That is why the VCP seeks every means to control the religions of Việt-Nam—anyone broaching a protest can be expected to go straight to jail. Even Buddhist temples must display the likeness of Hồ Chí Minh, whether it is a picture or a bust. Everywhere one can encounter public security officers disguised as Buddhist priests. The Catholic Church must have approval from the Party before it can ordain its priests or elevate them to the rank of bishops, or when it wants to recruit teaching personnel for the seminaries. Everything thus depends on the whims of the Party. No wonder every church ends up lacking everything.

Anyone daring to say a word, whether he is a Party member or not, in favor of pluralism and multipartyism, on behalf of freedom and democracy, or attacking Marxism or Uncle Hồ or the Communist Party of Việt-Nam, can expect to go straight to jail. Witness the cases of Messrs. Nguyễn Đan Quế, Đoan Viết Họat, Hoàng Minh Chính, Đo Trung Hiẽu, Nguyễn Đinh Huy and numerous others whom no one can possibly list all out.

Mr. McNamara's recent book on the war in Vietnam shows how little he understands Việt Nam and the Vietnamese people. Furthermore, he insulted the memory of those who have fought and sacrificed for the cause of freedom and democracy in Việt-Nam, which is closely linked to the same ideals in the world and in the United States itself. He failed to understand the finality of the collapse of Communism and the dimension of the victory of the Free World, which was due in no small part to the valiant struggle that we put up in Korea, Việt-Nam, and Afghanistan. He regretted the sacrifice in blood and money that went into the Việt-Nam war, but one should ask him: please tell us a good deed that does not cost anything! If that were the case, the whole world would be made up of good Samaritans! In retrospect, the war in Việt-Nam can be compared to a battle—a major battle if you want—that was lost but which in the end contributed to a victory on the grandest scale.

I have lived for more than 40 years in the very heart of Communism. I deeply realize that no pressure from the outside world can force the current leaders of Việt-Nam to adopt a pluralist and multiparty solution, to opt for freedom and democracy. For that is equivalent to abandoning their monopoly of power and giving up on their illegal gains. This will not happen until such time as the system disintegrates and collapses on its own. At the present time this disintegration process has reached a great depth and spread really wide.

But in the immediate future, I believe it is within the power of the United States and other free nations on earth to influence Hà Nội in many ways so that it will have to release the prisoners of conscience from their cruel places of exile and shameful prisons. This is especially urgent because they are near the exhaustion point, most of them having spent many years in jail, and therefore their minds and bodies have suffered greatly. That is why I would like to add my desperate voice to appeal to the conscience of mankind to work with determination and force the Vietnamese Communists to let go of all their prisoners of conscience. This should be done at once and unconditionally. Not only the families of the political prisoners but also the people of Việt-Nam yearn for this outcome every hour and minute of the day. Please do not let them down. Do not let them sink into despair and hopelessness!

To close my remarks, I would like to thank the government and Congress of the United States as well as all those who have done in any way to seek my release from Việt-Nam so that I could put my feet on the soil of this capital of the Free World and have this opportunity to address you with the above remarks.

Nguyễn Chí Thiện
November 8, 1995

July 21, 2005

Thân kính gởi anh Nguyễn Chí Thiện,

Cảm ơn anh gởi tặng quyển sách HỎA LÒ. Mọi truyện trong tập sách đã ghi lại một cách trung thực đời sống của anh ở địa ngục thế gian, tả gọn hơn trong bao nhiêu bài thơ. Sẵn đây, tôi gởi tặng anh quyển (FLOWERS FROM HELL/ HOA ĐỊA NGỤC, in năm 1984 lần đầu tiên, tôi mới tìm được. (Cuốn anh đã có là bản in lại năm 1985.)

Thân kính,

Huỳnh Sanh Thông

P.S. Tôi có đăng 3 bài thơ của anh trong tập ~~An~~ *An Anthology of Vietnamese Poems.*

Huỳnh Sanh Thông's Letter to Nguyễn Chí Thiện, 21 July 2005

July 21, 2005

Dear Esteemed Brother Nguyễn Chí Thiện,

Thank you for sending me as a gift your book *Hỏa Lò*. Every one of your stories is a faithful record of your life in this worldly inferno, which you have succinctly described in numerous poems. While we are on the subject, let me gift to you the book *Hoa Địa Ngục* (*Flowers from Hell*), first published in 1984 of which I happened to find one copy recently. (The one in your possession was only a 1985 reprint.)

Respectfully,

Huỳnh Sanh Thông

P.S. I have printed three of your poems in my *Anthology of Vietnamese Poems*.

(*Translation by Trương Anh Thụy, Canh Nam Press*)

(*original letter opposite*)

In 1984, while Nguyễn Chí Thiện was imprisoned at Hỏa Lò/Hanoi Hilton, the Council on Southeast Asia Studies at the Yale Center for International and Area Studies published *Hoa Địa Ngục* (*Flowers from Hell*), a bilingual edition of poems selected and translated by the Yale scholar Huỳnh Sanh Thông. The book was the first publication in the Lạc Việt Series at Yale. In 1985 it won the International

Poetry Prize at Rotterdam, inspiring a second edition by the Council on Southeast Asia Studies.

During that time, it was not known if the author were alive or dead, for there had been no word from the Hanoi Central Prison where he had been taken after delivering the manuscript of poems "Hoa Địa Ngục" on July 16, 1979. The British Foreign Service sent the manuscript to the School of Oriental Studies. The late Professor Paddy Honey circulated it to Vietnamese exiles in the United States, who published it first in the Vietnamese language press in late 1979 by an anonymous author. In early 1980, a security officer at the Hanoi Central Prison interrogated the prisoner Nguyễn Chí Thiện, thrusting a copy into his face and asking if he were the author. Elated that his mission to publish his poetry in the free world had occurred, Thiện replied that he was. Much of the solitary confinement that occurred for eight of the next twelve years of imprisonment was due to publication of his poetry and the world's response to it.

In April 2005 Nguyễn Chí Thiện was invited to Yale University by the Council on Southeast Asia Studies to speak at a Master's Tea. During the Yale visit, Thiện was brought to the New Haven home of Huỳnh Sanh Thông, at the latter's invitation. The letter printed here refers to this historic visit.

Design, typography,
layout, and production
by **H.G. Salome** of

Starksboro, Vermont USA

The Vietnamese fonts used in this work are available at www.linguistsoftware.com, +1-425-775-1130.